MAJOR JOHN WESLEY POWELL

1834–1902

THE COLORADO RIVER REGION
AND
JOHN WESLEY POWELL

THE GRA

From "F

The Colorado River Region and John Wesley Powell

A. John Wesley Powell: Pioneer Statesman of Federal Science
By MARY C. RABBITT

B. Stratified Rocks of the Grand Canyon
By EDWIN D. McKEE

C. Geologic History of the Colorado River
By CHARLES B. HUNT

D. The Rapids and the Pools—Grand Canyon
By LUNA B. LEOPOLD

GEOLOGICAL SURVEY PROFESSIONAL PAPER 669

*A collection of papers honoring Powell on
the 100th anniversary of his exploration
of the Colorado River, 1869–1969*

334993

UNITED STATES GOVERNMENT PRINTING OFFICE, WASHINGTON : 1969

UNITED STATES DEPARTMENT OF THE INTERIOR

WALTER J. HICKEL, *Secretary*

GEOLOGICAL SURVEY

William T. Pecora, *Director*

Library of Congress catalog-card No. 77–650223

For sale by the Superintendent of Documents, U.S. Government Printing Office
Washington, D.C.   20402 - Price $4.25 (cloth cover)

Foreword

A century ago John Wesley Powell—teacher, scientist, and veteran of the Civil War—set out to explore the unknown reaches of the Colorado River. He emerged from the forbidding canyons with a compelling interest in the nature of the western lands and how they could be developed for the greatest benefit to the Nation. A man gifted with imagination, yet always tempered by the scientist's appreciation for facts, Powell became one of the country's most vigorous proponents for the orderly development of the public domain and the wise use of its natural resources.

Throughout his lifetime, Powell stood firm in his belief that science, as a sound basis for human progress, should serve all the people, and he played an important role in organizing and directing scientific activities of the U.S. Government. His zeal led to the establishment of the Geological Survey in the U.S. Department of the Interior and the Bureau of Ethnology in the Smithsonian Institution.

On this 100th Anniversary of the Powell Colorado River Expedition, the U.S. Department of the Interior, Smithsonian Institution, and National Geographic Society (which Powell helped to found) have joined many organizations and individuals to recall the works of this man and to examine anew the imprints of his mind. His prescient concepts for the Nation's programs concerning people and their environment have been enhanced through a century of national development.

W. T. Pecora

Director, U.S. Geological Survey

Contents

————

John Wesley Powell: Pioneer Statesman of Federal Science

By MARY C. RABBITT

THE COLORADO RIVER REGION AND JOHN WESLEY POWELL

GEOLOGICAL SURVEY PROFESSIONAL PAPER 669–A

The exploration of the canyons of the Colorado in 1869
led to a career whose social and scientific significance
is perhaps more relevant today than ever before

Contents

JOHN WESLEY POWELL: PIONEER STATESMAN OF FEDERAL SCIENCE

By MARY C. RABBITT

SCIENCE IN AMERICA, 1869

In the middle decades of the 19th century, American science matured rather rapidly. The general scholar with an interest in natural history gave place to the specialist in a particular science, and the various sciences themselves became distinct from each other and from the general body of knowledge.

The geological sciences made especially rapid progress in America because of the opportunity and the necessity to explore the vast western territories. Although Clarence King later remarked [1] that before 1867 (when Congress authorized both the Geological Exploration of the Fortieth Parallel and the Geological and Geographical Survey of the Territories) "geology was made to act as a sort of camp-follower to expeditions whose main object was topographic reconnoissance," and that it amounted to "little more than a slight sketch of the character and distribution of formations, valuable chiefly as indicating the field for future inquiry," American geologists had, in fact, established a professional society, the Association of American Geologists, as early as 1840. Several years later this society became the American Association for the Advancement of Science. Several State surveys were founded in the 1830's, and by 1840, courses in geology were regularly included in the curricula of several colleges.

American scientists had been the most ready to accept Darwin's theory of the origin of species when it was proposed in 1859, perhaps in part because Asa Gray, the great American botanist, had paved the way by a series of articles so that evolution would not be charged with atheism, but in part because American scientists

were able to contribute much to the documentation of the theory. Darwin was elected to membership in the American Philosophical Society in 1869, long before receiving such honors elsewhere. By this time the American public was already becoming fascinated by the extension of the idea of evolution to fields other than biology.

Geology's sister science, geography, had gone through an almost complete metamorphosis from a descriptive and encyclopedic form to a quantitative and systematic science, largely as the result of the work of two German geographers, Karl Ritter and Alexander von Humboldt. Although their methods and philosophic approach were different, both stressed the interdependence of all phenomena on the earth's surface, and both looked for the general laws underlying the diversity of nature.

Arnold Guyot had introduced some of the new ideas to America in his Lowell Institute lectures in 1852, and his book "The Earth and Man" did much to popularize the new geography. In Guyot's words, geography dealt with "those incessant mutual actions of the different portions of physical nature upon each other, of inorganic nature upon organized beings, upon man in particular, and upon the successive development of human societies."

George Perkins Marsh, the forerunner of American conservationists, demurred. His "Man and Nature," published in 1864, was written to show that "whereas Ritter and Guyot think that the earth made man, man in fact made the earth," and he was fast making it uninhabitable by his wanton destruction, waste, and neglect. There was still, Marsh pointed out, "an immense extent of North American soil where the industry and folly of man have as yet produced little appreciable change." Hopefully, there, "with the present increased facilities for scientific observations, the future effects, direct and contingent, of man's labors can be measured and such precautions taken in the rural processes we call improvements, as to mitigate evils, perhaps, in some degree, inseparable from every attempt to control the action of natural laws." A more exact knowledge of the topography and climatic conditions of countries where the surface was yet unbroken was urgently needed, but the geological, hydrographical, and topographical surveys already being made in civilized countries were making such important contributions that within a short time there should be enough facts from which "to reason upon all the relations of action and reaction between man and external nature."

B. A. Gould, the retiring president of the American Association for the Advancement of Science in 1869, was not as optimistic. "The omens are less favorable for science in our own land than elsewhere, since there are peculiar obstacles to be encountered. These chiefly arise, directly or indirectly, from that characteristic in our national development, which assigns an exaggerated value to immediate utility, and a low estimate to what real utility is. It cannot be denied that the attainment of riches is becoming with us more and more the chief aim of existence."

Among other American failings, he observed that institutions of science were "dependent upon subsidies and gifts from individuals" and that the "governance and guidance of intellectual agencies" had been placed "in the hands of men who are not well fitted for their exercise." More than that, it had been forgotten that "the training of the school and the college is but a means, and not an end." Research was being neglected, and the scientist compelled "to earn his bread independently of his vocation, that is to say by work other than scientific research."

There were, however, he thought, hopeful signs for the future. "Science has few stronger friends than among the scholars of America," and "where science does have a foothold, her path is becoming smoothed and the sphere of her influence extended as never before."

"The magnificent, the stupendous march of scientific discovery in the recent past, leads to brilliant and almost limitless aspirations for the future. The range of human insight into the creation has been of late so wondrously expanded at each limit, that we are emboldened to expectations of scientific discovery, which at first seem utterly extravagant."

"What the future is to be," he told his audience on a hot August night at the annual meeting in Salem, Mass.,

"rests in great measure with the generation now upon the stage."

As he said these words, John Wesley Powell, who would have a large hand in shaping American science a decade or so later, might more properly have been described as waiting in the wings for his entrance cue. As Gould was delivering his address, Powell and eight others, hungry, bedraggled, and weary, were struggling in three small battered boats through the rapids in the Grand Canyon, looking hopefully for the break in the walls that would signify the end of the journey.

BEGINNINGS OF A SCIENTIST

In 1869 Powell was a relatively unknown professor of geology in a small Illinois college. He had been born in Mount Morris, in the western part of New York State, on March 24, 1834, the fourth child of Joseph and Mary Powell, who had emigrated from their native England in 1830 to carry the gospel of Methodism to the American frontier. He was named "John Wesley" in the hope that he would follow his father into the ministry, and his early training had a strong religious element.

The Powells moved to Jackson, Ohio, in 1838 and established themselves on a small farm. Jackson was at the crossroads of North and South, and feelings ran very high on the slavery issue. Because the Powells were strong abolitionists, the boy was unpopular with his schoolmates, and for a time, after he had been stoned by them, he was tutored by George Crookham, a successful farmer, an abolitionist active in the underground railway, and a self-taught naturalist. Crookham quickened young Powell's interest in nature, taking him on excursions into the fields and woods, sometimes with William Mather, who had been State Geologist of Ohio.

Powell's formal schooling was temporarily suspended when he was 12. The family moved to Walworth County, Wisc., and he had to take on the management of the farm. After 4 years of this he turned the farm over to his younger brother and left home in search of further schooling, but a year later he came back to move the family to Boone County, Ill.

In the fall of 1852, he obtained his first teaching position in Jefferson County, Wisc., and made great progress in his studies, especially in geography, as he endeavored to keep ahead of his students. Again, however, he was called home to help move the family, this time to Wheaton, Ill., where a new Wesleyan college was being established. His father promised to help him obtain a college education if he would study for the ministry, but he was already determined to become a scientist.

For a brief time he studied at Illinois College at Jacksonville, where he became acquainted with Jonathan Baldwin Turner, a well-known political liberal, who was committed to the improvement of education and agriculture, and to the advancement of the rights of the farmer. Only a few years before, Turner had developed the fast-growing osage orange as a means of fencing the prairie, a problem in which he had become interested so that a pattern of settlement could be established that would permit a common-school system. Turner also gave direction to Powell's development.

Except for a term at Illinois Institute at Wheaton and a few months at Oberlin College, Powell had no further formal education. His early twenties were spent in teaching, exploring (much of it along rivers), and collecting. Finally, he settled down to teaching at Hennepin, Ill., and when, in 1860, he was made the superintendent of schools, he set about organizing classes and preparing to teach mathematics and science.

With his strong convictions on slavery and the Union, Powell enlisted promptly when the Civil War began and gave distinguished service as a military engineer and artillery officer until January 1865, despite the loss of his right forearm, amputated after the Battle of Shiloh. He enlisted as a private and was discharged as Brevet Lieutenant Colonel, though the title of Major clung to him for the rest of his life.

After the war, he chose to become a professor of geology at Illinois Wesleyan University, a Methodist college at Bloomington. He was also curator of the Illinois State Natural History Society and gave courses at Illinois State Normal University. He was a popular teacher, for his students learned not only from books but through practical experience in the laboratory and in the field.

Some of the students accompanied him on his first trip West in 1867. To arrange this trip, he had to persuade the State legislature to provide a small endowment for the museum of the State Natural History Society and to be named curator by the trustees. Then, with his salary as curator, an allotment of $500 from the museum, an order for army rations from General U. S. Grant, railroad passes, and contributions from Illinois Industrial University and the Chicago Academy of Sciences, he equipped an expedition that spent the summer exploring and collecting in Middle and South Parks in the Colorado Rockies.

In 1868 he led a second expedition to Colorado. This time he devoted most of his attention to the geology, while the others, including his wife and his sister, Nell Thompson, engaged in collecting and other natural history studies. When fall came, the Powells moved over into the valley of the White River and established a winter camp. The winter was spent in exploring the canyons of the White River, the Green River, and the Yampa where it cuts through the Uinta Mountains. Many hours were also spent with the Ute Indians, who were camped nearby, while Powell learned their language and customs and traded with them to obtain items for the museums back home.

Finally, he made up his mind. The region to the southwest was largely unexplored, represented on the Government maps as a blank. There were many and fabulous stories about the Colorado River which flowed through it, of explorers who had disappeared, of places where the river disappeared underground, and of great falls. The Indians were afraid of the river. They said that long ago a chief, who was mourning the death of his wife, had been taken by a god to visit her in the happier land where she then dwelled so that he would cease to mourn. The trail to this beautiful land was the canyon of the Colorado. On their return, lest others who were discontented with this life should attempt to reach heaven before their appointed time, the god had rolled a river into the gorge, a mad, raging stream that would engulf anyone who tried. But, Powell said, "the thought grew into my mind that the canyons of this region would be a book of revelations in the rock-leaved Bible of geology. The thought fructified, and I determined to read the book."

THE BOOK OF REVELATIONS

In mid-March of 1869, the Powell party broke camp and through deep snow made their way across the mountains into Browns Park and thence to Fort Bridger, Wyo. The Powells went east, while the rest of the party remained in camp on Green River. Major Powell returned on May 11. He had been to Washington and obtained a renewal of the 1868 order authorizing Army posts to issue rations; he had obtained funds from the Illinois State Natural History Society, Illinois Industrial University, and the Chicago Academy of Sciences; he had arranged with a master boat builder in Chicago to build four boats in accordance with his own design, and he had had them shipped by rail to Green River City, Wyo.

As they made ready to leave Green River City on May 24, Major Powell wrote to the Chicago Tribune that the purpose of the trip was "to make collections in geology, natural history, antiquities and ethnology" and "to add a mite to the great sum of human knowledge." During the summer they would study the geography and geology of the valley of the Colorado. They would make a map showing the course of the river, determining the directions of each bend by compass and estimating the distances between bends, measuring altitudes by barometer, and determining astronomic stations every 50 miles. In addition, they would study the rocks exposed along the river and prepare geologic sections.

Ten started out: four guides from the preceding summer, Jack Sumner, Oramel Howland, William Rhodes Hawkins, and William Dunn; Walter Powell, the Major's youngest brother; Seneca Howland, Oramel's younger brother; George Bradley, whose release from the Army had been arranged by the Major; Andy Hall, 18-year-old veteran mule driver, bullwhacker, and Indian scout; and Frank Goodman, Englishman in search of adventure. Major Powell had planned a leisurely trip. They were equipped with 10 months' rations, and with guns, ammunition, and traps to add to their supplies, ample clothing, tools to build cabins for the winter and to repair the boats, and a variety of scientific instruments. These supplies were divided among the four boats, so the party would not be seriously crippled by the loss of one boat.

There were minor mishaps at the start, but the men soon settled down and moved down the river, naming the features as they went. On May 30 they passed through Flaming Gorge into the first series of canyons, and on through the Canyon of the Rapids, Kingfisher Canyon, and Red Canyon, by Ashley Falls, where they had the first long portage, to Brown's Hole. On June 8, shortly after they entered the Canyon of Lodore, one of the boats capsized and was dashed to pieces; with it went the clothing of the crew, one-third of the rations, and one-half the messkit, as well as some of the instruments and the map of the river to that point. Nine days later they lost most of the rest of the messkit in a mad dash to get away from a fire.

On June 18 they reached the junction of the Yampa and the Green and rested for a bit in Echo Park; 10 days later they arrived at the junction of the Uinta and the Green. A few supplies were obtained at the Indian agency, and some mail, and the Major had a chance to visit an old Indian chief and to inspect the Indians' fields. Frank Goodman left, having had enough adventure.

They started down the river again on July 6, through the Canyon of Desolation, and on the 16th arrived at the junction of the Grand and the Green. Major Powell had planned to stay at this point to observe the eclipse on August 7, but the rations were in such poor condition that they had to move on as soon as they determined the latitude and longitude.

On July 28, after passing through Cataract and Narrow Canyons, they came across the mouth of a stream not shown on any of their maps, and named it the "Dirty Devil." It was, according to Jack Sumner,

"filthy as the washing from the sewers of some large, dirty city." The next day they took time to climb up the cliffs to explore the ruins of some old Moqui (Hopi) houses, high on the canyon wall, that had last been inhabited perhaps a century or two before. On the last day of July they arrived at the mouth of the San Juan. By now, they were short of all rations except flour, coffee, and dried apples, and there was much grumbling, so after 2 days making observations, they pushed on, through Monument Canyon (later renamed "Glen Canyon"), past the Crossing of the Fathers, and the mouth of the Paria, which they did not recognize.

They stopped to observe the eclipse on August 7, but the weather was cloudy and it started to rain. The going became increasingly difficult as they continued down the river. About noon on the 10th the Major concluded that they had already passed the Paria and were coming to some other stream, and at 2 o'clock they reached it, the Chiquito or Little Colorado. By now, everyone except the Major was discontented. He was still happily studying the geology.

After 2 days in camp, on Friday, August 13, they started into the Grand Canyon. They had about a month's rations left—flour, a little rancid bacon, a few pounds of dried apples, and a large sack of coffee. Almost immediately they encountered long and difficult rapids. Then to make matters worse, it started to rain. The sun came out briefly, enabling them to dry out, but then the rain began again. The boats were leaking and had to be calked often. The river turned toward the northeast, and they feared they were headed back for the starting point. After they had come 120 miles (the Mormons had estimated the total distance as 70–80 miles) they began to wonder how much farther they had to go. On Wednesday, the 25th, they opened the last sack of flour.

On Friday, the 27th, after 2 weeks in the canyon, they came to a rapids that was as bad as any they had seen. All afternoon went by as they tried, and failed, to find a way around it. And below it they could see three more. There was food for only 5 days, and an unknown distance lay ahead of them. They had no choice but to try to run the rapids. The Howland brothers and Dunn refused to go on; the next morning, therefore, the guns, ammunition, and the few remaining provisions were divided, the small boat and the collections were cached. The three who were leaving climbed up the cliffs to go overland toward the settlements at the head of the Virgin River. The rest piled into the two large boats, and with all the courage they could muster dashed into the boiling waters, rowing as long as they could, and came out at the bottom of the rapids, soaked but right side up.

By 10 o'clock on Sunday morning they were out of the granite, the country began to open up, and a little after noon on Monday, August 30, they arrived at the mouth of the Virgin River, where three white men and a boy were fishing. The ordeal was over. The canyon had been conquered.

The expedition officially disbanded 2 days later. Major Powell and his brother left for Salt Lake City by way of St. Thomas and St. George, seeking word of the three who had left. The others continued down the Colorado, which was well known from this point to its mouth. The Major arrived in Salt Lake City on September 15 to receive a hero's welcome. By now, the word of his exploits had been front-page news in the newspapers of the country and the professor from Illinois was a national figure. In Salt Lake City, he learned that the Howlands and Dunn had been killed by Shivwits Indians. He stayed long enough to lecture to a large and appreciative audience about what he had seen on the Colorado, and then left for the East. He had already decided on a second expedition.

A third trip to Washington was more successful; Congress appropriated $10,000 for the exploration of the Colorado River and a strip of land along both sides during the year ending June 30, 1871. More important, Powell was assured that he could count on continued support.

Preparations for the second expedition were more thorough. First, Powell asked his brother-in-law, A. H. Thompson, to be the chief topographer and left with him notes from the first trip from which a preliminary base map could be prepared. Then, with F. M. Bishop and Walter Graves, who would be topographic assistants of the second expedition, he went West. Instead of carrying all the rations in the boats, they would have supplies brought down to the river. They knew of two points at which the river could be reached from settlements in Utah, but they were close together, and additional points would be needed. Jacob Hamblin, a Mormon who had spent many years in promoting peace with the Indians and who knew the country as well as any man, except perhaps the Indians, was hired as guide and interpreter, and with his assistance a second route to the mouth of the Paria was established. A council was held with the chiefs and principal warriors of the tribes so Powell could explain to them the purpose of the trip. All great and good white men, he told them, are anxious to know very many things; they spend much time in learning, and the greatest man is he who knows the most. The Indians named in Kapurats, meaning "One-arm-off," and agreed to be friends, to share their food with him, and to show him where to obtain water.

Then, although another route to the river should be found, the Major could not resist the opportunity to learn more of the Indians. Hamblin was going to visit the Moqui villages to the southeast and the Major went with him. After several weeks among the Indians, learning their language and observing their ways, he returned by way of Fort Defiance where he helped Hamblin establish a long-desired pact of friendship with the Navajos. To Hamblin he left the task of finding a way to the mouth of the Dirty Devil as the third supply point.

The second expedition left Green River on May 22, 1871. Except for Major Powell, none of the 1869 crew went on the trip. The new crew included—in addition to Thompson, Bishop, and Graves—E. O. Beaman, a professional photographer; Fred Dellenbaugh, a young man with artistic abilities; S. V. Jones, student of mathematics and surveying; J. F. Steward, an army acquaintance of the Major's and amateur geologist; Andrew Hattan, another army friend; Walter Clement Powell, the Major's cousin, and Frank Richardson, a family friend. Jack Hillers of Salt Lake City was a last-minute replacement for Jack Sumner who was snowbound. The boats were new, but similar to those that had served the first party. Rather than using a small lead boat, as in the first expedition, the Major had obtained an armchair which was lashed to the middle bulkhead of the *Emma Dean*, and from this perch he kept a lookout for danger ahead.

Remembering the trials of the first trip, the Major proceeded cautiously, and they reached the mouth of the Uinta almost without incident. Now and then while the current permitted, the three boats had even been lashed side by side and allowed to drift as the Major read to the men. At the Uintah Indian Agency came the first hint of trouble. A message from Hamblin said that it was not possible to take supplies to the mouth of the Dirty Devil. The Major took off for Salt Lake City, returned briefly to report that the river which Hamblin had thought was the Dirty Devil was actually the San Rafael, put Thompson in charge of the river party, and then took off again, determined to find a route down the Dirty Devil.

He rejoined the river party at Gunnison's Crossing at the end of August, without having found a practicable trail to the mouth of the Dirty Devil. The supplies were getting short, and the party again had to press on without adequate time for observations. One boat was cached at the mouth of the Dirty Devil, and they went on through Glen Canyon in two boats, noting to the northwest the "Unknown" Mountains, which were later named the "Henry Mountains." On October 6 they arrived at the Crossing of the Fathers where rations were waiting. The Major left for Kanab to make preliminary arrangements for the winter's work while the rest went on to the mouth of the Paria where they cached the other two boats.

As soon as they settled in winter camp, Thompson began preparation for the topographic map of the Kaibab and Kanab Plateaus and was occupied until February 21, 1872, measuring a 9-mile base line and setting up monuments for triangulation. Meanwhile, Major Powell and another party found a trail by which a pack train could reach the Grand Canyon at the mouth of the Kanab, thus assuring the food supply for the river party of the following summer.

Early in February, the Major left for the East, ostensibly to seek a new appropriation, but before leaving, he secured Thompson's promise to stay on even without salary if necessary. During this trip he not only secured the needed appropriation, but also made his first appearance at the Philosophical Society of Washington, where he presented an elaborate classification of valleys on the basis of his studies in the Colorado region, purchased a home in Washington, sold the home in Bloomington, and resigned from the university. He had settled on his life's work—to understand the West, first the land, and then those who inhabited the land.

While Powell was in the East, Thompson completed the preliminary map of the Grand Canyon region and at the end of May started out with several others for another try at the Dirty Devil route. He found the headwaters of the stream that should be the Dirty Devil, and the canyon was too steep to go down. Then from a point on the ridge, he observed that this stream turned east, cutting through the mountains, and then southeast to join the Colorado just above the San Juan. It was not the Dirty Devil. Both river parties had passed by its mouth without noting it. Thompson named it the "Escalante" in honor of the Spanish padre who had led an expedition from New Mexico to the region of Great Salt Lake and back in 1776. It was the last river added to the map of the United States.

Several days later, they found the true course of the Dirty Devil, and on June 22 passed down the long-sought route to the Colorado. The river was 15 feet higher than it had been the year before. Four of the party took the boat they had cached down to Lees Ferry at the mouth of the Paria while the rest went back to Kanab.

Powell arrived in August and took command of the party through Marble Canyon and into the Grand Canyon. Because of the greater height of the river, the boats were almost impossible to control, so when they reached Kanab Wash on September 7, Powell decided not to go on, and the second expedition through the canyons of the Colorado ended.

For the rest of the season Thompson continued the systematic mapping of the lower canyons, but Powell, after a brief study of Long Valley, went off riding around the district with the new Indian agent. He had already acquired a reputation for being able to deal with the Indians.

During most of 1873, Thompson continued in charge of the mapping while Powell was engaged in a study of the Indians. He had been appointed a special commissioner to visit the Indians of Utah and eastern Nevada and to help get them established on reservations. Between July and November, he visited all the bands known to live in the area, making a careful census of their numbers and condition and adding to his store of knowledge of their languages and customs.

The report of the special commissioners disclosed the unexpected fact that there were only 5,500 Indians in the whole territory. Because of the influx of white settlers who had occupied the best areas, the Indians had had to split into smaller and smaller bands in order to obtain the barest subsistence, and they were on the verge of extinction. Reservation sites were selected, but the commissioners pointed out that a reservation was not the whole answer. The reservation was not a pen where a horde of savages was to be herded but should be a school of industry and a home. The Indians should be taught trades and skills, and they should also be taught English, for the ideas and thoughts of civilized life simply could not be communicated to them in their own language.

The commissioners' recommendations of reservation sites were accepted and acted upon, but the rest of the report was ignored. The commissioners had really not expected anything else. Congress and the American public were not yet ready to accept responsibility for Indian welfare.

Once the Indian report was out of the way, Powell concentrated on completing the report on the exploration of the Colorado River. The competition for appropriations was keen, and becoming keener. Four surveys were now operating in the West (six, if one counted the Land Office surveys and the Coast Survey with its newly authorized geodetic work in the interior), and Powell's was the smallest and newest. Both the King and Hayden surveys had published substantial volumes, and the Wheeler survey had published several preliminary reports and maps.

The manuscript was completed and delivered to Secretary Joseph Henry of the Smithsonian Institution in June 1874. Its full title was "Exploration of the Colorado River of the West and Its Tributaries Explored in 1869, 1870, 1871, and 1872 Under the Direction of the Secretary of the Smithsonian Institution." The contents included what was purported to be a journal of the exploration of the Green and Colorado in 1869, an account of Powell's land exploration of 1870, and a report by Thompson on his trip to the mouth of the Dirty Devil. A second part contained Powell's geologic descriptions and discussion. The book is exciting reading still, but the journal of the exploration is actually a composite of the two river trips, and events have been switched around to heighten the drama, so it cannot be read as history.

The geologic discussion is another matter. In this, and in the "Report on the Geology of the Eastern Portion of the Uinta Mountains," which was published a year later, several important principles were first clearly stated.

The Major delighted in classifying the facts he observed. As he later explained, every stage in the progress of knowledge is marked by a stage in the progress of classification. He had proposed a classification of valleys to the Philosophical Society in 1872, two orders with three varieties in each, based on the relation of the stream to the dip of the rocks. From this classification he went on to a classification of valleys in relation to the stratigraphy or structural geology of the region, proposing the term "antecedent," for drainage established before, or antecedent to, the folding and faulting; "consequent," for valleys whose directions were dependent on the "corrugation"; and "superimposed," for those valleys whose present courses were determined by conditions in rocks that had since been removed by erosion.

The classic description of an antecedent stream is that of the Green River cutting its way through the Uinta Mountains:

"To a person studying the physical geography of this country, without a knowledge of its geology, it would seem very strange that the river should cut through the mountains, when, apparently, it might have passed around them to the east, through valleys, for there are such along the north side of the Uintas, extending to the east, where the mountains are degraded to hills, and, passing around these, there are other valleys, extending to the Green, on the south side of the range. Then, why did the river run through the mountains?

"The first explanation suggested is that it followed a previously formed fissure through the range; but very little examination will show that this explanation is unsatisfactory. The proof is abundant that the river cut its own channel; that the cañons are gorges of corrasion. Again, the question returns to us, why did not the stream turn around this great obstruction, rather than pass through it? The answer is that the river had

the right of way; in other words, it was running ere the mountains were formed; not before the rocks of which the mountains are composed, were deposited, but before the formations were folded, so as to make a mountain range.

"The contracting or shriveling of the earth causes the rocks near the surface to wrinkle or fold, and such a fold was started athwart the course of the river. Had it been suddenly formed, it would have been an obstruction sufficient to turn the water in a new course to the east, beyond the extension of the wrinkle; but the emergence of the fold above the general surface of the country was little or no faster than the progress of the corrasion of the channel. We may say, then, that the river did not cut its way *down* through the mountains, from a height of many thousand feet above its present site, but, having an elevation differing but little, perhaps, from what it now has, as the fold was lifted, it cleared away the obstruction by cutting a cañon, and the walls were thus elevated on either side. The river preserved its level, but mountains were lifted up; as the saw revolves on a fixed pivot, while the log through which it cuts is moved along. The river was the saw which cut the mountain in two."

Although there are some differences of opinion now whether the Green is an antecedent stream, later generations of geologists have used and developed this concept.

The second fundamental concept for which Powell must be credited is that of the "base level of erosion." In discussing the agencies and conditions that produced the more important topographic features in the valley of the Colorado, he pointed out that the primary agency is "upheaval" and the second is erosion. The latter depended on the character of the displacement in the upheaval, the texture and constitution of the rocks, and the amount and relative distribution of the rains. The higher the region the greater the amount of rainfall, and hence the eroding agency increased in some well-observed ratio from the low to the high lands. Moreover, the power of running water in eroding and transporting material increased with the velocity of the stream so that the degradation of the rocks increased with the inclination of the slopes.

"We may consider the level of the sea to be a grand base level, below which the dry lands cannot be eroded; but we may also have, for local and temporary purposes, other base levels of erosion, which are the levels of the beds of the principal streams which carry away the products of erosion. (I take some liberty in using the term level in this connection, as the action of a running stream in wearing its channel ceases, for all practical purposes, before its bed has quite reached the level of the lower end of the stream. What I have called the base level would, in fact, be an imaginary surface, inclining slightly in all its parts toward the lower end of the principal stream draining the area through which the level is supposed to extend, or having the inclination of its parts varied in direction as determined by tributary streams.) Where such a stream crosses a series of rocks in its course, some of which are hard, and others soft, the harder beds form a series of temporary dams, above which the corrasion of the channel through the softer beds is checked, and thus we may have a series of base levels of erosion, below which the rocks on either side of the river, though exceedingly friable, cannot be degraded. In these districts of country, the first work of rains and rivers is to cut channels, and divide the country into hills, and, perhaps, mountains, by many meandering grooves or water-courses, and when these have reached their local base levels, under the existing conditions, the hills are washed down, but not carried entirely away."

William Morris Davis, who called Powell "one of the bolder explorers on the high seas of theory," said that this idea of base level had been more or less consciously present in the minds of geologists, but its actual definition was of the greatest service to physiographers.

A SURVEY PROPER

Before Powell completed the manuscript on the exploration of the Colorado, Congress had taken note of the rivalry among the four surveys. The immediate cause was the encounter between the Hayden and Wheeler surveys during the summer of 1873, as both prepared to map the same area, but the underlying issue was one of civilian scientist versus military man in the mapping of the West. In April 1874, the House of Representatives asked President Grant to inform them about the surveys operating west of the Mississippi and the practicability of consolidating them, or of defining the geographic limits to be embraced by each.

President Grant, as an old Army man, was naturally sympathetic to the military cause. There was no question, he said, that surveys for sectioning the public lands should be under the control of the Interior Department, but where the objective was to complete the map of the country or to collect information on the unexplored parts of the country, it mattered little which department had control. The choice should depend first on which could do the work best and then on which could do it most expeditiously and economically. However, as exploring expeditions needed military escorts, and as the Engineer Corps was composed of scientific gentle-

men who had to be paid whether exploring or not, he thought his conditions could be best fulfilled by having the Army make the surveys.

The President also transmitted the views of officers of the War Department and the Interior Department. The Secretary of the Interior included opinions from both Professor Hayden and Major Powell. Professor Hayden highlighted the issue by pointing out that "much greater efficiency has always been gained where the leader of the survey is himself an ardent worker in geology and science generally." Major Powell took a different approach: "There is now left within the territory of the United States no great unexplored region, and exploring expeditions are no longer needed for general purposes * * *. A more thorough method, or a survey proper, is now needed."

The House Committee on Public Lands held hearings which lasted the better part of 2 weeks and became extremely acrimonious, particularly in exchanges between Lieutenant Wheeler and Professor Hayden. Major Powell was called as the hearings went into the second week. His concern was chiefly with the methods of mapping, or rather, with the efficiency of the mapping. He had brought along a blackboard on which he could draw diagrams, and proceeded to instruct the committee. The meander method, used by the Army, he dismissed as not accurate enough for geological purposes. There were two methods based on triangulation from a base line. Clarence King had used a base line determined by astronomic methods in the early part of the Fortieth Parallel survey but had abandoned it as not sufficiently accurate. The better method was triangulation from a measured base line. This had been King's final method and Powell's method in his work in northern Arizona and southern Utah, and Hayden had adopted it in the past year. Powell disagreed politely with the President; military escorts were not always necessary. They were in fact a hindrance, for the presence of troops always aroused the hostility of the Indians. All surveys for scientific and economic purposes he thought should be in one department, the Interior Department, and should be made by civilians.

In stressing the need for a general survey, or "a survey proper," Powell made a special plea for determining the areas that could be redeemed by irrigation. "All of the country west of the 100th or 99th meridian, except a little in California, Oregon, and Washington Territory, is arid, and no part of that country can be cultivated, with the exceptions I have mentioned; no part of it can be redeemed for agriculture, except by irrigation. When every spring, and stream, and body of water in all that region of country is taken out and used, less than three per cent of the entire area will be under cultivation, so that, under the best circumstances, I believe that of more than two-fifths of the whole area of the United States not more than three per cent can eventually be cultivated. Now, the extent and position of those areas that can be redeemed should be known."

Then he warned them: "Already the land surveys are being extended over broad districts of country which can never be settled, on which no drop of water can be had. Over the country which I have surveyed I have carefully noted the extent of the streams and the extent of the valleys that can be redeemed, and I have the data necessary for the construction of a map showing these facts."

Only a few months before, George Perkins Marsh had told the Congress that irrigation, far from being a panacea, was the source of many problems. Knowledge of western climates and soils was virtually nonexistent. No one knew how much land was irrigable, or whether enough water was available to make irrigation profitable. Before embarking on major irrigation works, the country required a comprehensive hydrographical survey.

The committee considered all the testimony, and the memorials submitted from college faculties and leading scientists, all favoring civilian control of the scientific surveys. It concluded that the surveys under the War Department, insofar as they were necessary for military purposes, should be continued, and that all other surveys for geographic, topographic, and scientific purposes should be placed under the Interior Department. The Powell survey was transferred from the Smithsonian Institution to Interior and was given a larger appropriation than ever before. Nothing was done about the problems of irrigation.

Powell's warning about the extent of the irrigable lands was repeated by the Commissioner of the General Land Office in his report for 1875. West of the 100th meridian, he said, were very limited areas where irrigation made agriculture possible, and throughout most of the area, title could not be obtained honestly under the homestead laws. Vast areas were suitable for grazing, but limiting acquisition to a quarter section, and requiring cultivation, made such use impracticable. Congress responded this time by passing the Desert Land Act on the last day of the last session of the Grant administration. This act made it possible to purchase 640 acres of public land for $1.25 an acre, 25¢ down and $1 in 3 years. Part of the acreage, however, was to be irrigated within the 3 years, and no provision was made for bringing water to the claims or even ensuring that water was obtainable.

A few weeks after passage of the Desert Land Act, Major Powell told the spring meeting of the National Academy of Sciences that the land system of the country, with regard to purchase, preemption, or homestead plans, was not suitable for the arid region. In that region, land as mere land was of no value. The water privilege was what was valuable. Rich men and stock companies had already appropriated all the streams and were charging for the use of water. There was very little land left that a poor man could turn into a farm.

Carl Schurz, a reform-minded senator from Wisconsin, became Secretary of the Interior when Rutherford B. Hayes became President in March 1877, and by fall he had several recommendations for legislative action: for forest conservation, for leasing lands west of the 100th meridian for pasturage where they were not suitable for agriculture, for amending the Desert Land Act so the desert character and quality of the land were established before entry was permitted, and for establishing the office of Surveyor-General, and abolishing the contract system of surveying the public lands.

The Schurz recommendations received scant support in Congress, though the House Committee on Public Lands held hearings in the spring of 1878 on a bill "to provide a more economic and accurate survey of the public lands." Major Powell was the first witness and seemingly was credited with being the author of the bill. He told them that the system of parceling the public lands into townships and sections and the method of measuring these parcels and determining their position had been devised more than 80 years before for the great valley of the Mississippi. They were well suited to that region, but in the great mountain region of the West, some modifications were needed.

His studies indicated that about 2.8 percent of the Territory of Utah was irrigable, in patches along the streams, and that Utah was perhaps slightly below the general average. In Utah, 23 percent of the land was valuable for timber and of no value for agriculture; this percentage was probably a fair average for the arid region as a whole. The timber lands were high on the plateaus and mountains. In between the timber lands and the agricultural lands were those valuable for pasturage only, and as the growth of grass in an arid climate was scant, pasturage farms had to be large, not less than 2,560 acres. Pasturage farms should be laid out with waterfronts on the springs and little streams to prevent a monoply of the water, and each should have a small tract of irrigable land near the home of the resident. If the pasturage farms were laid out with waterfronts, the homes could be grouped so that schools, churches, and other social institutions would be possible.

The system of surveying should be adapted to the type of land. It was unnecessary to survey timberlands in parcels as small as 160 acres, so a combination of chaining and triangulation would be suitable. Pasturage lands should be laid out in irregular tracts, so triangulation should be used. Mineral claims could be surveyed by chain or tape, but claims should be connected by triangulation. Surveying is properly a question of scientific engineering, and a man so qualified should have charge of the work to protect the interests of the Government and the people alike.

The bill did not get very far. It was drawn to change the method of surveying the public lands, and that was bad enough, but there was a suspicion that it would change the system of parceling the public lands as well, and that idea was anathema.

In his testimony, the Major had given the committee a preview of parts of his "Report on the Lands of the Arid Region of the United States." Two days later he delivered the manuscript to the Commissioner of the General Land Office.

The Major had intended to write a work on the Public Domain, including the swamps of the southeast Atlantic and Gulf coasts, the Everglades, the flood plains of the great southern rivers, and the lake swamplands of the north-central region. All these lands required drainage or protection from overflow. The problem of the arid lands was more pressing, however, as thousands were migrating there every year; he had therefore decided to publish first that part of the whole report that dealt with the arid lands.

It was more than a report; it was a program, including proposed legislation, for orderly development of the West. Within the arid region, which constituted about 40 percent of the country, the annual rainfall was not enough to sustain an economy based on the traditional patterns of the humid regions. Only a small part was irrigable, and cooperative labor or capital was necessary to develop irrigation. Reservoir sites should be selected and reserved so there would be no problem later in increasing irrigation by storage of water. Timberlands could not be used as farmlands; they were valuable for forests only and must be protected from fire. Pasturage lands were of value only in large quantities, and the farm unit there should not be less than 2,560 acres. Pasturage farms needed small tracts of irrigable land and waterfronts; the plots, therefore, should be shaped by the terrain, and residences should be grouped to secure the benefits of local social organizations.

The first edition of the Arid Lands report was printed in August 1878, and a second edition was ordered very soon thereafter, but the reforms called for in the book were controversial and too far in advance of the times to be acted on.

That same spring the Committee on Appropriations, in the face of the continuing depression after the financial crisis of 1873 and the continuing rivalry of the western surveys, had again asked the Secretaries of Interior and War for an accounting of the cost of the surveys and opinions about consolidating them. Secretary Schurz replied with letters from Professor Hayden and Major Powell. The Hayden Survey had received appropriations amounting to $615,000 in the 10 years of its existence. Appropriations for the Powell survey had been only $209,000, but in addition, he had had Army rations for 25 men and the assistance of two Army officers, Captains Clarence Dutton and Garrick Mallery. With his reply, Powell included a map showing the atlas sheets established by the Department of the Interior and the overlap among the various surveys. The Army also submitted a map showing its proposed atlas, on a different basis from that proposed by the Department of the Interior. Of the two Army surveys, the Exploration of the Fortieth Parallel under Clarence King had cost $383,711.85, and the Wheeler survey had cost $368,770.55.

In the ensuing discussions over appropriations for the coming year, during which drastic cuts were proposed, Hayden's friends rose to his defense, and in the closing days of the fiscal year, the Sundry Civil Expenses bill was passed with funds included for both the Powell and the Hayden Surveys. The Wheeler Survey funds came from the Army appropriations. On the final day of the session, Congressman Abram Hewitt of New York inserted in the Sundry Civil Expenses bill an amendment asking the National Academy of Sciences to advise the Congress on a "plan for surveying and mapping the Territories of the United States on such general system as will, in their judgment, secure the best results at the least possible cost." Congressman Hewitt, a wealthy iron manufacturer and former chairman of the Democratic National Committee, was one of the founders of the American Institute of Mining Engineering and its president in 1876. He was also a close friend of Clarence King, and it is likely that the idea of asking the Academy's advice had come from King.

The Academy was without a president at the time. Joseph Henry, its distinguished president of many years, had died on May 13, 1878, and it was not until August when the Acting President, Professor O. C. Marsh of Yale, returned from Europe that a committee was appointed. The committee included no member of the existing surveys but was composed of a "distinguished group of scientists who would judge matters objectively": Professor James D. Dana of Yale, Professor William Barton Rogers of the Massachusetts Institute of Technology, Professor J. S. Newberry of Columbia, Professor W. P. Trowbridge of Columbia, Professor Simon Newcomb of the Nautical Almanac, and Professor Alexander Agassiz of Harvard. Such a committee was sure to favor civilian control of the surveys and to call for high standards of scientific work.

The committee, in turn, asked the Secretaries of War and Interior for information and opinions. The Secretary of the Interior sent to the committee, without comment, reports from the Commissioner of the General Land Office, who thought that combining a geological and geographical survey with the survey of the public lands might be both beneficial and economical but who went on record as opposed to any change in the rectangular system of surveying; from Professor Hayden, who thought that combining the geological and geographical surveys with the public land surveys would be fatal to the former; and from Major Powell who said: "The prosecution of the work by a number of autonomous organizations is illogical, unscientific, and in violation of the fundamental law of political economy * * *. The work should be unified or integrated by placing it under one general management, and the division of labor should have a scientific basis; that is, it should be differentiated so that there shall be a division for geographical work embracing all methods of mensuration in latitudes, longitudes, and altitudes, absolute and relative; and the representation of the results in appropriate charts. There should be a department of geology embracing all purely scientific subjects relating to mining and agricultural industries. If ethnology, botany, and zoology are to be embraced in the general scientific survey, each subject should have but a single organization, with a single head subordinated to the general plan * * *. The present multiplication of organizations for all of these purposes is unscientific, excessively expensive, and altogether vicious; preventing comprehensive, thorough, and honest research, stimulating unhealthy rivalry, and leading to the production of sensational and briefly popular rather than solid and enduring results."

The Major pleaded for a change in the Land Office surveys which had produced a vast mass of material that was "of imperfect value in the parceling of the lands, of little or no value in the consideration of economic questions, and absolutely valueless for scientific purposes." He went on—"A proper scientific survey embracing the geography of the public domain with the parceling of the lands, and the geology with all the physical characteristics connected with it is necessary for the following reasons: First, to secure an accurate parceling of the public lands and enduring boundary lines. Second, for the proper administration of laws relating to the public lands. Third, for a correct and full knowledge of the agricultural and mineral resources of the lands. And fourth, for all purposes of abstract science."

The Coast Survey already had a transcontinental triangulation survey in progress and had a large number of persons trained in geographical science. As two systems of triangulation were unnecessary, "the one now in progress should be made the basis of all future geographical work in the United States." He thought it would be inadvisable for the Government to sustain and endow research in the various branches of zoology and botany, except in a limited way and for special purposes. Ethnology, on the other hand, should be supported by the General Government, for the work was of great magnitude and the opportunity was fast disappearing because of the rapid change in the Indian population.

The committee's report, approved at a special meeting on November 6, 1878, contained several recommendations. Existing surveys could be grouped under two heads: surveys of mensuration and surveys of geology and economic resources of the soil. The Coast and Geodetic Survey was best prepared to undertake the complete surveys of mensuration; in view of the paramount importance of the public lands, the Coast and Geodetic Survey should be transferred to the Department of the Interior and renamed the "Coast and Interior Survey." An independent organization, to be called the United States Geological Survey, should be established in the Department of the Interior to provide a thorough knowledge of the geological structure, natural resources, and products of the public domain, and a classification of the lands of the public domain. The existing surveys should be abolished. The contract system of surveying the public lands should be discontinued. A commission should be formed to consider codification of laws relating to the survey and disposition of the public domain.

The report was submitted to the Congress on the opening day of the session and was referred to the House Committee on Appropriations. Hayden, King, Powell, and the Engineers began lining up support or opposition. Powell prepared material for the newspapers, lobbied with Senators and Congressmen, and needled others into action. Legislation embodying the Academy plan was incorporated into the Legislative, Executive and Judicial appropriations bill which was introduced on

February 10, 1879. To Chairman John D. C. Atkins of the House Committee on Appropriations, the practical question was whether the plan proposed by the Academy promised the best results at the least cost, or whether a modified version of the plan that had been in use deserved approval. On the basis of cost alone, he thought that the new scheme might be justified, though it seemed scarcely necessary to plead for a system that so admirably combined the scientific with the practical and useful.

Major Powell had supplied background material to General James A. Garfield, who spoke in favor of the legislation on the following day. As a general principle, Garfield said, that the United States ought not to interfere in matters of science but should leave its development to the people themselves. The obvious exceptions to this principle were the scientific inquiries necessary to intelligent exercise of the Government's functions, investigations concerning whole classes or all classes of people, and those which could not be successfully made by private individuals because of their great magnitude and cost.

Representative Peter Wigginton of California had also obtained material from Major Powell. He was particularly interested in a radical change in the land survey system. Representatives from the public lands States, however, were opposed.

The climactic speech was that of Representative Abram Hewitt, who urged all to read carefully Major Powell's letter included with the Academy report in order to learn all the advantages of the bill. He then went on to make an eloquent appeal for a survey of the mineral wealth of the country to aid American industry. The geological survey, though, was not the point of contention. It was not until an amendment was proposed making the Coast and Interior Survey responsible for all surveys of position and mensuration, except the public-land surveys, that the bill was acceptable.

The House was concerned with many controversial subjects, pensions and civil rights among them, and did not pass the bill until February 25, 1879. Other appropriations bills were passed more readily, including the Sundry Civil Expenses bill which contained appropriations for the, as yet, unestablished Geological Survey. In the closing hours of the session, both bills came to conference; but as the day went on it became clear that it would be difficult, if not impossible, to obtain agreement on the Legislative, Executive, and Judicial bill, which contained a provision to end Federal supervision of elections on which the House and Senate held opposing views. Representative Hewitt, who was one of the conferees, added to the Sundry Civil Expenses bill the

pertinent clauses from the Legislative, Executive, and Judicial bill that would establish the Geological Survey and provide for its publications, abolish the existing western surveys, and create a commission to codify the public-lands laws. This bill was accepted and passed by both houses, and President Hayes signed it into law on March 3, 1879. The third and final session of the 45th Congress came to an end without passing the bill in which the enabling legislation was originally included. The transfer of the Coast Survey to the Department of the Interior and the plan to discontinue the contract system of land-parceling surveys died with the bill.

Once the Survey bill was passed, the appointment of the director became an important issue, for the new director would be a member ex officio of the Commission to Codify the Land Laws. There was considerable sentiment in favor of Hayden, who had been longest in the field, so Powell wrote to Congressman Atkins "If Dr. Hayden is appointed all hope of further reform of the system of land surveys is at an end or indefinitely postponed." Powell himself was not a serious candidate for the office. He had been the principal proponent of change in the land-parceling surveys, and that provision had been eliminated from the bill. His interest in geology was primarily in landforms and land use rather than in the mineral-resource studies that were emphasized in the final legislation; moreover he was very much interested in his ethnological studies, for which an appropriation had also been made in the Sundry Civil bill that included the Survey legislation. Hence, he threw his support to Clarence King, and King was appointed the first director of the United States Geological Survey.

Powell was made a member of the Commission to Codify the Land Laws when it was established on July 1, 1879, and both Captain Clarence Dutton and Joseph Stanley-Brown, who had been the Major's secretary, were made members of the staff. The commission spent the last 5 months of 1879 traveling throughout the West, gathering evidence and opinions. The Arids Lands report was widely distributed, and questionnaires were published in journals and newspapers. The majority of those on the commission accepted Powell's thesis that most of the West was too dry for agriculture without irrigation and too dry to profit from any features of a land system suited to the more humid conditions of the East. They were unwilling, however, to set the system aside and preferred an attempt to adjust it to the special conditions of the West. Powell himself could think of no way of carrying out his plan without halting settlement at least temporarily, and the commission would not sponsor changes that would impede settlement. The legislation that they proposed included a system of classifying the public land, reducing the price of unsold land, and providing for the pasturage homestead that Powell had proposed. The Congress accepted the report and authorized its printing. That was as far as it went.

While Powell was busy with the commission, organizing the Bureau of American Ethnology, and other activities, King set about organizing the Geological Survey. There were ambiguities in the Survey legislation. The Director was charged with responsibility for "classification of the public lands, and examination of the geologic structure, mineral resources, and products of the national domain." What kind of classification of the public lands did Congress have in mind? And what was the national domain—the whole United States, or only the public lands? When the difficulty was pointed out, the House passed and sent to the Senate a resolution extending the field of the Geological Survey to the entire United States; but action in the Senate was deferred by a technicality, and eventually the resolution was defeated. Discouraged by the restrictions on the Survey's field of activity, King resigned as soon as James A. Garfield became President in 1881, and John Wesley Powell became the second Director of the Geological Survey.

Powell made no immediate change in the plan of operations or methods of investigation established by King, but in the "Second Annual Report," his first as Director, there was one substantial contribution that was his own. A large amount of material was ready for publication, and in the Director's words, "it seemed wise to adopt a common system of general nomenclature, a uniform color scheme for geographic geology, a system of conventional characters for diagrams, and a form for geologic and topographic charts and atlases." The adoption of nomenclature, he pointed out, was to an important extent an attempt to establish the categories of classification, and every stage in the progress of knowledge is marked by a stage in the progress of classification. There was no attempt to fix permanent categories, for that would be futile in a "nascent" science, but on the other hand, diverse terms for the same classes and distinctions should be eradicated. "A multiplication of means for like purposes in the presentation of scientific subjects is a characteristic of low development, in the same manner as is the multiplication of organs for like purposes in a living being. Economy of time and thought is the goal to be obtained."

The color scheme should represent common usage, should not commit the geologist to distinctions and correlations not warranted by the facts, should be composed of easily distinguishable colors, should be obtainable with the greatest economy in printing, should provide for distinctions needed in different parts of the country, and should make use of all parts of the color scale.

Lithologic characters were also to be shown by conventional signs. "Cartographic colors and diagrammatic characters constitute the geologic alphabet, and its value will depend, first, on simplicity; second, on systematic consistency; third, on general usage." The value of the system described in the Second Annual Report is shown by the fact that, although it has been modified in detail since its adoption, basically it is still in use.

The problem of the field of operations of the Geological Survey was solved the following year. In his first budget, submitted in April 1882, the Director asked for an increase of $100,000 for the work in the Western States and an additional 100,000 to extend the work into the Mississippi Valley and the Appalachian region. The items were not approved in the report of the Committee on Appropriations, but when the bill was submitted to the House in July, Mr. Atkins, who had helped steer through the Survey legislation in 1879, moved to amend the item for the Geological Survey by adding "and continue preparation of a geological map of the United States." When he was challenged that this was an attempt to extend operations, he admitted it, and the amendment was changed to read "of the national domain of the United States." When the Sundry Civil bill was passed on August 7, the additional phrase had been deleted from the amendment, and the Survey's appropriation for the year was nearly $258,000. Demurely, the Director announced in his annual report: "Prior to the beginning of the present fiscal year it was doubted whether the Geological Survey was authorized by law to extend its operations into the eastern portion of the United States, but in the act making appropriations for the fiscal year 1882–'83 the Survey was required to make a geologic map of the United States. Authority, therefore, was given to extend the operations of the Survey over the entire country to the extent necessary for that purpose. The preparation of a geologic map necessitates the preparation of a topographic map, as topography is the basis of geologic representation."

The Major had, at long last, achieved his "survey proper." A. H. Thompson who had been the chief topographer of the Powell Survey, was promptly added to the Survey staff, and the seven districts planned by King came into being. Topographic work was begun in the South Atlantic and South Mississippi districts and three western districts before the end of August 1882.

THE MOST COMPREHENSIVE SCIENCE

Almost as soon as he became Director, Powell added paleontology to the Survey program. Lester Ward was appointed paleontologist, though the appointment was also intended to encourage him to continue his sociological writing. O. C. Marsh was persuaded to join the Survey staff, though he kept his laboratory at Yale; C. D. Walcott and C. A. White were placed in charge of still other laboratories. Separate chemical and physical laboratories were set up, and the programs were expanded from their modest beginnings under King. A library was begun, and the publications program was organized. Once the field of the Survey was clearly defined and the topographic work underway, preparation of a preliminary geologic map was begun by W J McGee, and a thesaurus of American geologic formations was started, as well as a bibliography of North American geology. (The classification scheme for the bibliography bore the Powell imprint, all its adjectives ending in "ic": Volcanic, Diastrophic, Hydric, Glacic, Eolic, Biotic, Anthropic, Lithic, Petromorphic, Geochronic, Choric, Geomorphic, and Economic Geology and Geologic Technology.)

Survey appropriations increased steadily, and by fiscal year 1885 were close to the half million that King had considered the ideal. Other scientific agencies were growing as well. By 1884 the trend had become so pronounced that Congress was prompted to charge a joint commission of the Senate and House of Representatives "to consider the present organization of the Signal Service, Geological Survey, Coast and Geodetic Survey, and the Hydrographic Office of the Navy Department with a view to secure greater efficiency and economy of administration of the public service in said Bureaus."

The Coast Survey, the oldest of the four bureaus, was first authorized in 1807. Although its first superintendent had insisted that it be civilian controlled and truly scientific, time and again transfer to the Navy had been proposed and more than once accomplished. Now such a transfer was again being proposed. The original function, a survey of the coast, was not yet accomplished, but the bureau had taken on others, including hydrographic studies and geodetic surveys in the interior. The Navy had also been collecting hydrographic information since the 1840's and had set up a separate Hydrographic Office in 1865. The Signal Service was really the weather bureau, as the meteorological observations that had been authorized in 1870 had been expanded into research as well. In 1881 a departmental task force had concluded that there was no natural connection between the military and the weather bureau,

but a bill to transfer the function to the Interior Department had remained in committee. The Geological Survey was only 5 years old, but under Powell's aggressive leadership it had already become a broadly based and truly national scientific agency and was engaged in an extensive topographic mapping program. Potentially, if not in fact, there was overlap with the Coast Survey mapping.

The Joint Commission, usually called the Allison Commission after its chairman, Senator William Allison, called upon the National Academy of Sciences for advice. A new Academy committee was named, but its report rather pointedly observed that Congress' failure to carry out the Academy's recommendation for two surveys within the Interior Department had inevitably resulted in a defect in cooperation between the Coast Survey and the Geological Survey. The Signal Service, they thought, could be divided between civilian and military. The Coast Survey and the Hydrographic Office should not be combined, though consolidation of the hydrographic work might be reconsidered after the survey of the coast had been completed.

The Academy Committee sought to establish a general principle on the relation of science to government. The Government should not undertake any work that could be equally well done by the enterprise of individual investigators, and it should confine itself to the increase and systematization of knowledge tending to promote the general welfare. Management of a scientific bureau required a combination of scientific knowledge and administrative ability; they therefore proposed that a department of science be established to direct and control the purely scientific work of the Government. However, recognizing the improbability that Congress would take such action, they proposed alternatively that the scientific work he reorganized into four bureaus which would be placed in one department, the work to be coordinated by a permanent commission.

The commission hearings opened in December 1884, with Major Powell as first witness. He was questioned on the Survey's authority to do geodetic work and to extend its work into the "old" States, even about the necessity for topographic maps as a basis for geologic maps.

In presenting his views on the organization of the scientific work of the Government, Powell recognized two types of scientific investigations: construction based on scientific principles, and investigations designed to furnish information to the people. The latter investigations, he pointed out, could not be planned and executed according to plan. If they could, this would mean that the facts were already known, and if the facts were known, the investigations would be unnecessary. He agreed with the Academy that all scientific work should be under one management, and that it should be led by scientists, but personally he would prefer to have the Smithsonian Institution in charge.

A few days later Major Powell was back to present Interior Department's argument against transferring the topographic work of the Geological Survey to the Coast Survey. There is an ideal order, he told them in which the various kinds of surveys—topographic, geographic, geologic, geodetic, cadastral, and parceling—should be undertaken, but practically speaking, the ideal cannot be followed because the land is usually occupied before governments are established. In the United States, experience had shown that topographic mapping under the control of geologists was better and less expensive than if done by some other organization. "Geology is the most comprehensive science studied by man. It draws on all other sciences for its materials. Its most fundamental connection is with topography, because geology in all its branches has for its purpose, either directly or remotely, the explanation of the topography."

He went on to discuss coordination among scientific bureaus. It would be possible to start with any bureau and show its relation to the rest and by so doing make it appear to be the center about which the others gathered. "Science is a fabric of complex structure, and scientific research is by multifarious lines. Many are the ways to interrogate nature and discover her laws." A central organization would have many advantages. It could serve as the Government's scientific authority to which legislative and administrative questions could be addressed. It could also serve to coordinate and stimulate work done by other organizations or by private enterprise, though it could not control the work of others. The Major noted that "scientific men, competent to pursue original research, are peculiarly averse to dictation and official management," but are "anxious that their several labors may be filled into the grand system of scientific operations for the development of knowledge."

Major Powell came out of the hearings with a greatly enhanced reputation, but the hearings had not been completed when Congress adjourned on March 3, and on March 4, 1885, there was a new administration, the first Democratic administration in 25 years. There were investigations of bureaus, rumors of changes, and innumerable seekers after office.

Some evidence of inefficiency was found in the Coast Survey, and the Superintendent was forced to resign. The investigators of the Geological Survey, however, concluded that it was efficiently run and that its accounts were well kept. President Grover Cleveland appointed the head of the investigating team as the new Super-intendent of the Coast Survey, dismaying both the career service and the scientific community at large, and Major Powell's success, in contrast, led to some feeling of bitterness.

When the commission reopened its hearings it was with an entirely new tone. Alexander Agassiz, the head of Harvard's Museum of Comparative Zoology, a man of great wealth, who had had a long association with the Coast Survey, had come to the defense of the Coast Survey and had raised certain fundamental questions about the relation of government to science. He concluded that the centralization of science in Washington would lead to disaster. His thesis was typical of the laissez-faire attitude of the day: "Competition is the ideal of scientific activity, and the government should limit its support of science to such work as is within neither the province nor the capacity of the individual or of the universities, or of associations and scientific societies."

Congressman Hilary Herbert wrote to Agassiz inquiring whether the work of the Geological Survey could be brought within proper bounds. It seemed to the Congressman that Major Powell was transcending the rule that Agassiz had laid down about the Government's role in science. He asked specifically about the various studies of the Comstock Lode, about paleontology, and about topography. Agassiz replied that the mining industry studies all seemed to him to fall within the limits of private investigation. Paleontology was one of those things that private individuals and learned societies could do just as well as the Government. They would, in fact, do it more cheaply. As for topography, a geologic map without it was impossible; but if the States did not want a topographic map enough to pay for it, it seemed plain that they did not want the Government to pay for it either!

When Agassiz's letter was made a part of the record of the commission, Powell prepared a reply. He gave credit to Agassiz for the work he had done. But, he said, a hundred millionaires could not do the scientific research work now done by the General Government, and it was questionable whether scientific research and the progress of American civilization should wait until the contagion of Agassiz's example inspired a hundred millionaires to do likewise.

Again Powell affirmed his stand on what scientific research the Government should undertake. First, the Government should not promote research in those fields where private enterprise could be relied on for good and exhaustive work, especially while vast fields where private enterprise could not work were still unoccupied by agents of the Government. In the geologic field, some individuals, notably some able college professors, had made contributions to the geologic surveys, but their contributions, in comparison with those of the official surveys, were small. Historically speaking, Government had had an important share in geology.

The Government should promote the welfare of the people by providing for investigations in those fields most vitally affecting the great industries in which people engaged. Not only mining but agriculture profited from Geological Survey investigations.

Then there was the problem of efficiency. "The results of local investigation are of general value to many districts, and a knowledge of the geology of one locality must be derived from an examination of many other localities." Thus, a survey "should be organized on the broadest territorial base possible" for one such organization could accomplish more than 20 with the same amount of money spread among them.

In conclusion, Powell took a firm stand against Agassiz's idea of competition. "Possession of property is exclusive; possession of knowledge is not exclusive; for the knowledge which one man has may also be the possession of another. The learning of one man does not substract from the learning of another, as if there were a limited quantity of unknown truth. Property may be divided into exclusive ownership for utilization and preservation, but knowledge is utilized and preserved by multiple ownership. That which one man gains by discovery is the gain of other men. And these multiple gains become invested capital, the interest on which is all paid to every one, and the revenue of new discovery is boundless. It may be wrong to take another man's purse, but it is always right to take another man's knowledge, and it is the highest virtue to promote another man's investigation. The laws of political economy do not belong to the economics of science and intellectual progress."

A minority report proposed that the Geological Survey should expend no money for paleontology, except for the collection, classification, and proper care of fossils, and should publish only an annual report. Authors of other works might publish them at their own expense. The Survey would no longer need its physical plant, which the Secretary of the Interior was therefore to sell. The Coast Survey was to be transferred to the Navy because the "real scientists on this subject of nautical maps are educated sailormen, naval officers." Almost the entire scientific community rose to do battle.

The majority report required that the Geological Survey itemize the publication costs for which money was to be appropriated. The majority of the commission expressed themselves as having "no doubt of the wisdom of a geological survey of the whole country; the question of the propriety of its being done by the General Government they considered as settled by existing legislation." Moreover, they were of the opinion that "the administrative part of the Bureau is well conducted, and with economy and care, and discloses excellent administrative and business ability on the part of its chief." The Coast Survey was left in civilian hands, a tacit acknowledgment that scientific bureaus should be administered by scientists. Although no action was taken at the time about the Signal Service of the Hydrographic Office, and no department of science was established, the General Government had accepted a role in scientific research.

At the end of fiscal year 1885, in the midst of the Allison Commission hearings, the Director was able to announce that at last a plan had been developed for publishing the topographic map of the United States that was reasonably economic and met other requirements as well. The map was being made primarily for representation of the geology, but it would be useful for many other purposes was well: "in the study of drainage systems; in the study of the regimen of rivers; in the study of the great subject of irrigation; in the study of the distribution of forests; in the study of catchment areas for the supply of water to cities; in the study of the drainage of swamps and overflowed lands; in the study of soils and the classification of lands for agricultural purposes; and in the laying out of highways, railroads, and canals." The maps would also be useful in the event of war, but there was no demand more exacting than that of the geologist, and "if properly made to meet his want they will subserve all the purposes of the civil engineer, the agriculturist, the military engineer, and the naturalist." It would not be long before an opportunity would develop to test the usefulness of the maps.

By 1888 many were ready to admit that Powell had been right when he had said that the land laws were not suited to the lands of the arid region, that they worked to the advantage of the land speculator and the large landlord rather than the individual settler. An effort was made to repeal the Desert Land Act, the Timber Culture Act, and the Preemption Act, but it failed.

Moreover, a series of dry years had had disastrous effect on the east edge of the arid region, and those who had disregarded the warnings about irrigation were now seeking sources of water to supplement the deficient rainfall. On February 13, 1888, the Senate asked the Secretary of the Interior whether the Geological Survey should be asked to survey and segregate irrigable lands and reservoir and canal sites in the arid regions. This was the opportunity for which Major Powell had been waiting, and planning, for 10 long years. He had found no reason to change the conclusions of his report on the Lands of the Arid Region, though he had seen the problems become increasingly aggravated. By now, the smaller streams were mainly utilized, so the only course open was to concentrate on the larger streams. Utilization of the large streams would require cooperative enterprise. Still, that was no reason to delay the survey of irrigable lands.

During the 10 years, the Major had added to his plan. He now knew that by taking out water for irrigation in the upper reaches of streams, the amount of water and debris reaching the lower regions during floods would be reduced, and land there could be reclaimed as well.

In March 1888 the Congress called on the Secretary of the Interior to examine "that portion of the United States where agriculture is carried on by means of irrigation, as to the natural advantages for the storage of water for irrigation purposes with the practicability of constructing reservoirs, together with the capacity of streams, and the cost of construction and the capacity of reservoirs and such other facts as bear on the question."

Powell's program was transmitted to the Joint Committee on March 29. He had interpreted the area covered by the request as every place beyond the 20-inch-rainfall line, thus taking in two-fifths of the United States. To accomplish what was asked, he proposed first a topographic survey, which would permit a preliminary designation of irrigable lands; then a hydrographic survey to measure streamflow and plot catchment basins to make the designation more precise; and finally a preliminary engineering survey to determine the feasibility of construction. If appropriations were available, the job could be done in 6 or 7 years; he estimated that the total cost would be 5.5–7 million dollars.

The Irrigation Survey was authorized in the appropriations bill passed on October 2, 1888. In order to prevent speculation, the House added an amendment that all the lands that might be irrigated by the reservoirs and canals to be located by the survey should be withdrawn from entry. Lest this be too drastic, an additional amendment authorized the President, at his discretion, to restore any or all lands to entry.

Powell was ready. Captain Clarence Dutton was placed in overall charge of the Irrigation Survey, and A. H. Thompson was in charge of the topographic work. Fieldwork began without delay in New Mexico, Colorado, Nevada, and Montana, and a training camp was established on the Rio Grande at Embudo, N. Mex., where a group of men was instructed in the methods of measuring the flow of rivers and other hydrographic

techniques. In March 1889, Congress appropriated another $250,000 for the survey, and in April, the Major was ready to certify the first reservoir site.

Powell accompanied the Senate Committee on Irrigation on its inspection tour of the arid regions in the summer of 1889 at the invitation of its chairman, Senator Stewart. During the trips he addressed two constitutional conventions meeting in preparation for admission of territories to statehood. To the North Dakota convention, he made a plea for State control of water rights. In the eastern part of the State, he reminded them, there was sufficient rainfall and in the western a permanent dependence on irrigation. The danger was in the middle region. "Years of abundance will come and years will come of disaster, and between the two the people will be prosperous and unprosperous, and the thing to do is to look the question squarely in the face. * * * There's almost enough rainfall for your purposes, but one year with another you need a little more than you get. * * * There are waters rolling by you which are quite ample to redeem your land and you must save these waters. * * * Don't let these streams get out of the possession of the people. * * * Fix it in your constitution that no corporation—no body of men— no capital can get possession of the right of your waters."

To the Montana Constitutional Convention he presented a still more radical proposal, speaking, he said, "as an old pioneer, not as a statesman," that the county boundaries should be drawn on the basis of geography. "In the western half of America, the local, the state, the territorial county governments, and the regulations and the national government are in no sense adapted to the physical conditions of the country."

There were 35 million acres of land in Montana that could be redeemed by irrigation, but only if every drop of water falling on the land remained within the State. A man in any given drainage basin must be interested in every part of it because the entire drainage basin gathers the water that he needs. The primary unit of organization in the arid lands should be the drainage basin which would practically have a county organization.

Although his eloquence had little effect on the constitutional conventions (only Wyoming wrote into its constitution the principle that water rights were tied to the land), he continued in a barrage of speeches, magazine articles, innumerable letters, and meetings to explain his points. The best and safest agriculture, and the oldest, was irrigation agriculture. Perhaps 20 percent of the western lands could be reclaimed by irrigation, but that 20 percent added up to more land than had been tilled so far in the Nation. The water to reclaim that 20 percent would have to come from the large rivers. Dams on the large rivers, if properly engineered, would provide protection from floods and permit a controlled flow that would prevent wasteful runoff and allow the reclamation of arid lands at the headwaters and swamplands near the river mouths.

Laws governing the ownership or use of interstate or international rivers must be worked out and a plan devised to obtain the means to construct the enormous engineering works necessary for development of the great rivers; such construction was beyond the capabilities of an individual or a company. The first step, however, was a systematic and careful survey, and that, without question, was a proper function of the Government's scientific bureaus.

The times were not ready for Powell's kind of planning. At first, the General Land Office continued to issue patents on claims, and speculators kept track of the Government surveying parties in order to stake claims promptly on prospective reservoir and canal sites. The Commissioner of the Land Office on August 5, 1889, ordered the local offices to cancel all claims filed after October 2, 1888. In the ensuing furor, the Land Office, for a time, was forced to issue patents again, but with the warning that they might be invalidated. In April 1890 the Solicitor General ruled that as soon as Congress had appropriated money for the Irrigation Survey, all irrigable lands were reserved; as no one would know which were the irrigable lands until the Survey should certify them, all claims filed after October 2, 1888, had to be invalidated. The amendment designed to prevent speculation had, in effect, repealed the land laws and closed the public domain. The President could reopen it, but the President did not. There was immediate and mounting pressure on Congress to do so.

The public, and the lawmakers, wanted a quick answer to the irrigation problem, not a slow, careful survey and the preparation of topographic maps before the irrigation works could be certified.

In April 1890 Powell submitted his plan of operations for the coming year with a request for an appropriation of $720,000. Before the House Appropriations Committee could open hearings, the Senate passed a resolution demanding to know how much, if any, of the money appropriated for irrigation surveys had been diverted to topographic work, and, if so, by what authority the money appropriated by Congress for one purpose could be diverted and used for another purpose for which an appropriation was also made.

The Senate hearings were prolonged and bitter. They began by questioning the propriety of Powell's being the source of information for Presidential proclamations that would sometime return the land to settlement. But he had not asked for these powers—Congress had given him a job to do. Where would such a survey as he was conducting lead? Was the Government to take over the whole business of irrigation? Major Powell pointed out that by the Desert Land Act a homesteader had to irrigate before he could obtain title, and he could not irrigate without knowledge or money. The least the Government could do would be to assure a homesteader that irrigation was possible. But how could the Government say that irrigation was possible, if the Government did not control the water? And could the Government control water without building dams and canals? The Major thought that the Government could simply refuse to sell or release lands unless they were irrigable. No sane settler would take a chance far from the mountains or from actual or proposed irrigation works. "Do you conceive that there is any risk or doubt in the Government's assuming that relation and undertaking to deal with the flow and use of water in the great streams? Do you think it is better than to leave it to nature and the common incidents of human life?" asked Senator Hale. "I think it would be almost a criminal act to go on as we are doing now, and allow thousands and hundreds of thousands of people to establish homes where they cannot maintain themselves," the Major replied.

This was the crux of the matter. Did the Government have the right, or the duty, to protect the people's welfare? Or should nature take its course? Congress was not yet ready to admit that the Government had this right, or this duty. The appropriation was cut to $162,500, all power of reserving irrigable land was eliminated, and the hydrographic survey was cut out. Powell's hope that science could provide for orderly settlement of the West had again come to naught.

HARVESTTIME OF SCIENCE

Despite the loss of the Irrigation Survey, the Survey appropriation that year was so large that the Survey was not seriously crippled. Despite a devastating personal attack on Powell when the long-standing feud between paleontologists O. C. Marsh and E. D. Cope was aired in the public press in January 1890, his standing remained high. The following year, however, the Survey appropriation was cut. More serious than the cut itself was the fact that salaries and programs were specified. In 1892 came a more drastic cut. Several of the principal scientists had to be discharged; others continued at reduced salaries or no salary in order to complete the work. Not only the Survey suffered. The Coast

and Geodetic Survey, the Fish Commission, the Smithsonian Institution, all were cut. The blow was actually against science generally, and Powell and the Survey as the leading scientist and scientific bureau were treated most severely.

In 1894, as soon as a successor, C. D. Walcott, was ready, Powell resigned as Director. The nerves in the stump of his right arm had regenerated, causing great pain, and he had to undergo surgery for the third time. Thereafter he devoted himself to the Bureau of American Ethnology and to writing. For many years he had planned to write a survey of man's knowledge and philosophy from savagery to the age of enlightenment. It was never finished. He died at Haven, Maine, on September 23, 1902.

At a meeting of the Geological Society of America not too long before he decided to resign, Powell reflected on the work of the Geological Survey. In describing the work of a scientific institution, he said that it is necessary to distinguish two stages in development, a "preliminary, or experimental, or preparatory stage, and the final or effective stage. During the first stage methods are devised, experiments are conducted, scientific apparatus is invented and subjected to trial, and the plan for the work is formulated; during the second stage the methods and apparatus are practically employed and the plans carried out."

The first stage he characterized as research, the second as applied science "and since it is the highest function of systemized knowledge to promote human welfare, the first stage represents the seed-time, the second the harvest-time of science."

John Wesley Powell's own career might be considered in the same terms. During his lifetime, though he was the leading scientist and the director of the leading scientific bureau in Washington, he only achieved the full realization of his ideal of science in the service of man for the brief instant of the Irrigation Survey.

Before Powell died, however, he had the satisfaction of knowing of the passage of the Newlands Act, establishing the Reclamation Service. Its first chief, and the first chief of the Bureau of Reclamation which succeeded it in 1907, was F. H. Newell, one of the first members of the Irrigation Survey. Powell's nephew, Arthur Powell Davis, was one of the first irrigation engineers and later Director of the Bureau of Reclamation. The Geological Survey continued under the able direction of C. D. Walcott in an ever-widening endeavor. The Bureau of American Ethnology continued fundamental studies in anthropology and ethnology as part of the Smithsonian Institution.

The conservation movement, which began with George Perkins Marsh, Carl Schurz, and John Wesley Powell, achieved full status at the time of the White House Conference of 1908, sparked by Gifford Pinchot, of the Forest Service, F. H. Newell, of the Reclamation Service, and W J McGee, whom Pinchot called the brains of the conservation movement. McGee had been one of Powell's closest associates in both the Geological Survey and the Bureau of Ethnology. The Major had a bet with McGee that his brain was larger than McGee's. (According to the autopsies, the Major won.)

G. K. Gilbert, who had joined the Powell Survey in 1874, became one of the world's leading geologists and continued to serve the Geological Survey until his death in 1918. Lester Ward, whose social philosophy was so like Major Powell's that it is difficult to decide who influenced the other, eventually left the Survey to become a professor of sociology. Forgotten for many years, like his friend Major Powell, he is now being recognized as one of the founders of the modern welfare state.

The reform of the land surveys, and the abandonment of the contract system of surveying, for which Powell fought so persistently, finally came about in 1910; but it was not until 1936, after a series of years of drought, that the public domain was finally closed. Then in 1950, the National Science Foundation was established, embodying some of Powell's ideas on a centralized administration of government science.

Major Powell throughout most of his life had a great vision of science as a means of progress for the human race. In one of his more flowery perorations to a talk at the Darwin memorial meeting in Washington in 1882, he said, "Let us not gird science to our loins as the warrior buckles on his sword. Let us raise science aloft as the olive branch of peace and the emblem of hope." It was in that same speech that he characterized the gift of science to man as hope. "Had philosophers discovered that the generations of living beings were degenerating they would have discovered despair. Had they discovered that life moves by steps of generations in endless circles—that what has been is, and what is shall be, and there is no progress, the gift of science to man would have been worthless. The revelation of science is this: Every generation in life is a step in progress to a higher and fuller life, science has discovered hope."

With the students of the Corcoran School of Science at its inauguration in 1884, he left an equally profound thought for our time, that science has enkindled charity. Not eleemosynary charity, as he called it, but philosophic charity. "It has at last been discovered that the world has always been full of error, and we are beginning to appreciate how much man has struggled through the ages from error to error toward the truth. We now know that false opinions are begotten of ignorance, and in the light of universal truth all men are ignorant, and as the scholar discovers how little of the vast realm of knowledge he has conquered he grows in philosophic charity for others. The history of the world is replete with illustrations to the effect that the greater the ignorance, the greater the abomination of unconforming opinion, and the greater the knowledge, the greater the charity for dissenting opinions."

NOTES AND REFERENCES

In preparing this account of John Wesley Powell, which emphasizes one aspect of a multifaceted career, an extensive list of publications and documents has been consulted, a list so long that, if it were reproduced in entirety, it would be almost as long as the paper itself.

For those who wish to learn more of Powell, the most complete biography is William Culp Darrah's "Powell of the Colorado" (Princeton, N.J., Princeton University Press, 1951). Wallace Stegner's "Beyond the Hundredth Meridian: John Wesley Powell and the Second Opening of the West" (Boston, Houghton Mifflin, 1954) is, Stegner says, the history of a career rather than of a personality, and as such, begins with the 1868 expedition. Other accounts are "John Wesley Powell: A Memorial to an American Explorer and Scholar," edited by G. K. Gilbert (Chicago, Open Court Publishing Co., 1903); "John Wesley Powell, 1834–1902," by W. M. Davis (U.S. National Academy of Sciences Biographical Memoirs, volume 8, 1915); and the chapter entitled, "John Wesley Powell: The Explorer as Reformer," in William H. Goetzmann's "Exploration and Empire" (New York, Alfred A. Knopf, 1966). Goetzmann also has chapters on the King, Hayden, and Wheeler surveys. Richard A. Bartlett's "Great Surveys" (Norman, University of Oklahoma Press, 1962) is an account of the field operations of the four surveys.

Much material on Powell is also included in A. Hunter Dupree's "Science in the Federal Government" (Cambridge, Harvard Univ. Press, 1957) and Thomas G. Manning's "Government in Science" (Lexington, Univ. Kentucky Press, 1968).

There are many accounts of the 1869 exploration. As mentioned in the text, Powell's own "Exploration of the Colorado River of the West" purports to be a journal of the 1869 trip but actually combines the first and second expeditions and hence is not good history. Most valuable is the Utah Historical Quarterly, volume 15, 1947, which includes biographical data on the members of the first expedition, "Major J. W. Powell's Report on his Explorations of the Rio Colorado in 1869" (from W. A. Bell, "New Tracks in North America," 2d ed., London, 1870), his letters to the Chicago Tribune, diary, and geological notes, as well as the diaries of George Bradley and Jack Sumner and letters by Walter Powell and O. G. Howland.

Material on the second expedition is more voluminous. A complete account is given in Frederick Dellenbaugh's "A Canyon Voyage" (New York, G. P. Putnam, 1908). The diary and letters of F. M. Bishop are included in the Utah Historical Quarterly, volume 15, 1947. Journals of Stephen Jones, John Steward, and Walter Clement Powell were published in volume 16–17 of the Quarterly. Almon Harris Thompson's journal, which includes entries to 1875, was published as volume 7 of the Utah Historical Quarterly.

Congressional documents provide a wealth of material. Of special interest are the reports of the Congressional hearings in 1874, found in the 43d Congress, 1st session, House of Representatives Executive Document 240 and Report 612; the testimony before the Committee on the Public Lands in March 1878 (45th Congress, 2d session, House of Representatives Miscellaneous Document 55); the documents pertaining to the consolidation of the surveys (45th Congress, 2d session, House of Representatives Executive Documents 81 and 88; 45th Congress, 3d session, House of Representatives Miscellaneous Document 5 and Senate Executive Document 21); the testimony before the Allison Commission (49th Congress, 1st session, Senate Miscellaneous Document 82); and the Irrigation Survey hearings (51st Congress, 1st session, House of Representatives Report 2407 and Senate Report 1466).

Valuable background material is found in George P. Merrill's "The First One Hundred Years of American Geology" (New Haven, Yale University Press, 1924); R. M. Robbins' "Our Landed Heritage." "The Public Domain 1776–1936" (Princeton, N.J., Princeton University Press, 1941); Stewart L. Udall's "The Quiet Crisis" (New York, Holt, Rinehart and Winston, 1963); and Walter Prescott Webb's "The Great Plains" (Boston, Ginn and Company, 1931) as well as in the other works cited.

Major Powell's own bibliography is lengthy. The Warman catalog in the Proceedings of the Washington Academy of Sciences, volume 5, 1903, lists 251 items, and although there is some duplication, the list is not complete. The principal works are the "Exploration of the Colorado River of the West and Its Tributaries," published in 1875; "Report on the Geology of the Eastern Portion of the Uinta Mountains," published in 1876; "Introduction to the Study of Indian Languages," first edition 1877 and revised edition 1881; and the "Report on the Lands of the Arid Region of the United States," published in 1878, all by the U.S. Government Printing Office.

Specific references for quotations in the text are as follows:

p. 1. Clarence King, First Annual Report of the U.S. Geological Survey; Washington, p. 4, 1880.

p. 1. Arnold Guyot, The Earth and Man: New York, Scribner's p. 21, 1886.

p. 1. George Perkins Marsh, Letter to Spencer Baird, May 21, 1860; Man and Nature: Cambridge, Mass., Harvard University Press, 1965 (The John Harvard Library reprint of 1864 edition), p. 49, 52.

p. 2. B. A. Gould, Address of the ex-president: American Association for the Advancement of Sciences 18th Annual Meeting, Salem, Mass. August 1869 Proceedings, p. 28, 29, 30, 32, 34.

p. 3. Major J. W. Powell's report on his explorations of the Rio Colorado in 1869, in W. A. Bell, New Tracks in North America (2d ed.): London, 1870; reprinted in Utah Historical Quarterly, v. 15 p. 21, 1947.

p. 3. J. W. Powell, letter to the Chicago Tribune, May 24, 1869; reprinted in Utah Historical Quarterly, v. 15, p. 74, 1947.

p. 4. John C. Sumner's Journal: Utah Historical Quarterly, v. 15, p. 116, 1947.

p. 6. J. W. Powell and G. W. Ingalls, Report of Special Commissioners on the condition of the Ute Indians of Utah; the Paiutes of Utah, northern Arizona, southern Nevada, and southeastern California; the Go-si-utes of Utah and Nevada; the northwestern Shoshones of Idaho and Utah; and the western Shoshones of Nevada; and report concerning claims of settlers in the Mo-a-pa Valley, southeastern Nevada: Washington, 1874.

p. 7. J. W. Powell, Exploration of the Colorado River of the West and its tributaries: Washington, p. 152, 1875.

p. 7. ibid., p. 203–204.

p. 8. 43d Congress, 1st session, House of Representatives Executive Document 240, p. 11 (Hayden) and p. 14, 53 (Powell).

p. 8. ibid., p. 53.

p. 9. New York Tribune, April 28, 1877, quoted in W. C. Darrah, Powell of the Colorado, p. 226.

p. 9. 45th Congress, 2d Session, House of Representatives Miscellaneous Document 55.

p. 10. 45th Congress, 3d Session, House of Representatives Miscellaneous Document 5, p. 2.

p. 11. J. W. Powell, Report on the Methods of Surveying the Public Domain to the Secretary of the Interior, at the request of the National Academy of Sciences, p. 5, 6, 10, 12.

p. 12. J. W. Powell to John D. C. Atkins, March 4, 1879.

p. 13. U.S. Geological Survey 2d Annual Report, 1880–81, p. XL, XLI, XLII, LIV, 1882.

p. 13. U.S. Geological Survey 4th Annual Report, 1882–83, p. XIII, 1884.

p. 14. 49th Congress, 1st Session, Senate Miscellaneous Document 82, p. 1.

p. 15. ibid., p. 169, 176–177, 178, 1014.

p. 16. ibid., p. 1081, 1082.

p. 16. 49th Congress, 1st Session, House of Representatives Report 2740, p. 52.

p. 16. U.S. Geological Survey 6th Annual Report, 1884–85, p. XVI, 1885.

p. 17. U.S. Geological Survey Tenth Annual Report, 1888–89, Part II, Irrigation (includes the resolutions and acts initiating the Irrigation Survey), 1890.

p. 17. Debates of the North Dakota Constitutional Convention 1889, p. 410–412.

p. 17. Proceedings and Debates of the Montana Constitutional Convention 1889, p. 820, 821.

p. 18. 51st Congress, 1st Session, Senate Report 1466.

p. 19. J. W. Powell, The Work of the U.S. Geological Survey: Science, v. 21. p. 15, 1893.

p. 19. J. W. Powell, Darwin's contributions to philosophy: Biological Society of Washington Proceedings, v. 1, p. 70, 66, 1880–82.

p. 20. J. W. Powell, The larger import of scientific education: Popular Science Monthly, v. 26, no. 4, p. 456, 1885.

Stratified Rocks of
the Grand Canyon

By EDWIN D. McKEE

THE COLORADO RIVER REGION AND JOHN WESLEY POWELL

GEOLOGICAL SURVEY PROFESSIONAL PAPER 669–B

*A history of stratigraphic
investigation in the
Grand Canyon region*

Contents

Illustrations

THE COLORADO RIVER REGION AND JOHN WESLEY POWELL

STRATIFIED ROCKS OF THE GRAND CANYON

By Edwin D. McKee

Abstract

The record of the earth's history in the walls of the Grand Canyon has been deciphered through hard work by many people during the past 100 years. Much still remains unsolved. John Wesley Powell's contributions were of a pioneering type, though he was not the first to discuss the rocks of the Grand Canyon. Far more important than his own observations and deductions in the field of stratigraphic geology was his tremendous influence upon the work of his associates and his successors. This chapter traces the evolution of thought concerning the stratified rocks of the Grand Canyon and summarizes present concepts of stratigraphic history as recorded in the walls of the canyon. A brief summary of available data and conclusions on each of the principal sedimentary units is presented.

INTRODUCTION

On the centennial of the epic boat trip down the Colorado River by Maj. John Wesley Powell and his party in 1869, it is appropriate that recognition be given to various phases of Powell's many scientific accomplishments, especially those related to his journey through the Grand Canyon. Accordingly, this chapter reviews one feature of the geology—the record of the stratified rocks—that was of great interest to Major Powell.

Our knowledge of the earth's history recorded in the walls of Grand Canyon is the result of hard work by many people during the past 100 years, yet much remains unsolved. Powell's contributions were of a pioneering type, though he was not the first to discuss the rocks of Grand Canyon. Far more important than his own observations and deductions in the field of stratigraphic geology was his tremendous influence upon the work of his associates and his successors. The objective of this chapter is to trace the evolution of thought concerning the stratified rocks of Grand Canyon and to show how our knowledge has increased since the time of Powell's epic journey.

This chapter also summarizes present concepts of stratigraphic history as recorded in the walls of Grand Canyon and thereby indicates the status of investigations at present. To accomplish this objective, a brief summary of available data and conclusions on each of the principal sedimentary units in Grand Canyon is presented.

The region discussed in this chapter is largely restricted to the area that includes Marble Canyon and Grand Canyon (fig. 1), though Powell's explorations of the Colorado River took him through a much larger area. These canyons are in the southwest corner of the Colorado Plateau and are entirely within the northern part of Arizona. As was recognized by Powell (1875, fig. 73), the Colorado Plateau is divided in this region by major faults and monoclines into a series of flat-lying blocks or steps. These blocks consist (north of the Colorado River, from east to west) of the Marble Platform and the Kaibab, Kanab, Uinkaret, and Shivwits Plateaus and (south of the river) the Coconino and Hualapai Plateaus.

Grand Canyon National Park, the area seen by most visitors to the region, includes only the eastern half of Grand Canyon or the part within the Kaibab Plateau and the eastern part of the Coconino Plateau (fig. 1). The Grand Canyon National Monument, less frequently visited but equally scenic, is mostly on the north side of the Colorado River within the Uinkaret and Kanab Plateaus.

Acknowledgments

Appreciative thanks are extended to L. C. Craig, Eleanor J. Crosby, P. T. Hayes, and R. B. O'Sullivan, of the U.S. Geological Survey, and to William Breed of the Museum of Northern Arizona, for many helpful suggestions and for constructive criticism during preparation of the manuscript.

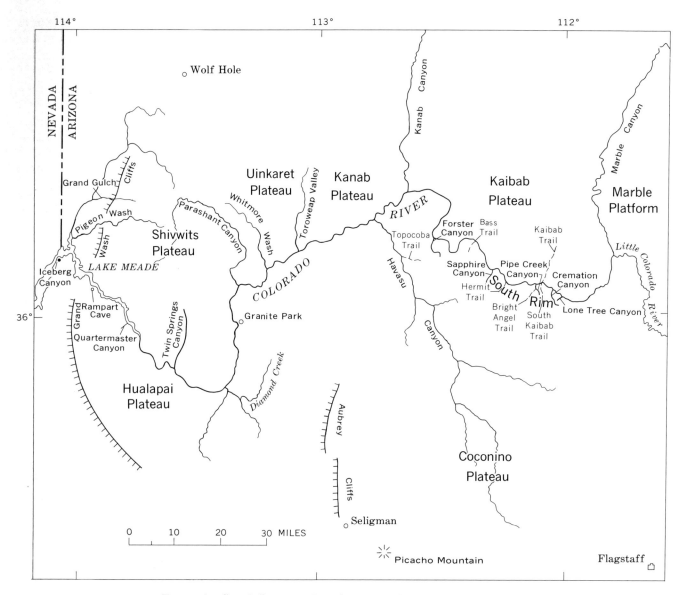

FIGURE 1.—Grand Canyon and environs, showing localities cited in text.

PIONEER STRATIGRAPHIC WORK— THE PRE-POWELL ERA

The earliest studies of Grand Canyon geology were made by Jules Marcou in 1853–54 and by J. S. Newberry in 1857–58. Marcou was a member of Lt. Amiel W. Whipple's expedition, which crossed northern Arizona while exploring for the U.S. Pacific Railroad; he examined strata similar to those of the Grand Canyon but in an area farther south (Marcou, 1856). Newberry, as geologist for a War Department expedition under Lt. J. C. Ives, recorded the Grand Canyon sections at Diamond Creek, along "Cascade River" (Havasu), and on "mesa at Camp 70" which was at Aubrey Cliffs north-

west of Seligman (Newberry, 1861). Both Marcou and Newberry attempted to classify and correlate the formations of the region; their conclusions were remarkable, considering the difficult conditions under which they worked and the state of general knowledge at the time.

The uppermost formation exposed in the canyon, now known as the Kaibab Limestone, was correlated by Marcou (1856, p. 170) with the European Magnesian Limestone of Permian age because of the high magnesium content in the rock where examined; this same limestone was correlated with the Upper Carboniferous by Newberry (1861, p. 70–73) on the basis of certain "known Carboniferous fossils." Subsequently, Marcou has been proved correct, although his evidence was not valid (that is, the chemical composition of the rock is insufficient basis for correlation), whereas New-berry was in error, though his reasoning was correct (that is, the fossils, including numerous productids, that he discovered were later shown to be Permian and not Carboniferous forms).

The Redwall Limestone, which forms a sheer cliff midway in the walls of the Grand Canyon, was considered in the 1850's as it is today, a stratigraphic marker to which less readily identified units both above and below could be referred. The Redwall was correlated correctly, as has since been demonstrated, with the "mountain limestone" of England ("lower Carboniferous" age) by both Marcou and Newberry. Evidence for this conclusion included brachiopods (listed as Spirifers), corals, and other fossils, as well as lithologic resemblances.

Resting on granite and underlying the "Mountain limestone" of Marcou in an area east of Picacho Mountain, south of Grand Canyon, is a reddish-brown sandstone (the Tapeats Sandstone of Cambrian age) which, probably because of its color and lithology, Marcou correlated with the "Old Red" or Devonian sandstone of England. This same unit farther north in Grand Canyon is mostly brown to purple. Newberry correlated it on the basis of lithology and stratigraphic position with the "Potsdam sandstone" (Cambrian age) of New York; thus, he was correct and Marcou was wrong in the age assignment.

Between the basal sandstone and the Redwall are strata that Newberry (1861, p. 55–56) referred to the "Silurian?" and "Devonian?" in his figure 12 (1861, p. 42; reproduced as fig. 2 in this publication). New-

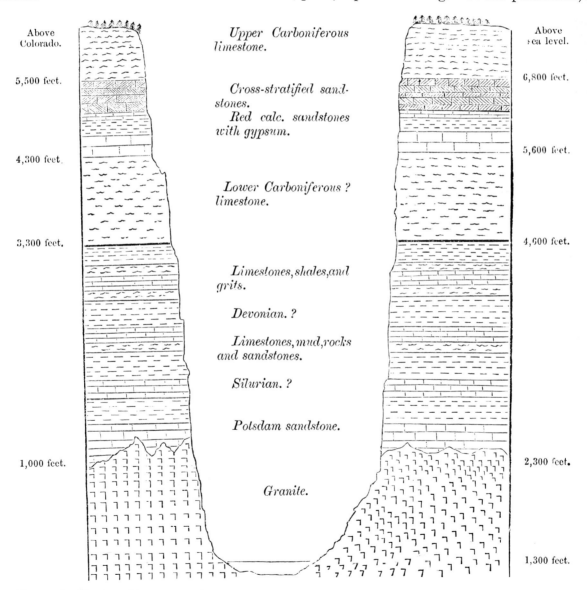

FIGURE 2.—Stratigraphic section of the Grand Canyon in high plateau along "mesa at Camp 70" which was near Aubrey Cliffs, northwest of Seligman. From Newberry (1861, fig. 12).

berry seemed very uncertain of the age of these strata, especially because recognizable fossils were not found. He was influenced in his correlations by lithologic character "much like that of some of the Chemung rocks" (Devonian of New York State) (1861, p. 56), and he noted the resemblance of certain structures to the "intermingled branches of *Chaetetes* which cover the surfaces of some of the Silurian strata" (1861, p. 56). The upper rocks in this sequence, which apparently were included with the Redwall by Marcou, have indeed proved to be of Devonian age, although even today little is known about them. The lower rocks that Newberry assigned to the Silurian? are absent in the area examined by Marcou; in Grand Canyon, where represented, they are now classed as Cambrian (Muav Limestone).

Newberry must also be credited for his attempts to reconstruct the history of deposition in the Grand Canyon area. He offered suggestions on paleogeography, genesis of gypsum, and some features of ecology, which, although elementary and in some cases incorrect as seen in the light of modern information, represent pioneer efforts of considerable significance.

JOHN WESLEY POWELL'S COLORADO RIVER TRIPS OF 1869 AND 1871–72

During two trips by boat down the Colorado River and through the Grand Canyon, Maj. John Wesley Powell not only explored unknown territory, but he also made many significant observations of little known features, especially in the field of geology. In his report on these explorations, Powell (1875) recorded many aspects of erosion and developed certain basic concepts of land destruction such as base level and stream antecedence. In addition, he described and classified the major types of structure, such as monoclines and faults, responsible for segmentation of the uplifted plateau. His original contributions to the youthful science of geology were numerous, and most of his concepts have proved to be valid.

In view of Powell's great interest in geology and keen powers of observation, the general lack of references in his report to the stratigraphy of Grand Canyon—the open book of earth history where stratification dominates the view—seems, at first, very surprising. Only the Carboniferous rocks were referred to by name, and the correlations suggested in the reports of earlier geologists were not mentioned; nor were ideas concerning the genesis of these strata discussed in detail. Perhaps the answer is that Powell was so beset with difficulties and so occupied with matters

of survival when in the Grand Canyon that he could give little thought to these matters; however, a more likely reason for the omission was his lack of any formal training in geology. At this stage in his career he had little knowledge of details of stratigraphy, and if he was familiar with the earlier work in the Grand Canyon area by Marcou and Newberry, there is nothing to indicate it. He was a self-trained and self-made man.

Despite the lack of general stratigraphic data in Powell's report, he must be credited with making the first reference to a very significant feature in the record of Grand Canyon history. His discussion of the two great unconformities, between early and late Precambrian and between Precambrian and Paleozoic strata, is classic. He not only correctly analyzed the sequence of events, but he showed in forceful language its meaning in terms of deposition, mountain building, volcanism, and erosion. Unfortunately his illustration of the three great rock sequences (reproduced as fig. 3 of this publication) is incorrectly drawn. (Note the relation of dipping upper Precambrian strata to the erosion surface on the underlying schists and granites.) In a later publication (Powell, 1876, table, p. 43), the correct relationships are shown. (See fig. 4 of this publication.) Nevertheless, he recognized that in the upper Precambrian or middle rock sequence, a topographic thickness of only a few hundred feet represents 10,000 feet of stratigraphic thickness, and he apparently visualized the tremendous amount of erosion that was required to bring about this base leveling or wearing away of mountains.

STRATIGRAPHIC WORK DURING THE EARLY DAYS OF THE U.S. GEOLOGICAL SURVEY

During the years immediately preceding the establishment of the U.S. Geological Survey, and for several decades thereafter, extensive studies were made of the stratified rocks of Grand Canyon by John Wesley Powell and a small group of his Washington, D.C., colleagues. Especially prominent in this connection are the names of G. K. Gilbert, A. R. Marvine, C. E. Dutton, and C. D. Walcott. Gilbert and Marvine actually did their early work while serving as geologists on the Wheeler Survey, but those studies were continued under auspices of the U.S. Geological Survey.

Between 1870 and 1890, contributions to an understanding of the stratified rocks in Grand Canyon were largely in the form of information on distribution, thickness, and lithology of various units, the collection

FIGURE 3.—Section in the north wall of the Grand Canyon illustrating the unconformity between (A) lower Precambrian schists and (B) steeply dipping upper Precambrian beds and the unconformity between (B) upper Precambrian and (C) Paleozoic strata. From Powell (1875, fig. 79).

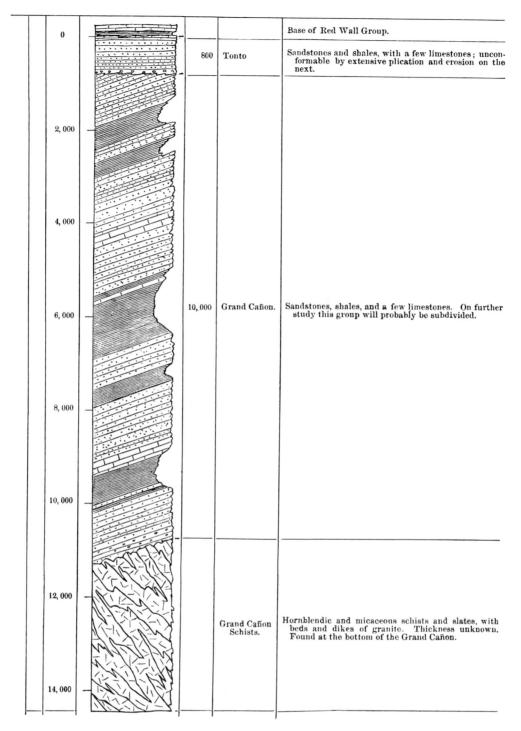

0			Base of Red Wall Group.
	800	Tonto	Sandstones and shales, with a few limestones; unconformable by extensive plication and erosion on the next.
2,000			
4,000			
6,000	10,000	Grand Cañon.	Sandstones, shales, and a few limestones. On further study this group will probably be subdivided.
8,000			
10,000			
12,000		Grand Cañon Schists.	Hornblendic and micaceous schists and slates, with beds and dikes of granite. Thickness unknown. Found at the bottom of the Grand Cañon.
14,000			

FIGURE 4.—Base of stratigraphic section in the Grand Canyon. From Powell (1876, p. 43).

and study of fossils from several formations, refinement of rock subdivisions and age assignments, and the application of local names for many of the rock units. Still lacking were any notable advances in the interpretation of depositional environments and in solving problems of genesis.

The first formal names to be given Grand Canyon rock units were the Tonto group, Redwall group, and Aubrey group, applied by G. K. Gilbert (1874; 1875a, p. 184) and later illustrated in graphic section (Marvine, 1875, fig. 82) as shown in figure 5 of the present report. According to Gilbert (1875a, p. 177), "it was found con-

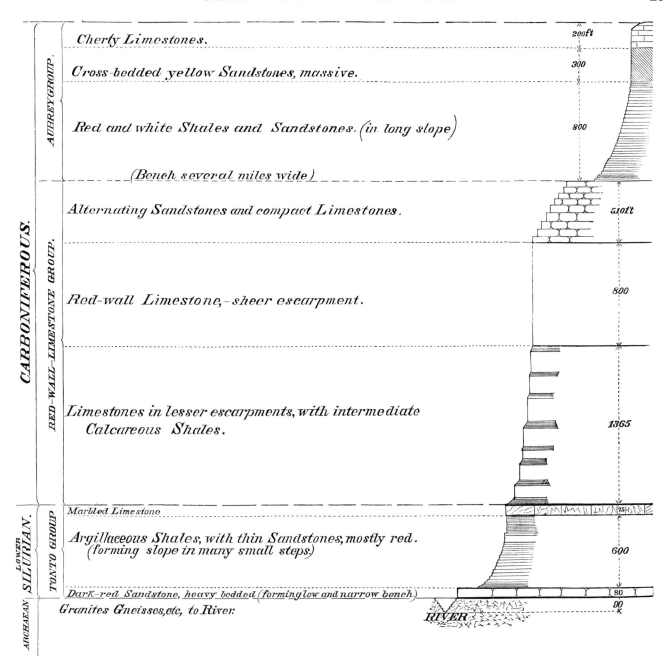

FIGURE 5.—Stratigraphic section at the mouth of the Grand Canyon. From G. K. Gilbert (in Marvine, 1875, fig. 82).

venient by Mr. Marvine and myself, to attach local names to the more important subdivisions [on the Colorado Plateau]." A short time later, Powell (1876, p. 60) presented a similar but more complete list of rock units, as follows: Upper Aubrey Group, Lower Aubrey Group, Redwall Group, Tonto Group, Grand Cañon Group, Grand Cañon Schists. Still later, rocks of Devonian age were recognized by Walcott (1883, p. 438) and named Temple Butte Limestone (Walcott, 1890, p. 50), as shown in his charts reproduced as figures 6 and 7 of this publication. Meanwhile, rocks of late Precambrian age belonging to Powell's Grand Cañon Group were studied in detail by Walcott (1883, p. 440; 1890, p. 50; 1894, p. 503; 1895, p. 329), who, after various revisions in classification and terminology, ultimately proposed (fig. 8) the adoption of Grand Canyon Series for the entire sequence and Unkar and Chuar for lower and upper subdivisions, called terranes by him (currently classified as groups).

Age assignments for most of the Grand Canyon for-

		PLANE OF UNCONFORMITY BY EROSION.
PERMIAN. 855 feet.	Upper Permian. 710 feet.	Gypsiferous and arenaceous shales and marls, with impure shaly limestones at the base.
		PLANE OF UNCONFORMITY BY EROSION.
	L. P. 145 ft.	Same as upper division with more massive limestone at the base.
		PLANE OF UNCONFORMITY BY EROSION.
CARBONIFEROUS. 3,260 feet.	Upper Aubry. 835 feet.	Massive cherty limestone with arenaceous gypsiferous bed passing down into calciferous sandrock.
	Lower Aubry. 1455 feet.	Friable reddish sandstones passing into more compact and massive beds below. A few filets of impure limestone are intercalated.
	Red Wall Limestone. 970 feet.	Arenaceous and cherty limestone 235 feet, with massive limestone beneath. Cherty layers, coincident with the bedding, in the lower portion.
		PLANE OF UNCONFORMITY BY EROSION.
	Devonian. 100 feet.	Sandstones and impure limestones.
		PLANE OF UNCONFORMITY BY EROSION.
SILURIAN. 785 feet.	? 235 feet.	Massive mottled limestone with 50 feet of sandstone at the base.
	Tonto Primordial. 550 feet.	Thin-bedded mottled limestone in massive layers. Green arenaceous and micaceous shales 100 feet, at the base.

Entire thickness of Paleozoic, 5000 feet.

FIGURE 6.—Classification of Paleozoic strata in the Grand Canyon. From Walcott (1880, p. 222).

		Feet.
Tertiary		815
Cretaceous		3,095
Jurassic (identified)		960
Jura-Trias		3,430
Carboniferous	Permian ____ 854	
	Upper Aubrey Limestone ____ 805	
	Lower " Sandstone ____ 1,485	4,106
	Red Wall Limestone ____ 962	
Devonian	Temple Butte Limestone	94
Cambrian	Tonto (calcareous and arenaceous shales) ____	
	" (sandstone)	1,050
Algonkian	Chuar (shales and limestones) ____ 5,120	
	Grand Cañon (sandstones, with lava flows in upper part) ____ 6,830	12,950
	Vishnu (bedded quartzite and schists) ____ 1,000+	
		26,500

FIGURE 7.—Terminology and thickness of stratigraphic units in the Grand Canyon. From Walcott (1890, p. 50).

mations continued to fluctuate during this period as one worker after another obtained new fossil evidence or reinterpreted old correlations. Not until many years later did the geologic periods that were determined for

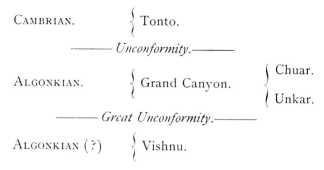

FIGURE 8.—Classification and age of lower rock units in the Grand Canyon. From Walcott (1895, p. 317).

various rock units finally become established, and not until relatively recent times have reliable data permitted assignment of rocks to smaller time units (geologic epochs) that could be accepted with confidence. For example, the Aubrey Limestone that had been considered Permian by Marcou and Carboniferous by Newberry, was classed as Permo-Carboniferous by Gilbert (1875a, p. 177) and by Marvine (1875, p. 213). Then, however, a detailed study of its fauna caused C. A. White (in Powell, 1876, p. 80) to state "* * * I therefore regard it as not improbable that the *time* of the Permian period may be represented in the Plateau Province by the Upper Aubrey Group * * *"; the age assignment, therefore, was changed back to the Permian where it remains today.

Other age assignments that changed repeatedly were those of the Tonto Group and the Grand Canyon Series. The Tonto was changed from Devonian ("Old Red") to Cambrian ("Potsdam"), to Primordial Silurian, to Carboniferous, and finally back to Cambrian, where it has remained since the middle 1880's. Assignment of its stratigraphic position within the Cambrian, however, continued to be changed until recent years, as shown in McKee and Resser (1945, p. 12), reproduced as figure 9 of this publication. Stratified rocks of the Precambrian Grand Canyon Series, first recorded by Powell (1875, p. 212) but not assigned an age, were later variously considered as Silurian (Powell, 1876; Dutton, 1882), Lower Cambrian (Walcott, 1883), and finally Precambrian (Walcott, 1886, p. 41). Today they are established as late Precambrian.

The most detailed stratigraphic work done in Grand Canyon during the last part of the 19th century was by Walcott. Not only did he measure numerous sections of various formations and make systematic collections of fossils that he later (1897–1925) described in 15 papers, but he also made many suggestions concerning paleogeography, sedimentology, and paleoecology.

Formation	Marcou 1856	Newberry 1861	Gilbert 1874	Powell 1875	Gilbert 1875	Walcott 1880	Dutton 1882	Walcott 1883	Walcott 1886	Walcott 1890	Walcott 1894
Muav.......	Devonian or Old Red sandstone	Potsdam	Primordial Silurian	Undetermined age	Primordial Silurian	Primordial Silurian	Carboniferous	Potsdam	Upper Cambrian to Ord. or Sil.	Upper Cambrian	....
Bright Angel								Potsdam	Upper Cambrian	Middle Cambrian	Middle Cambrian
Tapeats.....								....	....	....	Middle Cambrian

Formation	Walcott 1912	Noble 1914	Walcott 1918	Schuchert 1918b	Noble 1922	Walcott 1924 a and b	Moore 1925	Walcott 1925	Resser 1935	Stoyanow 1936	Wheeler and Kerr 1936
Muav.......	Upper Cambrian to Ord.	Middle Cambrian	....	Upper Cambrian	Upper Cambrian	Upper Cambrian	Upper Cambrian	....	....	Middle Cambrian	Middle Cambrian
Bright Angel	Middle Cambrian	Middle Cambrian	....	Middle Cambrian	Middle Cambrian	Upper Cambrian	Upper Cambrian	Upper Cambrian	Middle Cambrian	Middle Cambrian	Lower and Middle Cambrian
Tapeats.....	....	Lower or Middle Cambrian	Middle Cambrian	Middle Cambrian	Middle Cambrian	....	Upper Cambrian	....	....	Middle Cambrian	Lower Cambrian

FIGURE 9.—Changes in age assignment of Tonto Group. From McKee and Resser (1945, p. 12).

Among his most significant contributions to sedimentary stratigraphy are:

1. (Walcott, 1880). A description of the channeling and extensive erosion surface formed on Cambrian limestones before deposition of the Devonian.
2. (Walcott, 1883). An interpretation of the environment of deposition during late stages in developing the great pre-Paleozoic unconformity and a description of the buried knolls and ridges of Precambrian rocks projecting into the basal Cambrian strata that illustrate "the sea breaking off and burying with drifting sand, fragments of the rocky islands" (p. 439).
3. (Walcott, 1890). A detailed study of the fault movement that occurred after cessation of Precambrian sedimentation and before Cambrian sedimentation along the line referred to as the East Kaibab displacement. He pointed out that the downthrown side was to the west, rather than to the east, as in later movements, and that the movement in Precambrian time ranged from 400 to 4,000 feet.
4. (Walcott, 1894). A record of the volcanic history of late Precambrian time. True fissure eruptions were shown to be represented in the Unkar Group by dikes and by a series of lava flows interbedded with red sandstones. The dikes had been first noted by Powell (1875, p. 81) on his river trips.

5. (Walcott, 1895, p. 329). Recognition that the Grand Canyon Series, with its long history of "orographic movement and subsequent erosion" after deposition, must have formed in Precambrian time, as these events would have exceeded the time interval recognized as necessary for Lower Cambrian sedimentation in other regions.
6. (Walcott, 1895). The first detailed stratigraphic sections of upper Precambrian rocks in the Grand Canyon and measurements of the succession totalling 12,000 feet.

EXPANDED STRATIGRAPHIC STUDIES, 1900–1935

During the first third of the present century, studies involving the stratified rocks of Grand Canyon greatly increased, and many new geologists appeared on the scene. Probably some of the acceleration in geological activity was directly related to opening of the Bright Angel and El Tovar Hotels in 1896 and 1905, respectively, and to the construction of a branch line of the Santa Fe Railroad to the South Rim in 1901. This made the Grand Canyon much more accessible than before. Also, a general increase in the number of geologists and the spreading fame of the Grand Canyon probably contributed to an expansion of interest.

Many of the studies during this period were of local areas, were limited in scope, and merely added to the sum total of general knowledge. Among the contributors were such eminent geologists as F. L. Ransome (1908, 1916), N. H. Darton (1910, 1925), H. H. Robinson (1913), Charles Schuchert (1918a, 1918b), J. B. Reeside, Jr., and Harvey Bassler (1922), R. C. Moore (1925), and C. R. Longwell (1928). New descriptive data and, in some cases, detailed sections for various rock formations were recorded. Ideas concerning paleogeography, especially the probable locations of positive elements in neighboring regions, and the sources of sediments were suggested by Ransome (1916), Schuchert (1918a), and Darton (1925). Many paleontological papers by C. D. Walcott (1897–1925) were published, although his Grand Canyon fieldwork had been finished before 1900. Many Cambrian fossils from Grand Canyon were described by him, and one paper (Walcott, 1918) was devoted to the tracks and trails of trilobites and other invertebrates. Other trace fossils, consisting of reptilian footprints in the Permian Coconino Sandstone and probable amphibian tracks in the Supai Formation of Pennsylvanian and Permian age, were studied by Gilmore (1926, 1927, 1928).

Some new formation names were given and some type sections were selected during this period, and terminology was being stabilized. The names Supai Formation, Coconino Sandstone, and Kaibab Limestone were proposed by Darton (1910, p. 25–28) for units of the Aubrey Group. Likewise, Tapeats Sandstone, Bright Angel Shale, and Muav Limestone were proposed by Noble (1914, p. 41, 61) for divisions of the Tonto Group; Hotauta Conglomerate, Bass Limestone, Hakatai Shale, Shinumo Quartzite, and Dox Sandstone were proposed for units in the Unkar Group. (Noble, 1914, p. 41). A new formation, the Hermit Shale, was created from the upper part of the Supai (Noble, 1922, p. 64). Thus, most of the Grand Canyon formations as we know them today had been recognized and named by 1935.

The contributions of one geologist—Levi Noble—during the period 1900 to 1935 were outstanding. A very large fund of factual data, which has stood the test of subsequent checks was accumulated by Noble; furthermore, he attempted a considerable amount of thought-provoking interpretation. Like Newberry in the earliest days and Walcott somewhat later, he advanced ideas, using all the evidence at hand, to interpret the genesis of the various stratified rocks and to explain the missing intervals. Perhaps the most important feature of Noble's work, however, was the pattern of stratigraphic study that he promoted and that has strongly guided much subsequent investigation in the region.

Noble (1914, p. 60) recognized that although "the distribution and broader character of the [stratified] rocks of the Grand Canyon are familiar to every geologist * * *," details of stratigraphy were still very imperfectly known. He stated (p. 60) that "a close and accurate comparison and correlation of the thickness and character of the Paleozoic formations from place to place in the Grand Canyon must therefore depend on the results of future detailed work at many points." Noble (1922) then proceeded to follow his own advice; he produced a classic paper on detailed stratigraphy in which trends and changes in all Paleozoic formations of eastern Grand Canyon were described and analyzed for a distance of about 30 miles. This work set the stage for most subsequent studies, especially those involving paleogeography, the distribution of life, environment of deposition, paleoclimate, and other interpretive subjects.

One of the earliest attempts to analyze in detail available data bearing on the environment and history of the entire sequence of stratified rocks in Grand Canyon was presented by Noble (1914, p. 80–88). In his synthesis, he described his concepts of the genesis of each successive formation from bottom to top of the canyon walls and discussed for each unit such features as climate, advances and retreats of the sea, agents of sediment transport, and sources of sediment. An excellent illustration of Noble's (1914, p. 62) skill in describing and interpreting environmental features is seen in the following quotation:

Within the Tapeats sandstone is a record of marine planation that in these vertical sections, which include no soil, is preserved with a clearness that is almost beyond belief. The long southwestern face of the Unkar island monadnock was undercut by the waves of the sea in which the sandstone was deposited, and a cross section of this old sea cliff preserved in the Tapeats sandstone in the southern wall of Hotauta Canyon near the Colorado reveals clearly every detail of the structure; at the base of the cliff huge angular blocks of Shinumo quartzite are incorporated in the Tapeats sandstone in the places where they fell and lodged; farther out lie masses of bowlders, worn and rounded by the pounding of the waves; and these bowlders run into lenses of fine pebbly conglomerate, representing the shingle of the ancient beach, dragged out by the undertow. No more striking example of a fossil sea cliff can be imagined.

RECENT STUDIES (SINCE 1935) AND THEIR INTERPRETATION

The greatly increased number of geological investigations and the accelerated pace at which new data on Grand Canyon stratified rocks have become available since 1935 are impressive. One trend has been toward specialization as new techniques in field and laboratory work have been developed and as new information has become available from related fields or from surrounding regions. A second trend has been toward broad regional generalizations made possible by the large amount of comparative data accumulated and compiled and by the application of statistical methods of study.

In order to summarize the results of recent studies in the Grand Canyon area, each of the specific phases of geology involved is considered below. Within this framework, the principal contributions, including interpretations, are presented in chronological sequence, from oldest to youngest formation.

Rock Classification—Revisions And Additions

Few major changes in the nomenclature of the Grand Canyon stratigraphic column have been proposed since Noble's definitive work of 1922. Principal additions to the list of formations and groups are the Nankoweap Group of Van Gundy (1934), Pakoon Limestone and Queantoweap Sandstone of McNair (1951), Callville Limestone, and Toroweap Formation. The name Rama Formation was suggested (Maxson, 1961) for intrusive rocks of late Precambrian age in the Bright Angel quadrangle, but because farther east these igneous rocks include basaltic flows that are interbedded with strata of the Dox Sandstone, the desirability of applying this name is questionable.

Nankoweap Group is the term applied by C. E. Van Gundy (1934; 1951) to sandstones and shales formerly assigned by Walcott to the lower part of the Chuar Group and the upper part of the Unkar Group of late Precambrian age. It is described as having erosional unconformities both above and below and as having a thickness of about 300 feet.

The Callville Limestone (Longwell, 1921, p. 47; 1928) and the Pakoon Limestone (McNair, 1951, p. 524–525) (fig. 10B, this publication) are names originally given to rock units outside the Colorado Plateau but subsequently recognized in the walls at the west end of Grand Canyon. Both units are dominantly limestones that are laterally equivalent to parts of the Supai Formation in the eastern Grand Canyon area. Where the boundary between the Supai Formation and its carbonate equivalents should be drawn still is not known; clarification of this problem awaits further detailed work.

The Queantoweap Sandstone was described by A. H. McNair (1951, p. 525–526). It is the upper cliff member of the Supai Formation in western Grand Canyon and has long been known as the Esplanade Cliff unit.

Throughout most of the canyon area, this unit is considered the upper part of the Supai Formation.

The name Toroweap Formation (fig. 10A) was proposed by McKee in 1938 (p. 12–28) for lower members of the Kaibab Limestone of Darton (1910); the name Kaibab was restricted to the original upper units. This revision serves to emphasize dual transgression as represented by the limestone members of each formation and, in addition, gives recognition to the unconformity between these units and to differences in faunas of the two limestones.

Most of the recent revisions and additions to the classification and nomenclature of stratified rocks in Grand Canyon have involved units of member status. In the Cambrian, Mississippian, Pennsylvanian, and Permian rocks, such subdivisions have been recognized, and names have been applied to most of them.

In the Cambrian strata of Grand Canyon, key beds or marker beds of various types have been traced for many miles along canyon walls; these beds make feasible the recognition of intervening stratigraphic units, most of which have been given formal names (McKee and Resser, 1945, p. 80–110). These units consist of eight members and seven tongues, as illustrated in figures 11 and 12 of this report. Members are recognized within the carbonate rock sequence by virtue of certain marker beds, considered to be essentially time planes, that form bounding surfaces. Tongues of dolomite extend laterally from the limestone members into a sequence of shales, siltstones, and fine-grained sandstones. Thus, although the formation boundaries cross time planes because of transgressions and regressions, the members within these Cambrian strata do not.

The Redwall Limestone has been divided into four members, first tentatively designated by numbers and then by letters, as indicated in figure 13. The members were later given the formal names, in ascending order, of Whitmore Wash, Thunder Springs, Mooney Falls (fig. 14C), and Horseshoe Mesa (McKee and Gutschick, 1969, chap. 2). These well-defined units are based on distinctive lithologic features and are believed to represent two periods of marine transgression, each followed by a period of regression. They apparently are independent of time units as shown by faunal zones, especially those of foraminifers, that are abundant in these rocks.

Subdivision of the Supai-Hermit red-bed sequence is necessary if progress is to be made in unravelling the history of these rocks; however, difficulties are posed by the lack of extensive fossil zones that can be used as markers and by the similarity of different rock units. Fortunately, because datable limestones and dolomites intertongue with the red beds on the west and south, the

FIGURE 10.—Stratified rocks of Grand Canyon. *A,* View west from Twin Springs Canyon: (S,e) Supai Formation, Esplanade cliff unit; (H) Hermit Shale; (C) Coconino Sandstone; (T) Toroweap Formation; (K) Kaibab Limestone. *B,* View north from head of Pigeon Wash: (R) Redwall Limestone; (S,1) Supai Formation, lower cliff unit; (S,m) Supai Formation, middle cliff unit; (P) Pakoon Limestone of McNair (1951).

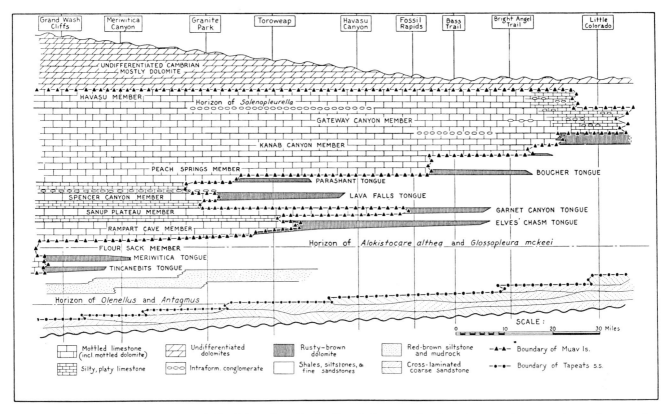

FIGURE 11.—Diagrammatic section of Cambrian deposits in Grand Canyon, showing stages in transgression and regression and distribution of facies from east to west. (Time planes are horizontal; actual thickness ranges from 1,500 feet in west to 800 feet in east.) From McKee and Resser (1945, fig. 1).

dating of major rock units in some areas has been accomplished. Furthermore, several thin conglomerate units (Fig. 14A) have been shown to be widespread and probably mark hiatuses between natural divisions within the rock sequence. In any event, faunal evidence from the limestones shows that the Pennsylvanian System is represented by rock equivalents of the Morrow, Des Moines, and Virgil Series and that a series equivalent (Atoka, Missouri) is missing between each two of these. Furthermore, rocks of Wolfcamp age of the Permian rest unconformably on rocks of Virgil age. Thus, although no formal names are as yet proposed and boundaries are not recognized in many areas, available evidence suggests that at least four definite subdivisions (members) occur with in the Supai-Hermit sequence.

Classification of the Kaibab Limestone (fig. 15) has been changed several times during the past half century. Three members (A, B, C) were recognized by Noble in 1922 (p. 68–70), but in a later, more detailed study, he (Noble, 1928, p. 52–54) included five members (A–E) in which the designations of individual units did not correspond with the earlier ones. When still another change in assignment became necessary because

of the designation of the Toroweap Formation (McKee, 1938, p. 18) (fig. 16, this report), the Greek letters α, β, and γ were used (descending order) for the members of each formation to avoid confusion with either of the earlier systems. The γ member is believed to represent the time of advancing seas, the β member the time of extended seas, and the α member the time of receding seas.

Refinements In Age Determination

Since 1886, rocks of the Grand Canyon Series have been considered Precambrian in age (Walcott, 1886, p. 41), and in 1890, they were referred to the "Algonkian" on the basis of stratigraphic position (Walcott, 1890, p. 50, 52). No fossils of diagnostic age have yet been found in these rocks, and no direct dating by potassium-argon, rubidium-strontium, or lead-uranium measurements has yet been reported, but new data have strengthened the stratigraphic evidence. Discovery that the Tapeats Sandstone is of Early Cambrian age, at least in western Grand Canyon, and that it is a continuous transgressive sand body across the region from west to

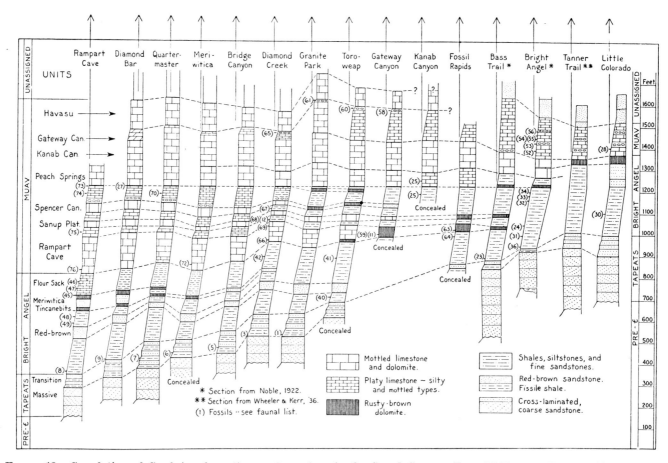

FIGURE 12.—Correlation of Cambrian formations and members in the Grand Canyon. From McKee and Resser (1945, fig. 2B).

east (McKee and Resser, 1945, p. 11–15) shows that the Grand Canyon Series is clearly older than earliest Cambrian. Unconformably underlying the series, moreover, are metamorphic rocks intruded by pegmatites that have a minimum age of 1,540 m.y. on the basis of rubidium-strontium measurements (Giletti and Damon, 1961). These measurements indicate that rocks immediately below the Grand Canyon Series either are to be correlated with the Mazatzal revolution (Damon and Giletti, 1961) or are younger, as argued by Wasserburg and Lanphere (1965, p. 755). In either case, the Grand Canyon Series must be considerably younger than the dated pegmatites.

Correlation between the Grand Canyon Series and certain other rocks long suspected to be of similar age—especially the Apache Group of southern Arizona and the Belt Supergroup of Montana and Idaho—involves many uncertainties. Nevertheless, recent studies of the Apache Group by Shride (1967, p. 80–81) have prompted him to suggest, on the basis of similar sequences of distinctive features, a correlation between parts of this group and lower units of the Unkar. He

believes that stratigraphic equivalents of the Dox Sandstone and the Chuar Group are absent in southern Arizona because of erosion prior to Cambrian deposition. Further progress in the matter of correlation probably must await the determination of absolute ages.

Today, the age of the Cambrian rocks of Grand Canyon seems to be well established, on the basis of extensive fossil collections. These collections consist mostly of trilobites and brachiopods and include some gastropods, Conchostraca, cystids, and sponges, described for the most part by C. E. Resser (in McKee and Resser, 1945, p. 185–220). Systematic collecting of these fossils has demonstrated that they occur in well-defined zones ranging from late Early Cambrian to approximately the middle of Middle Cambrian time (McKee and Resser, 1945, p. 29–33). Although many of the fossil genera have considerable vertical range, extending through much of the Cambrian of the area studied, the species are mostly very limited in range, being restricted to single members or rock units 150 feet thick or less. Three principal faunal zones in the Grand Canyon occur within a rock thickness of slightly

<table>
<tr><th></th><th colspan="2">Walcott, 1880</th><th colspan="2">Noble, 1922</th><th colspan="2">Gutschick, 1943</th><th colspan="2">Easton and Gutschick, 1953</th><th colspan="2">McKee, 1958</th><th colspan="2">McKee, 1960a</th><th colspan="2">This paper</th></tr>
<tr><td rowspan="2">Pennsylvanian and Permian</td><td colspan="2">Lower Aubrey group</td><td colspan="2" rowspan="2">Supai formation</td><td colspan="2" rowspan="2">Supai formation</td><td colspan="2" rowspan="2">Supai formation</td><td colspan="2" rowspan="2">Supai formation</td><td colspan="2" rowspan="2">Supai formation</td><td colspan="2" rowspan="2">Naco Formation (east)
Supai Formation (middle)
Callville Limestone, part (west)</td></tr>
<tr><td rowspan="5">Redwall limestone</td><td>A</td></tr>
<tr><td rowspan="4">Mississippian</td><td rowspan="2">B</td><td rowspan="4">Redwall limestone</td><td>Subdivision A</td><td rowspan="4">Redwall limestone</td><td>Member IV</td><td rowspan="4">Redwall limestone</td><td>Member IV</td><td rowspan="4">Redwall limestone</td><td>Top member</td><td rowspan="4">Redwall limestone</td><td>Member D</td><td rowspan="4">Redwall Limestone</td><td>Horseshoe Mesa Member</td></tr>
<tr><td rowspan="2">Subdivision B</td><td>Member III</td><td>Member III</td><td>Upper middle member</td><td>Member C</td><td>Mooney Falls Member</td></tr>
<tr><td>C</td><td>Member II</td><td>Member II</td><td>Lower middle member</td><td>Member B</td><td>Thunder Springs Member</td></tr>
<tr><td>D</td><td>Subdivision C</td><td>Member I</td><td>Member I</td><td>Bottom member</td><td>Member A</td><td>Whitmore Wash Member</td></tr>
<tr><td>Devonian</td><td colspan="2">Temple Butte limestone</td><td colspan="2">Temple Butte limestone</td><td colspan="2">Jerome formation</td><td colspan="2">Jerome formation</td><td colspan="2">Temple Butte formation</td><td colspan="2"></td><td colspan="2">Temple Butte and Muav Limestone* (north)
Martin Formation (south)</td></tr>
</table>

*Middle Cambrian

FIGURE 13.—Development of stratigraphic subdivision of the Redwall Limestone. From McKee and Gutschick (1969, table 1).

more than 1,000 feet, and because of the widespread distribution and abundance of some species, these fossils form excellent horizon markers, as shown in figure 17.

Little more is known today, concerning the age of Grand Canyon rocks assigned to the Devonian System, than was known in 1879 when Walcott (1880, p. 225) discovered "placoganoid fishes" in the walls of Kanab Canyon, a few miles above its junction with the main canyon. Additional fish specimens were found by Noble (1922, p. 51, 52) at Sapphire Canyon, and these were assigned to the genus *Bothriolepis* by Gidley; none, however, have been reported since. The early specimens from Grand Canyon are discussed in a restudy of Devonian fresh-water fishes from the Western United States by Denison (1951, p. 221, 230) who concurs in the generic identification and states that the genus is "a characteristic element of Late Devonian fresh-water faunas throughout much of the world" (1951, p. 223). In the most recent stratigraphic report on the Devonian of Arizona (McKee, in Poole and others, 1967, p. 887), the Temple Butte Limestone of Grand Canyon is shown as probably representing much of the Frasnian stage or lower part of the Upper Devonian Series. A suggestion is made that the Temple Butte is approximately correlative with the fossiliferous and well-dated Jerome Member of the Martin Formation in central Arizona, the fossils of which have been reported on by Teichert (1965).

In the Redwall Limestone, determination of fossil zones and consequent age assignments for various parts of the formation have resulted from extensive systematic fossil collecting within recent years (McKee and

FIGURE 14.—Some sedimentary features in stratified rocks of Grand Canyon. *A*, Conglomerate containing chert and jasper pebbles; forms key bed in lower part of Supai Formation, Whitmore Wash. *B*, Channel at top of thin-bedded carbonate rock of Cambrian age filled with poorly-bedded Devonian dolomite, Lone Tree Canyon. *C*, Massive limestone cliff formed by Mooney Falls Member of Redwall Limestone, Parashant Canyon. *D*, Cambrian-late Precambrian unconformity. Tapeats Sandstone resting on beveled surface of diabase in Dox Sandstone, Cremation Canyon. *E*, Cyclothem of (1) red bed, (2) aphanitic limestone, and (3) bedded gypsum (ascending order) in Toroweap Formation, Wolf Hole. *F*, Beds of (c) earthy chert, alternating with beds of (s) calcareous sandstone, Kaibab Limestone, near south Kaibab trail. *G*, Bedded chert (dark bands) alternating with aphanitic limestone (light bands) in Thunder Springs Member of Redwall Limestone, Iceberg Canyon.

Status	Environment—locality	Character	Other names—fauna
α member (upper)	Time of receding seas	Thin-bedded limestones, chemical precipitates, red beds, local cross-bedded sandstones	Bellerophon limestone of Powell; Super Aubrey of Huntington and Goldthwait; Harrisburg gypsiferous member of Reeside and Bassler; subdivision A of Noble, 1928
Facies 1	Western area, i. e. Toroweap and westward	Alternating red beds, gypsum deposits, and thin-bedded limestones	Fauna mostly molluscan, some brachiopods
Facies 2	Middle, eastern area, i. e. Hilltop to Little Colorado	Alternating thin-bedded limestones and red beds	Fauna molluscan
Facies 3	Southern and southeastern areas, i. e. Sycamore Canyon east over Mogollon Plateau	Thin-bedded limestones in great thickness; locally sandstones, cross-bedded and flat-bedded, mostly light-colored	Fauna not well known but probably like preceding
Facies 4	Apparently restricted to area of Rimey Jim Ranch between Flagstaff and Cameron	Massive magnesian limestone	Fauna molluscan, mostly gastropods
Facies 5	San Rafael Swell, along Fremont River, Circle Cliffs	Thin-bedded, magnesian limestone	Fauna not well known; mostly molluscan; correlation tentative
β member (middle)	Time of extended seas	Massive crystalline limestone, sandy limestone, and sandstone; in part with bedded and concretionary cherts	Subdivision A of Noble, 1922; subdivision B of Noble, 1928
Facies 1	Western area, i. e. from Hermit and Aubrey Cliffs west	Largely crystalline limestone, becoming sandy toward eastern border, concretionary chert abundant	Fauna of molluscoids, corals, and sponges
Facies 2	East, central area, near Kaibab Trail and Sycamore Canyon	Sandy limestone and sandstone beds alternating with bedded cherts	No fauna except on borders, where species of adjoining facies appear
Facies 3	Middle, eastern area, i. e. Point Imperial, Desert View Point	Fine, uniform-grained, non-calcareous sandstone, brown	Fauna molluscan
Facies 4	Eastern, southeastern, and southern areas, esp. on Mogollon Plateau, Little Colo. and Marble Canyons	Dolomitic limestones, in places sandy or alternating with sandstones	Fauna mostly molluscan
Facies 5	San Rafael Swell, along Fremont River, Circle Cliffs	Sandstones, sandy limestones, and limestones	Fauna largely of molluscoids correlation tentative
γ member (lower)	Time of advancing seas	Massive and thin-bedded, impure limestones	
Facies 1	Southern and southeastern area, i. e. on Mogollon Plateau	Magnesian limestones with sandy limestones	Fauna of large mollusks confined to Mogollon Plateau

FIGURE 15.—Classification of rock units in the Kaibab Formation. From McKee (1938, table 4).

Status	Environment—locality	Character	Other names—fauna
WESTERN PHASE			
α member (upper red)	Time of receding seas	Red beds, gypsum, chemical limestones	Subdivision B of Noble, 1922; subdivision C of Noble, 1928
Facies 1	Western area, i. e. from Hilltop westward	Red beds, thin-bedded limestones, gypsum deposits	No fauna except in one pelecypod limestone
Facies 2	Eastern area, i. e. from Fossil Mtn. to Hance Trail	Red beds	No fauna except in one pelecypod limestone
β member (limestone)	Time of extended seas	Massive limestones	Subdivision C of Noble, 1922; subdivision D of Noble, 1928
Facies 1	Western area, i. e. Toroweap and westward	Massive, crystalline and dense, marine limestones	Fauna of molluscoid types
Facies 2	Eastern area, i. e. Hilltop east to Desert View	Massive, impure, brackish-water limestones	Fauna of mollusks
γ member (lower red)	Time of advancing seas	Red beds, other sandstones and shales, gypsum in west	Subdivision E of Noble, 1928
Facies 1	Throughout area	Red beds and other sandstones. Gypsum reported in west, new facies?	No fauna
TRANSITION PHASE			
Intertongued type	Transition area, i. e. Hance Trail, Desert View, Sycamore Canyon	White cross-bedded sandstones fingering into red beds	No fauna
EASTERN PHASE			
Sandstone type	Eastern area, i. e. Little Colorado, Oak Creek Canyon	White cross-bedded and gnarly-bedded sandstones	No fauna

FIGURE 16.—Classification of rock units in the Toroweap Formation. From McKee (1938, table 2).

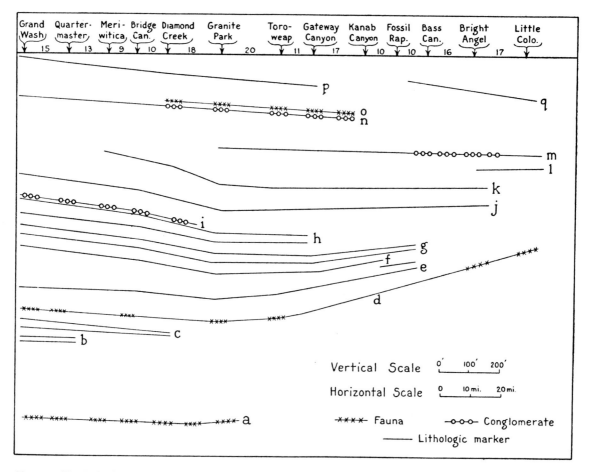

FIGURE 17.—Principal key beds and horizon markers considered to be approximate time planes in Cambrian deposits of the Grand Canyon: "(a) *Olenellus-Antagmus* horizon. (b) Tincanebits tongue, boundary beds. (c) Meriwitica tongue, boundary beds. (d) *Glossopleura-Alokistocare* horizon. (e) Rampart Cave member, basal beds. (f) Rampart Cave member, top beds. (g) Sanup Plateau member, boundary beds. (h) Spencer Canyon member, boundary beds. (i) Lower conglomerate beds. (j) Peach Springs member, basal beds. (k) Kanab Canyon member, basal beds. (l) Kanab Canyon member, middle beds. (m) Gateway Canyon member, basal beds and conglomerate. (n) Upper conglomerate bed. (o) *Solenopleurella* horizon. (p) Havasu member, top beds. (q) Top of Noble's 'Mauv C.'" From McKee and Resser (1945, fig. 3).

Gutschick, 1969, chap. 4). Foraminifers, brachiopods, and certain genera of corals occur in distinct zones; most other faunal groups seem to owe their distribution patterns to facies control. The foraminifers form six zones, two of which are divided into two subzones each, and this zonation represents an almost continuous faunal succession through the formation (Betty Skipp, in McKee and Gutschick, 1969, chap. 5). Among the corals, many forms are long-ranging, so they are not useful in zonation; but two species, *Dorlodotia inconstans* and *Michelinia expansa* form very distinctive widespread zones (W. J. Sando, in McKee and Gutschick, 1969, chap. 6). Brachiopods likewise seem to be useful as zone indicators, but details of their distribution and significance have not yet been published.

In the Redwall Limestone, rather good agreement has been attained in age determinations based on independent studies of the main faunal groups (McKee and Gutschick, 1969). Zones of foraminifers show an age range from late Kinderhook to middle? Meramec. Brachiopods from several localities confirm the Kinderhook age in the basal parts of the sections involved; brachiopods range upward through Osage and into Meramec forms in many sections. Corals likewise indicate a Meramec age for the uppermost beds in many places. In one locality (Bright Angel trail), a thin remnant of strata of Chester age, dated both by brachiopods and by foraminifers, has been preserved. In general, age determinations and the character of the faunas upon which these are based indicate a close relationship between the Redwall and other Mississippian Rocky Mountain formations such as the Madison, Leadville, Escabrosa, and Lake Valley Limestones.

The age assignment of the Supai-Hermit red-bed sequence, which has for a long time fluctuated between Pennsylvanian and Permian, seems finally to be stabilizing, as more and more diagnostic fossils are uncovered in various parts of the area and at different horizons. The age of the Hermit Shale was determined as "upper Lower Permian" by David White (1929, p. 38) on the basis of plant species in its relatively large flora. The Pakoon Limestone—a carbonate tongue extending into the upper part of the Supai Formation from the west—has been shown by McNair (1951, p. 525) to be Permian also, for it contains an abundance of diagnostic Wolfcamp fusulinids. More recently, numerous collections of invertebrate fossils, mostly brachiopods and fusulinids, have been made by the writer (unpub. data) from limestone tongues lower in the Supai, showing that Pennsylvanian rocks of Virgil, Des Moines, and Morrow age are also represented in the Supai.

Both the Coconino Sandstone and the Toroweap Formation, between the Hermit Shale and Kaibab Limestone, have long been assigned to the Permian System because of stratigraphic position. Virtually the only fossils that have been found in the Coconino are tracks considered reptilian, and although these are scarcely reliable for precise correlation on the basis of present knowledge, it is significant that some of the same forms occur also in the Lyons Sandstone of Permian age in Colorado (Gilmore, 1926, p. 5, 13). The fauna of the Toroweap is relatively small and nondiagnostic, but in general it is similar to that of the Kaibab, which has been correlated with the standard Permian of Texas. Thus, the Leonard age of the Toroweap seems well established.

The Kaibab Limestone that forms the rim of Grand Canyon and constitutes the youngest Paleozoic formation in northern Arizona is now believed almost certainly to be of late Leonard age (McKee and Breed, 1969). Correlation with the standard Permian sequence of Texas has been established on the basis of brachiopods (McKee, 1938, p. 170), mollusks (Chronic, 1952, p. 111), siliceous sponges (Finks, 1960, p. 36), and nautiloids (Miller and Youngquist, 1949, p. 9). Although these faunal groups do not all suggest correlation with the same rock unit in Texas, the youngest probable correlative in the Texas sequence is the Road Canyon Formation, formerly the "First Limestone member" of the Word Formation, which has been shown by Cooper and Grant (1966, p. E6) to belong to the Leonard Series.

Fossils of the Kaibab Limestone, especially the brachiopods, make possible rather firm correlations between it and Permian strata of surrounding areas. The typical brachiopod assemblage of the Kaibab occurs in the Concha Limestone of southern Arizona (Gilluly and others, 1954, p. 31; Bryant and McClymonds, 1961, p. 1329). This assemblage also is found in the section in the Confusion Range, western Utah, so the name Kaibab has been extended to that area (Hose and Repenning, 1959, p. 2178–2179). Farther east in Utah, all marine Permian strata seem to be of Guadalupe age and therefore are younger than the Kaibab (McKee, 1954, p. 21; Yochelson, 1968, p. 625).

Paleogeography And Paleotectonics

Many attempts have been made within recent years to reconstruct the geographic and tectonic features of various ages in the Grand Canyon region. Paleogeographic maps prepared by Stoyanow (1942, pl. 5) illustrate his views, largely derived from the study of invertebrate fossils, on the distribution of land and sea within Arizona during various parts of the Paleozoic. A series of isopach maps of the Paleozoic rocks of Arizona and adjoining areas was published in 1951 (McKee, 1951). More elaborate and detailed maps, both isopach and lithofacies, but only for certain Paleozoic systems, have since been prepared as parts of the paleotectonic map series of the U.S. Geological Survey (for example, the Permian System: McKee, Oriel, and others, 1967; also maps for Pennsylvanian and Mississippian Systems, unpub. data). These maps include Arizona. Finally, a detailed isopach map of Mississippian rocks of the Grand Canyon area, and one for each of the Redwall members, have been published by McKee and Gutschick (1969, figs. 2, 7, 16, 23, 28).

Information on paleogeography of upper Precambrian stratified rocks in Grand Canyon is meager, partly because reliable data on precise correlation with rocks of adjoining areas are lacking. Trends in lithofacies, especially the considerable increase westward in percentage of carbonate rock within the Bass Limestone and the greater proportion of sand in the Hakatai Shale of eastern Grand Canyon than farther west were pointed out by Noble (1914, p. 54). Van Gundy (1951) obtained a small amount of information on directional movements of currents for the Nankoweap Group of Van Gundy (1934) and for the Chuar Group (Trevor Ford and W. J. Breed, unpub. data). By and large, however, the location and distribution of geographic and tectonic trends and their relationship to trends that dominated the history of Paleozoic time are not yet known.

Analysis of various maps, and accompanying texts, of the Grand Canyon region for Paleozoic time shows that the early concept of a landmass, referred to as Mazatzal Land, separating basins of northern and southern Arizona, does not satisfy the test of isopach mapping. The geographic picture that has evolved (fig. 18) and that seems to be rather similar for all Paleozoic systems is that of two positive elements—the Defiance (or Defiance-Zuni) in northeastern Arizona and the Ensenada southwest of Arizona—and seas from the Cordilleran and Sonoran troughs to the northwest and southeast, respectively, advancing periodically across adjacent shelves to connect across the Arizona sag of Eardley (1949, fig. 2) in central Arizona. Some doubt exists concerning the validity of the Ensenada positive area, because the record of Paleozoic rocks is poor in southwestern Arizona (McKee, 1947); thickness trends, however, suggest a definite and considerable thinning toward that corner of the State.

Significance Of Unconformities

Because strata in the walls of Grand Canyon are not concealed, either by debris or by vegetation for long distances, buried erosion surfaces of various types and magnitudes appear as prominent features. A realization that these erosion surfaces may be the time equivalents

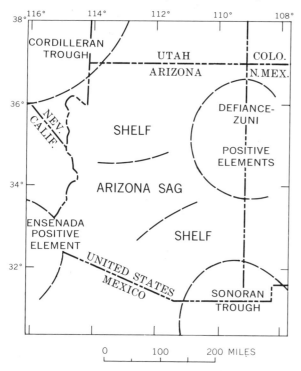

FIGURE 18.—Structural features of Arizona during middle part of Permian Period. Adapted from McKee and Breed (1969, fig. 2).

of great numbers of strata elsewhere in the geologic column makes their importance in the region's history apparent.

The most obvious and also the most significant of unconformities seen in the walls of Grand Canyon are those at the base of the Grand Canyon Series of late Precambrian age (fig. 19A) and at the bottom of the Tonto Group of Cambrian age (figs. 14D, 19A, and 19B). These unconformities were discussed by Powell (1875, p. 212), who pointed out that each represents a sequence of events of tremendous importance in earth history, including the formation of mountains by tectonic forces, the erosion of these mountains to a condition of base level, and, finally, the burial of the erosion surfaces by sediments of advancing seas.

Various aspects of these great unconformities have subsequently been examined and studied by many geologists, including Walcott, Noble, Hinds, Sharp, and McKee. The terms "Ep-Archean" and "Ep-Algonkian" were used by Hinds (1935, p. 4) in order to facilitate reference to each unconformity, and this procedure was subsequently followed in discussions by Sharp (1940) and by McKee (McKee and Resser, 1945). Principal features considered during investigation of the unconformities were the amount of relief on the erosion surfaces, the relative importance of marine as opposed to subaerial erosion, the duration of each period of erosion, and the climatic implications for each interval.

Probably the most conspicuous feature of the earlier or "Ep-Archean" erosion surface is its extreme flatness; it has relief not exceeding 20 feet in most areas and an observed maximum of 50 feet (Hinds, 1935, p. 10). In contrast, the "Ep-Algonkian" surface, although also referred to as a peneplain by some authors (Hinds, 1935, p. 49; Sharp, 1940, p. 1244), consists of a series of block-faulted quartzite ridges, some of which rise 800 and 900 feet above the general base of erosion (McKee and Resser, 1945, p. 117).

A weathered mantle from subaerial erosion is typical of both the "Ep-Archean" and "Ep-Algonkian" surfaces. Although only slight chemical weathering (on the "Ep-Archean" surface) was reported by Noble (1910, p. 524; 1914, p. 81) and a dominance of mechanical disintegration for both surfaces was suggested by Hinds (1935, p. 50), a depth of weathering of 10 feet beneath the "Ep-Archean" surface and as much as 50 feet beneath the "Ep-Algonkian" surface is recorded by Sharp (1940, p. 1264). The thesis of intense chemical weathering proposed by Sharp (1940, p. 1255–1257) is supported by his studies of the progressive changes of certain minerals such as biotite and feldspar, on evidence of residual concentrations of iron oxide, and on measurements of insoluble-residue accumulations.

FIGURE 19.—Major unconformities in Grand Canyon involving (1) Vishnu Schist (includes granite), (2) Grand Canyon Series, (3) Tonto Group, Cambrian. *A*, Unconformities between lower and upper Precambrian rocks and between upper Precambrian and Paleozoic rocks near Shinumo Canyon opposite Bass trail. From Noble (1914, pl. *8B*). *B*, Unconformity between lower Precambrian rocks and Paleozoic strata west of Quartermaster Canyon.

Marine erosion undoubtedly took part in shaping the ultimate landscape that was covered by transgressing seas during both late Precambrian and Cambrian times. Examples of its effects on quartzite islands, forming sea cliffs and other characteristic features (fig. 20B), and of its reworking of weathered material and of talus have been cited by Noble (1914, p. 62), Sharp (1940, p. 1265), and McKee (McKee and Resser, 1945, p. 120). Sharp (1940, p. 1265) contends, however, that these "marine processes have modified the topography of the surfaces only to a minor degree."

The periods of time represented by the two great unconformities in Grand Canyon must have been of great duration, as indicated by the record of events that these unconformities portray. The tremendous amount of time represented by the "Ep-Algonkian" unconformity so impressed Walcott (1910, p. 14) that he assigned it a name—the Lipalian interval—and he described it as "an era of unknown marine sedimentation between the adjustment of pelagic life to littoral conditions and the appearance of the Lower Cambrian fauna." The magnitude of this break in the record was later minimized by Hinds (1939, p. 306), who argued that Lipalian time was not one of long-continued emergence and that a great break in the record did not separate latest Precambrian from Cambrian time. On the other hand, calculations of the time involved in lowering by erosion a land surface of the height represented by the upper Precambrian strata of Grand Canyon were made by Sharp (1940, p. 1260–1261), who concluded that roughly 100 million years would have been required.

Other conclusions based on studies of the great unconformities have involved speculations on the climate during late stages of erosion and immediately preceding marine deposition after each hiatus. Despite earlier contentions to the contrary, a strong case was made by Sharp (1940, p. 1255) to indicate that in both "Ep-Archean" and "Ep-Algonkian" times dominantly humid conditions prevailed. The evidence included considerations of insoluble residues, nature and extent of weathering, lack of caliche, content of iron oxide in detritus, and type of residual feldspar.

Two relatively minor yet locally significant unconformities have been recorded from within the upper Precambrian strata of the Grand Canyon (Van Gundy, 1951, p. 954–955). On the basis of these two stratigraphic breaks, the Nankoweap Group of Van Gundy (1934) was separated from the Unkar and Chuar Groups. The earlier of the unconformities is described as being formed on top of basaltic lava flows of the Unkar which were eroded to an irregular surface and, in many places, covered by a conglomerate of basalt and sandstone debris. The later unconformity likewise is marked by an erosion surface and a conglomerate, and it underlies magnesian limestone of the Chuar.

Compared with the two great unconformities formed during and at the close of Precambrian time, others that have left their records in the walls of Grand Canyon are small. Nevertheless, the significance of various later erosion intervals, in terms of time involved if not of total volume of rock removed, is considerable. Most notable of these time breaks are the pre-Devonian, pre-Pennsylvanian, and pre-Triassic unconformities. More difficult to recognize, but nevertheless of significance because of the hiatus involved, are unconformities underlying rocks of the Mississippian and Permian Systems of this area.

An unconformity involving a hiatus of considerable magnitude—Late Cambrian, Ordovician, Silurian, and Early and Middle Devonian time—has been recognized at the top of the Cambrian sequence of the Grand Canyon. This break in the record is marked by a surface of erosion that in places consists of relatively narrow channels, as much as 100 feet or more deep, that were subsequently filled with sediment of Late Devonian age (fig. 14B). Such erosional irregularities were noted first by Walcott (1880, p. 221; 1883, p. 438); a detailed description of them, accompanied by sketches (fig. 21), as found along a 28-mile stretch of Grand Canyon walls, was subsequently given by Noble (1922, p. 49–51). Since then, few new data concerning the nature of this erosion surface have been obtained, but observations by the writer indicate that channels similar to those described also occur locally beneath thick Devonian sections in western Grand Canyon. Where no channels occur, the boundary between strata of Cambrian and Devonian age (Mississippian in parts of eastern Grand Canyon), commonly is difficult to recognize.

A pre-Mississippian unconformity is represented by a flat, even surface between dolomite units of Devonian (locally Cambrian) age and Mississippian age in eastern Grand Canyon (Noble, 1922, p. 53), but in many places it is obscure. Farther west, the unconformity is marked by a surface of slight relief and local conglomerates, so in places it is more readily located but is still not conspicuous (McKee and Gutschick, 1969, chap. 2). Nowhere is there evidence of large uplift that would cause marked dissection of the region or form angular unconformable relations between formations; beveling of the surface across a wide area, however, may have taken place. Faunal evidence suggests that a hiatus occurred, involving all of Kinderhook time in the east and much of it in western Grand Canyon (McKee and

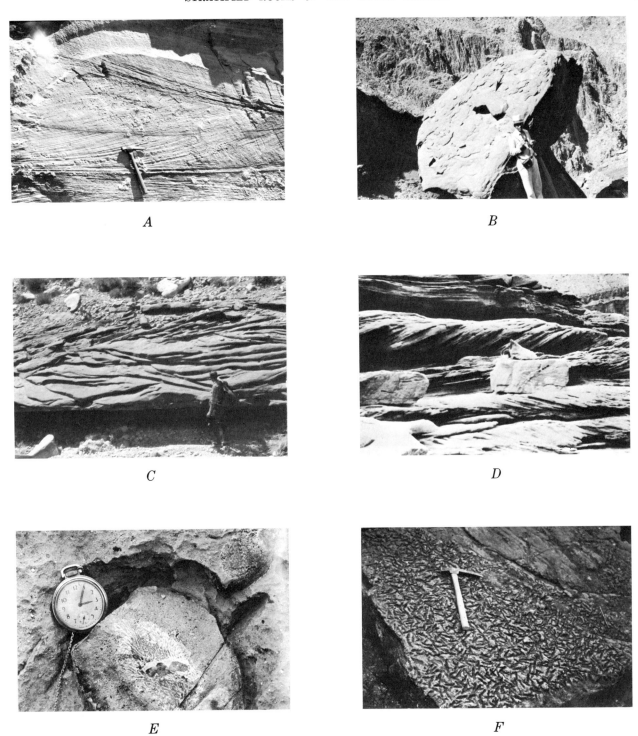

FIGURE 20.—Fossils and sedimentary features in stratified rocks of Grand Canyon. A, Wedge-planar cross-strata of Coconino Sandstone near Bright Angel trail. B, Boulder of upper Precambrian Shinumo Quartzite incorporated in fallen block of Cambrian Tapeats Sandstone, near south Kaibab trail. C, Trough-type cross-strata in upper part of Supai Formation, along Topocoba trail. D, Tabular-planar cross-strata in Tapeats Sandstone at Forster Canyon. E, Siliceous sponge, *Actinocoelia*, forming nucleus of spherical chert concretion, Kaibab Limestone, Hermit trail. F, Probable worm borings in upper part of Tapeats Sandstone near Grand Wash Cliffs.

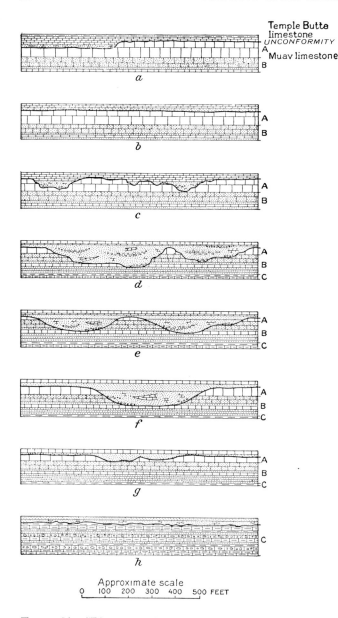

FIGURE 21.—"Diagrammatic sketches showing general character of unconformity between Temple Butte limestone and Muav limestone at eight localities between Garnet Canyon and Cottonwood Creek, Grand Canyon, Ariz. *a*, Garnet Canyon; *b*, Bass Canyon; *c*, Ruby Canyon; *d*, Turquise Canyon; *e*, Slate Creek; *f*, Hermit Creek; *g*, Pipe Creek; *h*, Cottonwood Creek." From Noble (1922, fig. 3).

Gutschick, 1969). The later part of Late Devonian time may also be unrepresented in rocks of this region, though evidence is scant (Poole and others, 1967, p. 887).

Between the Redwall Limestone of Mississippian age and the Supai Formation of Pennsylvanian age is an unconformity which, though scarcely noticeable in most places along the walls of Grand Canyon, is, nevertheless, an excellent record of erosion by solution. A rugged, irregular karst surface with local relief ranging from 3 to 40 feet forms the top of the Redwall (McKee and Gutschick, 1969). Depressions on this surface include channels of through-flowing streams, indicated by well-rounded cobbles and pebbles of chert and other durable materials that partially fill them; also included are ancient sinkholes, many of which contain angular fragments of locally derived limestone or dolomite. Elevations on the erosion surface consist of flat-topped ridges and low mesas or buttes that have been surrounded and buried by blankets of red mud and, in some places, by initial deposits of thin-bedded calcium carbonate of the Supai Formation. In many other places, caverns and solution-enlarged shrinkage cracks, partly filled with red mud of the Supai, extend down into the Redwall.

The hiatus represented by the unconformity at the top of the Redwall is between rocks of Meramec age (probably Osage in eastern Grand Canyon) and those of Morrow age—well above the base of the Pennsylvanian System. One exception is along the Bright Angel trail where a remnant of Chester-age rocks caps the Redwall (McKee and Gutschick, 1969). In the Grand Canyon area, no appreciable reduction of the original thickness of the Redwall occurred during pre-Supai erosion, for only the thin upper member is affected.

Probably the least well known of the important unconformities in the Grand Canyon sequence of stratified rocks is that between the Pennsylvanian- and Permian-age rocks. This stratigraphic break is marked by an overlying conglomerate of rounded gravel, composed largely of limestone, siltstone, and sandstone that seem to be locally derived. The conglomerate commonly has been considered intraformational, but detailed studies by the writer (unpub. data) show that it is persistent and extends from one end of Grand Canyon to the other. It is a gravel sheet that thins and thickens within short distances and is absent locally; it rests on an undulatory, channeled surface which in places has been eroded to form depressions 30 or 35 feet deep. In western Grand Canyon this excellent marker bed lies between marine units containing fossils that indicate Virgil (Late Pennsylvanian) age below and Wolfcamp (Early Permian) above.

The top of the Kaibab Limestone, which forms the rim of Grand Canyon, is in the approximate position of the Permian-Triassic unconformity, although in only a few places on the rim do overlying Triassic rocks remain to preserve the ancient erosion surface. This unconformity has been the subject of many detailed studies: Dake (1920); Longwell (1925); Baker, Dobbin, McKnight, and Reeside (1927); and McKee (1938, p. 55–61; 1954).

The hiatus represented by the break between the Kaibab Limestone and the Moenkopi Formation involves the time between the Leonard or early part of the Permian and the middle stage (*Meekoceras* zone) of the Early Triassic. It is calculated, therefore, in terms of some tens of millions of years. Physical evidence of the unconformity consists of irregular surfaces of erosion, of basal conglomerates, and, in some areas, of angular discordance. The most conspicuous record of vigorous erosion is in southwestern Utah and southern Nevada, where narrow valleys or canyons, 100 to 700 feet deep and partly filled with large pebbles and boulders, are reported (Longwell, 1921, p. 49; Reeside and Bassler, 1922, p. 60). In contrast, in the region east and north of the Grand Canyon, Ariz., the surface is generally flat and even, and pebbles in the basal conglomerate are small and subangular.

Interpretations of the pre-Moenkopi erosion surface differ materially. This surface has been attributed both to marine planation (Dane, 1935, p. 52–53) and to subaerial channeling by stream floods (Longwell, 1925, p. 106). The large channels, at least, seem to have been cut and largely filled by locally derived gravels before the first marine deposits were laid down.

Advances In Sedimentology

During the past 30 years, a considerable amount of information has been obtained on the sedimentology of certain Grand Canyon formations—especially those of Cambrian age and the Redwall and Supai. The petrology of most other rock units of Grand Canyon has been studied to some degree but still offers many problems.

In contrast to most other rock units, strata of late Precambrian age have received scant attention from the standpoint of sedimentation and facies interpretation, especially considering their great thickness and probable importance in earth history. Early references to the abundance of ripple marks and shrinkage cracks were made by Walcott (1895, p. 323) and Noble (1914, p. 47), and the presence of salt molds and other sedimentary structures is known. According to Walcott (1895, p. 325), the basal conglomerate was an "old sea-beach * * *"; "sand and a few beds of calcareous mud accumulated" in this sea. Walcott described how "flow after flow of basaltic lava poured out through these [fissures] over the sea-bed" (p. 325), while sand deposition continued between flows. In brief, he visualized a "great inclosed basin, or mediterranean sea" in which these sediments accumulated (Walcott, 1895, p. 327).

More recent study of the upper Precambrian strata of Grand Canyon by Van Gundy (1951) was concentrated on the petrography and sedimentary structures of a single small segment of strata—the Nankoweap Group of Van Gundy (1934). On the basis of mineral determinations, grain texture, and sorting observations, and evidence of strain shadows and inclusions in the quartz, a source for these rocks from the Unkar basalts and from lower Precambrian metamorphic and silicic igneous rocks was postulated. Directional trends of ripple marks indicate a regional current flow largely from south to north, and the absence of salt molds (in contrast with their presence in the Unkar beds below) suggests that depositing waters were not high in salt content. The conclusions of Van Gundy (1951, p. 959) were that rocks of this group were deposited in a body of shallow water, possibly a lagoon, bay, or estuary, connected with the ocean and containing mudflats or tidal flats.

The sequence of Cambrian rocks in Grand Canyon includes many different and distinctive types. These types have been analyzed with regard both to distribution and to petrologic characteristics (McKee and Resser, 1945, p. 37–79). Distribution of the rocks seems to have been determined largely by the environmental factors responsible for various facies; these facies apparently migrated across the region during marine transgression and regression in Cambrian time.

Approximately a dozen main lithologic facies are recognized in the Cambrian strata of Grand Canyon. These facies include a transgressive series, consisting, from shore seaward (east-west), of conglomerate, coarse-grained sandstone, fine-grained sandstone (fig. 22B), green shaly mudstone, glauconitic ferruginous beds, rusty-brown dolomite, *Girvanella* limestone, and mottled aphanitic limestone. The sequence is repeated in five principal steps (fig. 12; fig. 27) that record stages of transgression across the region. Deposits of regression, in contrast, include some very different lithologic facies, such as silty micaceous platy limestones, a distinctive type of glauconite bed, and thin-bedded intraformational edge-wise conglomerates. These strata are believed to have formed at times when sedimentation had built up approximately to the base level of deposition; this permitted only a very limited accumulation of permanent deposits because of the slow rate of concurrent basin sinking.

The Cambrian rocks of Grand Canyon offer one of the best documented illustrations of the mechanics of transgression (McKee and Resser, 1945, p. 133–138). Evidence is available both from the Tapeats Sandstone and from the Muav Limestone. Continuously exposed rock surfaces across wide areas and the presence of thin marker beds approximating time planes show that

FIGURE 22.—Primary structures in stratified rocks of Grand Canyon. A, Wedge-planar cross-strata in middle part of Call-
ville Limestone, Grand Gulch mine trail. B, Interference ripple marks in fine-grained sandstone of Bright Angel Shale,
Pipe Creek Canyon. C, Eolian-type ripple marks on steeply dipping cross-strata in Coconino Sandstone, Kaibab trail. D,
Large-scale, tabular-planar cross-strata in middle cliff of Supai Formation, Havasu Canyon.

transgression consisted of a series of rapid advances,
with pauses of considerable duration between each
advance. During pauses, the sea floor was relatively
stable, and little sediment could accumulate because of
high base level, as shown in figure 23. Thus, periodic,
rather than continuous, advance of the sea occurred.

Detrital sedimentary rocks of the Cambrian, especially the coarse-grained sandstones, lend themselves
well to statistical studies of texture and structure.
Analyses show that the trough-type crossbedding,
which consists of successive, superimposed channels, each
filled either symmetrically or asymmetrically with dipping foresets, is very common, but that medium-scale

tabular-planar and wedge-planar crossbeds also are
present (fig. 20D). (Terminology for crossbeds according to McKee and Weir (1953).) Directional studies of
cross lamination indicate a regional current trend from
east to west. In some local areas, islands of Precambrian
quartzite served to deflect the currents (McKee and
Resser, 1945, p. 125–131), and directions of dip on
crossbeds are very different in such places. Studies of
degrees of sorting, skewness, and other properties of
the sand grains have permitted reasonable speculations
on depth of water, rate of sand accumulation, and
other environmental considerations in reconstructing
the history of the Tapeats Sandstone.

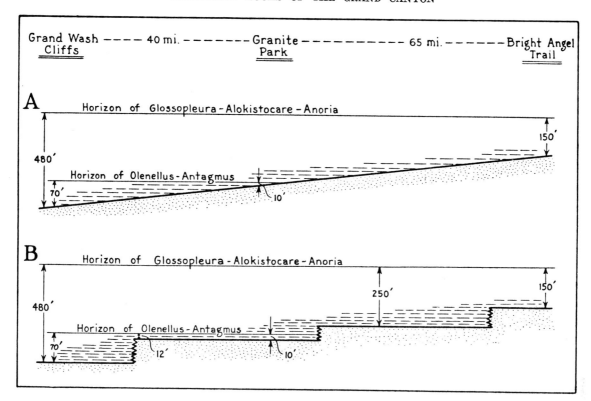

FIGURE 23.—Reconstruction of boundary between coarse sand and shale developed during transgression of the Cambrian sea. A. Based on field data only. B. Based on field data plus various theoretical considerations. From McKee and Resser (1945, fig. 12).

The Redwall Limestone of Mississippian age has recently been the subject of monographic treatment (McKee and Gutschick, 1969). The sedimentology was given careful consideration, along with stratigraphy, paleontology, and other aspects of the formation. Carbonate rocks that form most of the Redwall were found to be remarkably free of all detrital materials, but bedded chert constitutes a significant part of two of the four members. Dolomite, which forms a considerable part of the carbonate rock, is largely restricted to the lower part of the formation and is mostly in the relatively thin sections of eastern Grand Canyon. This, with other evidence, supports the concept that the dolomite was formed by normal diagenesis on the sea floor at an early stage after deposition.

Limestone of the Redwall includes both granular and aphanitic types, and these types alternate in a cyclic arrangement within the upper two members of the formation across a wide area. Although grain size of clastic carbonate particles may bear no relation to depth or distance from shore, studies of the Redwall suggest that cycles in this formation, recognized by differences in grain size, probably resulted from systematic changes in water depth that effected differences in

wave base (McKee, 1960a, p. 231). The granular limestone of the Redwall includes three principal varieties that can readily be recognized: peloidal, skeletal, and oölitic. These varieties commonly occur in separate beds, but mixtures of two or all of them are not uncommon.

A semiquantitative study of bedded chert in the Thunder Springs Member (fig. 14*G*) of the Redwall was made at selected localities throughout the Grand Canyon region to determine relations and distributional trends of rock types and of fossils (McKee, 1960b). Through the analysis of a series of sample plots, a few of which are shown in figure 24, the probable time of chert development, on or beneath the sea floor, was determined to have been at a very early stage of diagenesis and before the associated calcium carbonate of the eastern Grand Canyon had been changed to dolomite. Furthermore, it was shown that types and relative abundance of animals in the Redwall sea differed according to paleogeographic location and(or) type of associated sediment.

An attempt has been made to determine the degree of turbulence (energy potential) represented by various parts of the Redwall (McKee and Gutschick, 1969, chap.

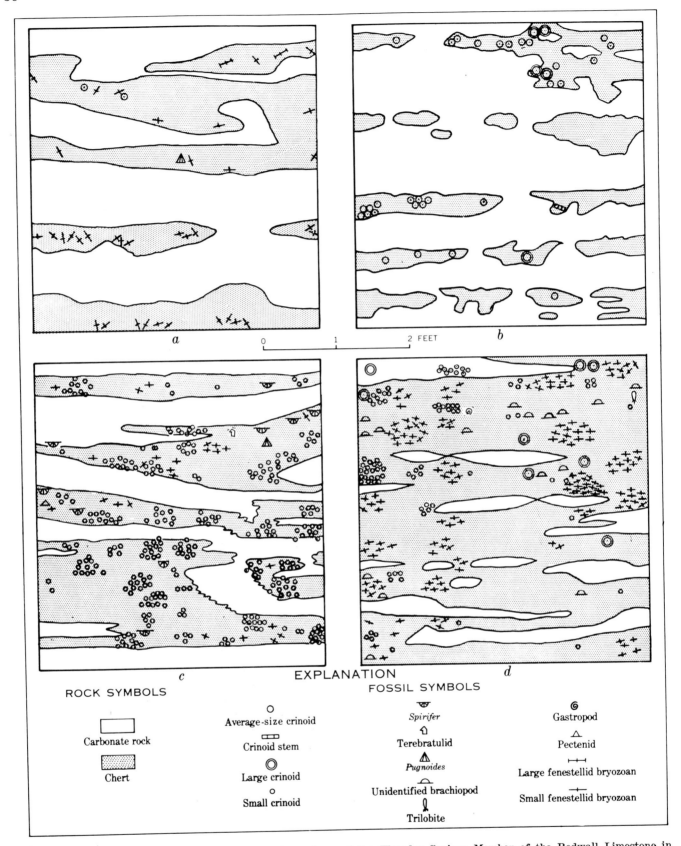

FIGURE 24.—Sample plots from four vertical outcrop faces of the Thunder Springs Member of the Redwall Limestone in Arizona, showing distribution of chert, carbonate rock, and associated fossils. From McKee (1960b, fig. 210.1).

14. The principal evidence used in these determinations is the size and character of clastic grains in the carbonate rock, although the attitude and condition of included fossils locally also contributed evidence. In general, the aphanitic limestones, believed to have originated as lime muds, were most probably accumulated in quiet-water environments. Oölitic limestones are considered to represent environments of moderate energy potential—agitated, warm, and very shallow waters; peloidal limestones probably originated in waters of moderate to strong turbulence; skeletal or bioclastic limestones, in general, represent deposits from wave or current agitation of considerable magnitude, at least as compared with the energy conditions of other facies in the Redwall.

Sedimentology of the Supai Formation and overlying Hermit Shale has been much neglected until recent times, probably because, as in most red-bed formations, distinctive traceable rock units and widespread recognizable fossil zones are scarce. This paucity of dependable criteria for correlation has made difficult the determination of regional trends in the properties of sediments and in the distribution of contemporaneous facies. Before the 1960's, contributions to the depositional history of these red beds, therefore, had consisted only of a series of measured sections and a general description of texture, crossbedding, and other sedimentary features by Noble (1922, p. 60) and of a classic report on the flora of the Hermit Shale by David White (1929), in which the significance of mudcracks, salt molds, rain pits, and other sedimentary structures is discussed.

Recent sedimentologic work on the Supai and Hermit, largely by the writer and associates (unpub. data), has consisted of gathering data on thickness, lithofacies, textural properties, calcium-magnesium ratios, and current-direction data for various rock units. The usefulness of these data has depended on successfully working out a stratigraphic framework within which they could be plotted. A series of maps has been prepared, using material from measured sections that are distributed geographically as a net covering the Grand Canyon area and that are divided into five stratigraphic or vertical units within the red-bed sequence.

Current-vector maps based on average directions of crossbedding dips were made for the Supai (fig. 20C, fig. 22D) and correlatives (fig. 22A) as long ago as 1940 (McKee, 1940), although at that time most of the stratigraphic divisions of the Supai were not recognized, and results were therefore rather generalized. A southerly direction of sediment transport, determined at that time, has been substantiated by subsequent more detailed studies, made throughout a wide area and for each subdivision of the Supai. Further support for the concept of current movement in that direction has been provided through the compilation of maps showing grain-size distribution. Maximum grain sizes, dominant size grade, and percentage of grains greater than fine-grained all indicate a source to the north. Studies of calcium/magnesium ratios indicate that a marine environment lay both to the west and south.

Isopach and lithofacies maps for the upper or Permian part of the Supai-Hermit sequence (McKee, Oriel, and others, 1967, pls. 3A, 3B) show two lobes of minimum thickness extending southward into northern Arizona from southwestern Utah; they are composed largely of sandstone and mudstone but include increasing percentages of limestone westward. Maps of corresponding areas for various parts of Pennsylvanian time (lower part of Supai) show somewhat similar patterns, as illustrated, in part, by a total Pennsylvanian isopach map (fig. 25).

As a result of studies cited above, the Supai Formation is currently interpreted as a deltaic deposit. Evidence includes the lobate form of the deposit, its alternating sandstone and mudstone deposits that tongue into limestone in two directions, the character of its flora and fauna, and the types of sedimentary structures included. It apparently was built up by rivers that flowed southward from southern Utah, and it merged into marine deposits to the west and south. Its total development involved at least four phases within Pennsylvanian and Permian time.

The Coconino Sandstone is, perhaps, best known in the field of sedimentology because of its use during a pioneer study of current-vector analysis. Reconstruction of current orientation through determination of average dip directions of cross-lamination in the Coconino was made by Reiche (1938) in the Grand Canyon region and has served as a model for statistical studies of this type. Previous considerations of the Coconino—its petrography, minor sedimentary structures (fig. 22C), geometry of the sand body, and geomorphic features—had already indicated (McKee, 1933, p. 113) a probable eolian origin of the formation. Later, experiments on the forming of reptilian tracks in loose sand and comparison of these tracks with footprints in the Coconino, probably eliminated all reasonable doubt concerning the genesis of the Coconino as a desert dune deposit (McKee, 1944). Additional evidence of eolian origin based on sedimentary structures (fig. 20A) was recorded by McKee (1945).

The Toroweap Formation and Kaibab Limestone have not yet been studied using modern techniques and

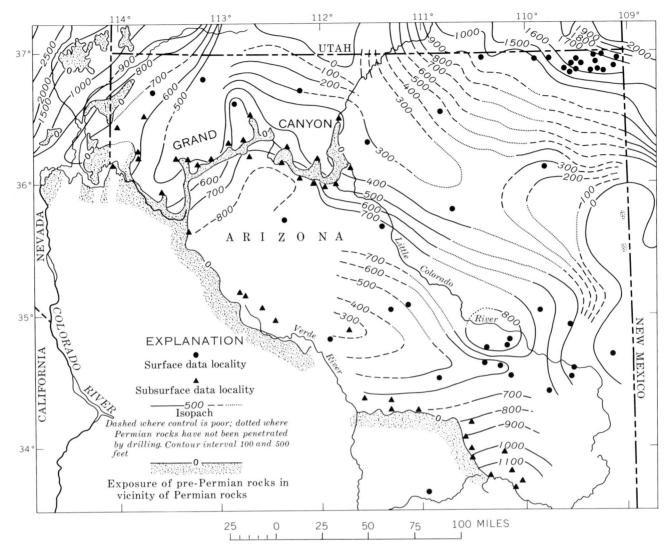

FIGURE 25.—Isopach map of northern Arizona for the Pennsylvanian System.

methods of carbonate-rock analysis, but the rock units of which these formations are composed were classified and described as lithologic facies (McKee, 1938) at a time when the concept of facies was still not widely understood in the United States. Interpretation of the environments represented by these facies was based on composition, texture, structure, fauna, and paleogeographic considerations; continental, marine, and intermediate environments were recognized.

A sedimentologic feature of the Kaibab that has been given considerable attention and is significant in the history of this formation is the genesis of the bedded chert (McKee and Breed, 1969). Evidence that the chert beds (fig. 14F) were formed by silica introduced by rivers from the land and deposited by inorganic processes in an area where fresh and marine waters mingled is furnished by (1) the gradation from clean sand into

pure calcium carbonate within the belt of bedded chert deposits, (2) a complete change in fauna from near-shore molluscan on the east to normal marine brachiopod-bryozoan-echinoid on the west, and (3) the cyclic occurrence of the chert (figs. 26, 27).

Both the Kaibab and the Toroweap are cyclic in character (McKee, 1964, p. 284). Each formation includes sediments of transgression, followed by those of regression; these formations consist of three vertical lithic divisions or members that have been characterized as deposits of an advancing sea, deposits of the most extended sea, and deposits of a receding sea (McKee, 1938, p. 35). Furthermore, within the regressive units (upper members) of each formation, cyclic sequences of smaller magnitude are recognized. Each of these sequences consists of a succession of beds of red sandstone, aphanitic limestone, and gypsum, from the bottom

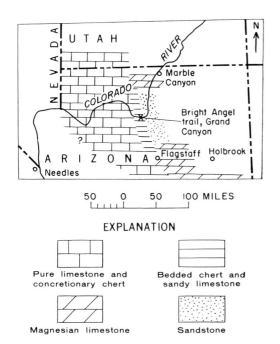

FIGURE 26.—Facies distribution in middle member of Kaibab Limestone, Arizona and Utah. From McKee (1964, fig. 3).

up (fig. 14*E*) ; this succession is interpreted as the result of a period of detrital accumulation followed by evaporite precipitation.

Paleontology And Paleoecology

The problem of why traces of life are so uncommon in rocks of late Precambian age, especially when fossils are abundant and well developed in the Cambrian strata directly above, has intrigued geologists since the early days of geologic science. Attempts to discover recognizable plants or animals in these rocks have been many, yet results have been meager and mostly inconclusive. In the Grand Canyon, the normal difficulty of travel and of access to the upper Precambrian beds has been a deterrent to collecting material, but aside from this fact, study has been difficult because traces of life are both rare and obscure.

Presence of a fragmentary fauna in the Chuar Group of late Precambrian age was announced by Walcott in 1883 (p. 441) and in 1886 (p. 43) ; the evidence was later summed up (Walcott, 1895, p. 327) as "a minute discinoid or patelloid shell, a small Lingula-like shell (which may be a species of *Hyolithes*) and a fragment * * * of a trilobite * * *." The small discinoid shell was believed phosphatic and was subsequently assigned to a new genus and species, named by Walcott (1899, p. 234) *Chuaria circularis.* Still later, Walcott's *Chuaria* was discussed by White (1928, p. 599), who states that it "may be of plant origin, and can hardly be a bivalve." Additional specimens of this form have recently been found in the Chuar by Trevor Ford and W. J. Breed (unpub. data), who discuss the many uncertainties in classifying it and the differences of opinion on its interpretation. Meanwhile, the other questionable organic forms referred to by Walcott (1899, p. 235) have been largely discredited for various reasons.

Since Walcott's announcement, a few other reports of fossil animals from the Grand Canyon Precambrian have been placed on record. An impression in sandstone of the Nankoweap Group, attributed to a jellyfish medusa, was reported by Van Gundy (1937a, p. 314; 1937b, p. 304), discussed by Hinds (1938, p. 186), and

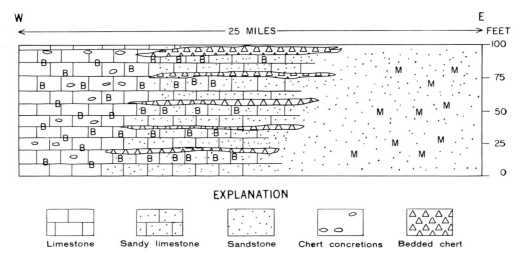

FIGURE 27.—Schematic cross section of part of middle member of Kaibab Limestone near eastern end of Grand Canyon. B indicates brachiopod fauna, and M indicates molluscan fauna. From McKee (1964, fig. 2).

later named and described by Bassler (1941, p. 522, pl. 64), who, however, stated that he "has become less certain of his first opinion as to the animal nature of the specimen * * *." Other "jellyfish-like impressions" have been reported by Alf (1959, p. 62) from the Unkar Group. The validity of the various claims is still in question, however, and many scientists remain skeptical. (See the opinion of G. Stiasny in Bassler (1941, p. 521).)

The evidence for a clearly defined flora in the form of stromatolites in the upper Precambrian rocks of Grand Canyon is much more definite than is the evidence for a fauna. Reference to "a stromatopora-like form [in the Chuar Group] that is probably organic" was made by Walcott in 1895 (p. 327). The structure of that form was regarded as possibly corresponding to that of Cryptozoon, and the form was referred to Cryptozoon? occidentale by J. W. Dawson (in Walcott, 1899, p. 233). When the algal Collenia was created (Walcott, 1914, p. 110), the form was placed in that genus. Recent studies by Trevor Ford, University of Leicester, England, and W. J. Breed, Museum of Northern Arizona, Flagstaff, Ariz., have shown that stromatolites, including those reported by Walcott, occur at three widely separated horizons in the Chuar Group (unpub. data).

In the Bass Limestone of the Unkar Group, near the base of the upper Precambrian sequence in Grand Canyon, four distinct forms of organic origin, including Collenia, and two or three others of problematic type, were collected and reported by White (1928, p. 598), but unfortunately they were never fully described. Studies of the Bass Limestone and its algal deposits are currently being undertaken by Michael O'Connor, Department of Geology, East Carolina University, Greenville, N.C.

The fauna of the Cambrian rocks of Grand Canyon has become well known through the work of C. E. Resser (in McKee and Resser, 1945, p. 171). He made an attempt to describe all Cambrian fossils that had been collected from the canyon up to 1945; so far as known, no additional species have been collected and described since that date. These fossils represent 76 localities, extending from the foot of Marble Canyon on the east to the Grand Wash Cliffs, more than 100 miles to the west. They represent many zones within the Tapeats Sandstone, Bright Angel Shale, and Muav Limestone.

The Cambrian fauna of Grand Canyon consists of 47 species of trilobites, which constitute the most conspicuous and abundant element, 16 species of brachiopods, and several species of gastropods, mostly Hyolithes. Also included are numerous species of Conchostraca, sponge spicules, an Eocrinus, worms (fig. 20F) and algal colonies of the form known as Girvanella. Distribution of trilobites clearly was controlled by facies; those in green shales are different from those in limestone. The Conchostraca are confined to red, ferruginous sandstones and most but not all species of brachiopods are in the medium- to coarse-grained, near-shore sandstones.

The fauna of the Devonian Temple Butte Limestone of Grand Canyon is poorly known; consequently, uncertainty exists about the environment of deposition of this formation. The armored placoderm known as Bothriolepis, found near the base of the formation both at Kanab Canyon (Walcott, 1883, p. 438) and Sapphire Canyon (Noble, 1922, p. 52), is considered to be a freshwater form. However, an assemblage of "Cyanthophylloid corals, casts of brachiopods, and gastropods," including some forms typical of a marine environment, has also been reported from the Devonian strata of Kanab Canyon (Walcott, 1883, p. 438). Probably on this basis, the suggestion is made by Denison (1951, p. 257) that "this is a near-shore facies, deposited in the advancing Chemung sea * * * the only fishes reported * * * must have been transported from a nearby land." Until additional diagnostic fossils are found, further speculation along these lines seems futile, but a rugged relief of as much as 100 feet at the formation base gives cause for question concerning a marine origin.

Knowledge of the faunas of the Mississippian Redwall Limestone has greatly increased during the past two decades. From one of the least known faunas in the formations of Grand Canyon, it has become perhaps the best known. This increased knowledge is primarily the result of a team effort in which eight paleontologists made detailed studies in their specialties, each contributing a chapter to a monograph on the Redwall Limestone (McKee and Gutschick, 1969). In addition, several other paleontologists examined fossils representative of minor groups and contributed data to the general report. Both stratigraphic and ecologic aspects of the various assemblages have been considered by these investigators.

Brachiopods, corals, foraminifers, and crinoids are the most common fossils in the Redwall Limestone; gastropods, cephalopods, pelecypods, bryozoans, and blastoids are fairly common; trilobites, fish, ostracods, holothurians, and algae are also represented. Altogether, 17 groups of animals and one group of plants have been recorded from 500 stations. The nine fossil groups that represent the greater part of the entire fauna are distributed in distinctive combinations or associations within members of the formation. Typical associations are coral-brachiopod-crinoid, brachiopod-bryozoan, and coral-foraminifer-brachiopod.

Important data on the age and correlation of Redwall subdivisions have been furnished by studies concerning vertical zoning of the corals (W. J. Sando, in McKee and Gutschick, 1969) and studies of foraminifer zonation (Betty Skipp, in McKee and Gutschick, 1969). Much information on ecological and geographical features of the Redwall has likewise been provided by these studies. Interpretation of environmental features has been greatly furthered by studies of the mollusks by E. L. Yochelson, bryozoans by Helen Duncan, blastoids by D. B. Macurda, crinoids by J. C. Brower, and cephalopods by W. M. Furnish (in McKee and Gutschick, 1969). Data on the nature of bottom sediment, the turbulence of the water (energy factor), the turbidity, and the depth of water have been obtained from some of these faunal studies.

Scarcity of fossils in the red-bed sequence composed of the Supai Formation and the Hermit Shale has made practical subdivision of these rocks difficult. A moderately large flora from the Hermit Shale, consisting of 35 species of terrestrial plants, has been studied and described by David White (1929); these plants clearly indicate an Early Permian age. Only a few poorly preserved plants have been reported from the Supai, and these furnish little evidence of age. Other fossils in the red beds are a few trackways of vertebrate animals from both the Supai Formation and the Hermit Shale, two wing impressions of insects from the Hermit (Carpenter, 1927; 1928), and numerous deposits formed from algal growth, mostly in the Supai (White, 1927, p. 369). In some of the algal deposits plant forms and structures have been retained.

General time relations based on zones of marine fossils can be projected laterally in the walls of Grand Canyon, because red beds of the Supai intertongue westward with carbonate rocks commonly referred to the Pakoon Limestone of McNair (1951) and the Callville Limestone. Brachiopods from the lowest unit of the Supai throughout the western half of Grand Canyon establish the age of the basal Supai as Early Pennsylvanian (Morrow). Fusulinids, corals, and brachiopods from the Pakoon or uppermost limestone establish its age as Early Permian or Wolfcamp. Between these units of Morrow and Wolfcamp age, fossils are relatively rare and age determinations correspondingly less certain, but on the basis of both brachiopods and small foraminifers, the strata probably represent Des Moines or Virgil age or both. Determinations of these fossils have been made by R. C. Douglass and L. G. Henbest (foraminifers), R. E. Grant (brachiopods), and W. J. Sando (corals), of the U.S. Geological Survey.

The fauna of the Coconino Sandstone consists exclusively of tracks and trails; no skeletal parts or other organic remains have yet been found. On the basis of these footprints and trails, 17 genera and 22 species of animals have been described by Gilmore (1926, 1927, 1928). The tracks are considered to be mostly reptilian, and they represent a wide variety of quadrupedal forms. Some animals apparently were the size and shape of small lizards, others had large feet and long strides, and still others were short limbed and wide bodied. In addition, a few burrows of wormlike creatures and trails of invertebrates, probably insects, are locally present. The tracks and trails are clearly impressed; most footprints show toes, claws, and heel marks on the long, steeply-dipping surfaces of cross strata of which the Coconino is composed.

General composition of the marine faunas of the Kaibab Limestone and, to a lesser extent, the Toroweap Formation has been known a long time. Some of the common forms were collected and described by geologists of the earliest expeditions (Marcou, 1858; Newberry, 1861). In following decades, extensive lists of fossil determinations were prepared, most notably by G. H. Girty between 1910 and 1930, and published in the reports of many geologists. A summary of the paleontology and descriptions of the brachiopods of these formations was prepared by McKee in 1938 (pt. 2). Since then many additional forms, representing most of the faunal groups, have been reported and in some cases described; these additions have been listed and discussed by McKee and Breed (1969).

As currently recognized, the fauna of the Kaibab and Toroweap includes 7 genera of fish; 10, of crustaceans; 34, of brachiopods; 16, of bryozoans; 9, of corals; 34, of gastropods; 35, of pelecypods; and 13, of cephalopods. In addition, the Annelida, Porifera (fig. 20E), scaphopods, echinoids, and crinoids are represented. The distribution of most of these fossils was controlled by facies. The nature of this distribution was not recognized in the early days when the so-called *Productus* fauna and the *Bellerophon* fauna were considered indicators of different ages. Later, it was demonstrated through field relations that most of the brachiopods (*Productus* fauna) were restricted to relatively pure limestones and represented normal marine environments, whereas pelecypods and gastropods (*Bellerophon* fauna) were dominant in the near-shore sandstones and the magnesian limestones of contemporaneous age and represented brackish and (or) supersaline environments (McKee, 1938, p. 133).

Studies of the physical factors that have probably been responsible for the faunal distribution patterns in both the Kaibab and Toroweap formations have been made by a number of geologists (McKee, 1938, p. 134–142; Nicol, 1944, 1965; Chronic, 1952). The principal factors considered were bottom character, temperature, depth, marine currents, salinity, amount of light, and turbidity. For some of these factors, direct evidence is recorded in the rock, but for others, inferences had to be made from various types of evidence.

CONCLUSIONS

During the past 100 years, increasing investigation of stratified rocks in the Grand Canyon has been responsible for a rapid expansion in the accumulation of facts; as might be expected, these new facts have been significant in the evolution of ideas about the regional history. From the number of recent discoveries that have modified earlier concepts, it is evident that changes in our ideas concerning Grand Canyon rocks may be expected to continue for a long time. This is especially true in such features as the genesis of certain rocks, the significance of many fossils, and various environments of deposition.

As Powell recognized during his boat trips in 1869 and 1871–72, clear exposures of the strata and the general lack of structural disturbance offer nearly ideal conditions for the study of these rocks. Many geologists subsequently have realized that opportunities are exceptionally good for testing theories concerning natural processes and for demonstrating the detailed record of such phenomena as transgression and regression, cyclic sedimentation, facies relationships, diastems, and others. Thus, the Grand Canyon has proved to be one of the world's finest laboratories for illustrating various geological principles, especially those related to the history of stratified rocks.

REFERENCES

Alf, R. M., 1959, Possible fossils from the early Proterozoic Bass Formation, Grand Canyon, Arizona: Plateau, v. 31, no. 3, p. 60–63.

Baker, A. A., Dobbin, C. E., McKnight, E. T., and Reeside, J. B., Jr., 1927, Notes on the stratigraphy of the Moab region, Utah: Am. Assoc. Petroleum Geologists Bull., v. 11, no. 8, p. 785–808.

Bassler, R. S., 1941, A supposed jellyfish from the pre-Cambrian of the Grand Canyon: U.S. Natl. Mus. Proc., v. 89, no. 3104, p. 519–522.

Bryant, D. L., and McClymonds, N. E., 1961, Permian Concha Limestone and Rainvalley Formation, southeastern Arizona: Am. Assoc. Petroleum Geologists Bull., v. 45, no. 8, p. 1324–1333.

Carpenter, F. M., 1927, A fossil insect from the lower Permian of the Grand Canyon: U.S. Natl. Mus. Proc., v. 71, art. 23, 4 p.

———— 1928, A new protodonatan from the Grand Canyon: Psyche, v. 35, no. 3, p. 186–190.

Chronic, Halka, 1952, Molluscan fauna from the Permian Kaibab Formation, Walnut Canyon, Arizona: Geol. Soc. America Bull., v. 63, no. 2, p. 95–165.

Cooper, G. A., and Grant, R. E., 1966, Permian rock units in the Glass Mountains, west Texas: U.S. Geol. Survey Bull. 1244-E, 9 p.

Dake, C. L., 1920, The pre-Moenkopi (pre-Permian?) unconformity of the Colorado Plateau: Jour. Geology, v. 28, no. 1, p. 61–74.

Damon, P. E., and Giletti, B. J., 1961, The age of the basement rocks of the Colorado Plateau and adjacent areas: New York Acad. Sci. Annals, v. 91, p. 443–453.

Dane, C. H., 1935, Geology of the Salt Valley anticline and adjacent areas, Grand County, Utah: U.S. Geol. Survey Bull. 863, 184 p.

Darton, N. H., 1910, A reconnaissance of parts of northwestern New Mexico and northern Arizona: U.S. Geol. Survey Bull. 435, 88 p.

———— 1925, A résumé of Arizona geology: Arizona Bur. Mines Bull. 119, 298 p.

Denison, R. H., 1951, Late Devonian fresh-water fishes from the western United States: Fieldiana—Geology, v. 11, no. 5, p. 221–261.

Dutton, C. E., 1882, Tertiary history of the Grand Canyon district: U.S. Geol. Survey Mon. 2, 264 p., atlas.

Eardley, A. J., 1949, Paleotectonic and paleogeologic maps of central and western North America: Am. Assoc. Petroleum Geologists Bull., v. 33, no. 5, p. 655–682.

Easton, W. H., and Gutschick, R. C., 1953, Corals from the Redwall limestone (Mississippian) of Arizona: Southern California Acad. Sci. Bull., v. 52, pt. 1, p. 1–27.

Finks, R. M., 1960, Late Paleozoic sponge faunas of the Texas region—The siliceous sponges: Am. Mus. Nat. History Bull., v. 120, art. 1, 160 p.

Gilbert, G. K., 1874, On the age of the Tonto sandstones [abs.]: Philos. Soc. Washington Bull. 1, p. 109.

———— 1875a, Report on the geology of portions of Nevada, Utah, California, and Arizona * * *: U.S. Geog. and Geol. Surveys West 100th Meridian (Wheeler), Rept., v. 3, p. 17–187.

———— 1875b, Report on the geology of portions of New Mexico and Arizona: U.S. Geog. and Geol. Surveys West 100th Meridian (Wheeler), Rept., v. 3, p. 503–567.

Giletti, B. J., and Damon, P. E., 1961, Rubidium-strontium ages of some basement rocks from Arizona and northwestern Mexico: Geol. Soc. America Bull., v. 72, no. 4, p. 639–643.

Gilluly, James, Cooper, J. R., and Williams, J. S., 1954, Late Paleozoic stratigraphy of central Cochise County, Arizona: U.S. Geol. Survey Prof. Paper 266, 49 p.

Gilmore, C. W., 1926, Fossil footprints from the Grand Canyon: Smithsonian Misc. Colln., v. 77, no. 9, 41 p.

———— 1927, Fossil footprints from the Grand Canyon; second contribution: Smithsonian Misc. Colln., v. 80, no. 3, 78 p.

———— 1928, Fossil footprints from the Grand Canyon; third contribution: Smithsonian Misc. Colln., v. 80, no. 8, 16 p.

Gutschick, R. C., 1943, The Redwall limestone (Mississippian) of Yavapai County, Arizona: Plateau, v. 16, no. 1, p. 1–11.

Hinds, N. E. A., 1935, Ep-Archean and Ep-Algonkian intervals in western North America: Carnegie Inst. Washington Pub. 463, 52 p.

———— 1938, An Algonkian jellyfish from the Grand Canyon of the Colorado: Science, new ser., v. 88, no. 2278, p. 186–187.

———— 1939, Pre-Cambrian formations in western North America: Sixth Pacific Sci. Cong. Proc., p. 289–309.

Hose, R. K., and Repenning, C. A., 1959, Stratigraphy of Pennsylvanian, Permian, and Lower Triassic rocks of Confusion Range, west-central Utah: Am. Assoc. Petroleum Geologists Bull., v. 43, no. 9, p. 2167–2196.

Longwell, C. R., 1921, Geology of the Muddy Mountains, Nevada, with a section to the Grand Wash Cliffs in western Arizona: Am. Jour. Sci., 5th ser., v. 1, no. 1, p. 39–62.

——— 1925, The pre-Triassic unconformity in southern Nevada: Am. Jour. Sci., 5th ser., v. 10, p. 93–106.

——— 1928, Geology of the Muddy Mountains, Nevada, with a section through the Virgin Range to the Grand Wash Cliffs, Arizona: U.S. Geol. Survey Bull. 798, 152 p.

McKee, E. D., 1933, The Coconino sandstone—its history and origin: Carnegie Inst. Washington Pub. 440, p. 77–115.

——— 1938, The environment and history of the Toroweap and Kaibab formations of northern Arizona and southern Utah: Carnegie Inst. Washington Pub. 492, 268 p.

——— 1940, Three types of cross-lamination in Paleozoic rocks of northern Arizona: Am. Jour. Sci., v. 238, no. 11, p. 811–824.

——— 1944, Tracks that go uphill: Plateau, v. 16, no. 4, p. 61–72.

——— 1945, Small-scale structures in Coconino sandstone of northern Arizona: Jour. Geology, v. 53, no. 5, p. 313–325.

——— 1947, Paleozoic seaways in western Arizona: Am. Assoc. Petroleum Geologists Bull., v. 31, no. 2, p. 282–292.

——— 1951, Sedimentary basins of Arizona and adjoining areas: Geol. Soc. America Bull., v. 62, no. 5, p. 481–505.

——— 1954, Permian stratigraphy between Price and Escalante, Utah, in Intermountain Association Petroleum Geologists, Portions of high plateaus and adjacent canyon lands, central and south-central Utah, 5th Annual Field Conference, 1954: Salt Lake City, Utah, p. 21–24.

——— 1958, The Redwall limestone, in New Mexico Geological Society, Guidebook of the Black Mesa basin, northeastern Arizona, 9th Field Conference, October 16–18, 1958: p. 74–77.

——— 1960a, Cycles in carbonate rocks: Am. Jour. Sci., v. 258–A (Bradley Volume), p. 230–233.

——— 1960b, Spatial relations of fossils and bedded cherts in the Redwall Limestone, Arizona, in Short papers in the geological sciences: U.S. Geol. Survey Prof. Paper 400–B, p. B461–B463.

——— 1964, Permian and Triassic cycles involving chemical sediments, northern Arizona, in Merriam, D. F., ed., Symposium on cyclic sedimentation: Kansas Geol. Survey Bull. 169, nos. 1–2, p. 283–286 [1966].

McKee, E. D., and Breed, W. J., 1969, The Toroweap Formation and the Kaibab Limestone, in Kottlowski, F. E., and Summers, W. K., eds., the San Andres Limestone, a reservoir for oil and water in New Mexico: New Mexico Geol. Soc. Spec. Pub. 3. [In press.]

McKee, E. D., and Gutschick, R. C., 1969, History of the Redwall Limestone of northern Arizona: Geol. Soc. America Mem. 114, 612 p.

McKee, E. D., Oriel, S. S., and others, 1967, Paleotectonic maps of the Permian System: U.S. Geol. Survey Misc. Geol. Inv. Map I–450, 164 p.

McKee, E. D., and Resser, C. E., 1945, Cambrian history of the Grand Canyon Region. Part 1, Stratigraphy and ecology of the Grand Canyon Cambrian: Carnegie Inst. Washington Pub. 563, p. 3–168.

McKee, E. D., and Weir, G. W., 1953, Terminology for stratification and cross-stratification in sedimentary rocks: Geol. Soc. America Bull., v. 64, no. 4, p. 381–390.

McNair, A. H., 1951, Paleozoic stratigraphy of part of northwestern Arizona: Am. Assoc. Petroleum Geologists Bull., v. 35, no. 3, p. 503–541.

Marcou, Jules, 1856, Résumé and field notes: U.S. Pacific Railroad Explor. (U.S. 33d Cong., 2d sess., Senate Ex. Doc. 78 and House Ex. Doc. 91) v. 3, pt. 4, Geol. Rept., p. 165–171.

——— 1858, Geology of North America: Zurich, Zurcher and Furrer; New York, Wiley and Halstead, 144 p.

Marvine, A. R., 1875, Report on the geology of the route from St. George, Utah, to Gila River, Arizona, examined in 1871: U.S. Geog. and Geol. Surveys West 100th Meridian (Wheeler), Rept., v. 3, p. 189–225.

Maxson, J. H., 1961, Geologic map of the Bright Angel quadrangle, Grand Canyon National Park, Arizona: Grand Canyon Nat. History Assoc., scale 1:48,000, text.

Miller, A. K., and Youngquist, W. L., 1949, American Permian nautiloids: Geol. Soc. America Mem. 41, 218 p.

Moore, R. C., 1925, Geologic report on the inner gorge of the Grand Canyon of Colorado River: U.S. Geol. Survey Water-Supply Paper 556, p. 125–171.

Newberry, J. S., 1861, Geological report, in Ives, J. C., Report upon the Colorado River of the West: U.S. 36th Cong., 1st sess., Senate and House Ex. Doc. 90, pt. 3, 154 p.

Nicol, David, 1944, Paleoecology of three faunules in the Permian Kaibab formation at Flagstaff, Arizona: Jour. Paleontology, v. 18, no. 6, p. 553–557.

——— 1965, An ecological analysis of four Permian faunas: Nautilus, v. 78, no. 3, p. 86–95.

Noble, L. F., 1910, Contributions to the geology of the Grand Canyon, Arizona; the geology of the Shinumo area: Am. Jour. Sci., 4th ser., v. 29, p. 369–386, 497–528.

——— 1914, The Shinumo quadrangle, Grand Canyon district, Arizona: U.S. Geol. Survey Bull. 549, 100 p.

——— 1922, A section of the Paleozoic formations of the Grand Canyon at the Bass trail: U.S. Geol. Survey Prof. Paper 131, p. 23–73.

——— 1928, A section of the Kaibab limestone in Kaibab Gulch, Utah: U.S. Geol. Survey Prof. Paper 150, p. 41–60.

Poole, F. G., and others, 1967, Devonian of the Southwestern United States, in Oswald, D. H., ed., International symposium on the Devonian System, Calgary, Alberta, September 1967: Calgary, Alberta Soc. Petroleum Geologists, v. 1, p. 879–912.

Powell, J. W., 1875, Exploration of the Colorado River of the West and its tributaries: Washington, D.C., U.S. Govt. Printing Office, 291 p.

——— 1876, Report on the geology of the eastern portion of the Uinta Mountains and a region of country adjacent thereto: Washington, D.C., U.S. Geol. and Geog. Survey Terr. (Powell), 218 p.

Ransome, F. L., 1908, A comparison of some Paleozoic and pre-Cambrian sections in Arizona [abs.]: Science, v. 27, new ser., p. 68–69.

——— 1916, Some Paleozoic sections in Arizona and their correlation: U.S. Geol. Survey Prof. Paper 98–K, p. 133–166.

Reeside, J. B., Jr., and Bassler, Harvey, 1922, Stratigraphic sections in southwestern Utah and northwestern Arizona: U.S. Geol. Survey Prof. Paper 129–D, p. 52–77.

Reiche, Parry, 1938, An analysis of cross-lamination; the Coconino sandstone: Jour. Geology, v. 46, no. 7, p. 905–932.

Resser, C. E., 1935, Nomenclature of some Cambrian trilobites: Smithsonian Misc. Colln., v. 93, no. 5, Pub. 3295, 46 p.

Robinson, H. H., 1913, The San Franciscan volcanic field, Arizona: U.S. Geol. Survey Prof. Paper 76, 213 p.

Schuchert, Charles, 1918a, On the Carboniferous of the Grand Canyon of Arizona: Am. Jour. Sci., 4th ser., v. 45, p. 347–361.

———— 1918b, The Cambrian of the Grand Canyon of Arizona: Am. Jour. Sci., 4th ser., v. 45, p. 362–369.

Sharp, R. P., 1940, Ep-Archean and Ep-Algonkian erosion surfaces, Grand Canyon, Arizona: Geol. Soc. America Bull., v. 51, no. 8, p. 1235–1270.

Shride, A. F., 1967, Younger Precambrian geology in southern Arizona: U.S. Geol. Survey Prof. Paper 566, 89 p.

Stoyanow, A. A., 1936, Correlation of Arizona Paleozoic formations: Geol. Soc. America Bull., v. 47, no. 4, p. 459–540.

———— 1942, Paleozoic paleogeography of Arizona: Geol. Soc. America Bull., v. 53, no. 9, p. 1255–1282.

Teichert, Curt, 1965, Devonian rocks and paleogeography of central Arizona: U.S. Geol. Survey Prof. Paper 464, 181 p.

Van Gundy, C. E., 1934, Some observations of the Unkar group of the Grand Canyon Algonkian: Grand Canyon Nature Notes, v. 9, no. 8, p. 338–349.

———— 1937a, Jellyfish from Grand Canyon Algonkian: Science, new ser., v. 85, no. 2204, p. 314.

———— 1937b, Nankoweap group of the Grand Canyon Algonkian [abs.]: Geol. Soc. America Proc. 1936, p. 304.

———— 1951, Nankoweap group of the Grand Canyon Algonkian of Arizona: Geol. Soc. America Bull., v. 62, no. 8, p. 953–959.

Walcott, C. D., 1880, The Permian and other Paleozoic groups of the Kanab Valley, Arizona: Am. Jour. Sci., 3d ser., v. 20, p. 221–225.

———— 1883, Pre-Carboniferous strata in the Grand Canyon of the Colorado, Arizona: Am. Jour. Sci., 3d ser., v. 26, p. 437–442, 484.

———— 1886, Second contribution to the studies on the Cambrian faunas of North America: U.S. Geol. Survey Bull. 30, 369 p.

———— 1890, Study of a line of displacement in the Grand Canyon of the Colorado, in northern Arizona: Geol. Soc. America Bull., v. 1, p. 49–64.

———— 1894, Pre-Cambrian igneous rocks of the Unkar terrane, Grand Canyon of the Colorado, Arizona, with notes on the petrographic character of the lavas, by J. P. Iddings: U.S. Geol. Survey Ann. Rept. 14, pt. 2, p. 497–524.

———— 1895, Algonkian rocks of the Grand Canyon of the Colorado: Jour. Geology, v. 3, p. 312–330.

———— 1897, Cambrian Brachiopoda: Genera *Iphidea* and *Yorkia*, with descriptions of new species of each and of the genus *Acrothele*: U.S. Natl. Mus. Proc., v. 19, p. 707–718.

———— 1898, Cambrian Brachiopoda; *Obolus* and *Lingulella*, with description of new species: U.S. Natl. Mus. Proc., v. 21, p. 385–420.

———— 1899, Pre-Cambrian fossiliferous formations: Geol. Soc. America Bull., v. 10, p. 199–244.

———— 1901, Cambrian Brachiopoda—*Obolella*, subgenus *Glyptias*; *Bicia*; *Obolus*, subgenus *Westonia*; with descriptions of new species: U.S. Natl. Mus. Proc., v. 23, p. 669–695.

Walcott, C. D., 1902, Cambrian Brachiopoda—*Acrotreta; Linnarssonella; Obolus*; with descriptions of new species: U.S. Natl. Mus. Proc., v. 25, p. 577–612.

———— 1905, Cambrian Brachiopoda with descriptions of new genera and species: U.S. Natl. Mus. Proc., v. 28, p. 227–337.

———— 1908, Cambrian geology and paleontology I: No. 3, Cambrian Brachiopoda, descriptions of new genera and species: Smithsonian Misc. Colln., v. 53, no. 3, p. 53–165.

———— 1910, Cambrian geology and paleontology II; No. 1, Abrupt appearance of the Cambrian fauna on the North American continent: Smithsonian Misc. Colln., v. 57, no. 1, p. 14.

———— 1912a, Cambrian geology and paleontology II; No. 6, Middle Cambrian Branchiopoda, Malacostraca, Trilobita, and Merostomata: Smithsonian Misc. Colln., v. 57, no. 6, p. 145–228.

———— 1912b, Cambrian Brachiopoda: U.S. Geol. Survey Mon. 51, pt. 1, 872 p.; pt. 2, 363 p.

———— 1914, Precambrian Algonkian algal flora: Smithsonian Misc. Colln., v. 64, p. 77–156.

———— 1916a, Cambrian geology and paleontology III; No. 3, Cambrian trilobites: Smithsonian Misc. Colln., v. 64, no. 3, p. 157–258.

———— 1916b, Cambrian geology and paleontology III; No. 5, Cambrian trilobites: Smithsonian Misc. Colln., v. 64, no. 5, p. 303–570.

———— 1918, Cambrian geology and paleontology IV; No. 4, Appendages of trilobites: Smithsonian Misc. Colln., v. 67, no. 4, p. 115–216.

———— 1924a, Cambrian geology and paleontology IV; No. 9, Cambrian and Ozarkian Brachiopoda; Ozarkian Cephalopoda and Notostraca: Smithsonian Misc. Colln., v. 67, no. 9, p. 477–554.

———— 1924b, Cambrian geology and paleontology V; No. 2, Cambrian and lower Ozarkian trilobites: Smithsonian Misc. Colln., v. 75, no. 2, p. 53–60.

———— 1925, Cambrian geology and paleontology V; No. 3, Cambrian and Ozarkian trilobites: Smithsonian Misc. Colln., v. 75, no. 3, p. 59–146.

Wasserburg, G. J., and Lanphere, M. A., 1965, Age determinations in the Precambrian of Arizona and Nevada: Geol. Soc. America Bull., v. 76, no. 7, p. 735–757.

Wheeler, R. B., and Kerr, A. R., 1936, Preliminary report on the Tonto group of the Grand Canyon, Ariz.: Grand Canyon Nat. History Assoc. Bull. 5, p. 1–16.

White, David, 1927, Study of the fossil floras in the Grand Canyon, Arizona: Carnegie Inst. Washington Year Book 26, p. 366–369.

———— 1928, Algal deposits of Unkar Proterozoic age in the Grand Canyon, Arizona: Natl. Acad. Sci. Proc., v. 14, no. 7, p. 597–600.

———— 1929, Flora of the Hermit Shale, Grand Canyon, Arizona: Carnegie Inst. Washington Pub. 405, 221 p.

Yochelson, E. L., 1968, Biostratigraphy of the Phosphoria, Park City, and Shedhorn Formations: U.S. Geol. Survey Prof. Paper 313-D, p. 571–660.

Geologic History of
The Colorado River

By CHARLES B. HUNT

THE COLORADO RIVER REGION AND JOHN WESLEY POWELL

GEOLOGICAL SURVEY PROFESSIONAL PAPER 669–C

*Thirty million years of changes
in the rivers and canyons that
Powell was first to explore*

Grand Canyon, as sketched by W. H. Holmes of the Powell Survey and published in Dutton's monograph (1882) on Grand Canyon. View is about southeast along the axis of the Kaibab upwarp. In the distant skyline, right, is San Francisco Mountain (F) and other volcanoes in the volcanic field south of Grand Canyon. The plateau surface is Permian limestone (Kaibab Limestone); the canyon walls seen in this view are mostly the Permian, Pennsylvanian, and Mississippian formations. Altitude of the rim here is about 8,200 feet; bottom of the canyon (out of sight) is below 3,000 feet. San Francisco Mountain, about 70 miles away, is above 12,600 feet.

Contents

Illustrations

Tables

GEOLOGIC HISTORY OF THE COLORADO RIVER

By Charles B. Hunt

Abstract

John Wesley Powell clearly recognized that the spectacular features of the Colorado River—its many grand canyons—were dependent upon the structural history of the mountainous barriers crossed by the river. He conceived of three different historical relationships between rivers and structural features: (1) Newly uplifted land surfaces have rivers that flow down the initial slope of the uplift; these relationships he termed **consequent.** (2) A river may be older than an uplift that it crosses because it has been able to maintain its course by eroding downward as the uplift progresses; this relationship he named **antecedent.** (3) An uplifted block may have been buried by younger deposits upon which a river becomes established. The river, in cutting downward, uncovers the uplifted block and becomes incised into it; this relationship he called **superimposed.**

The geologic history of the Colorado River involves all three relationships. In addition, although the position of the river course through a particular structural barrier may have been the result of superposition, the depth of the canyon at that point may be largely due to renewed uplift of the barrier; such deepening of the canyon, therefore, is due to antecedence. The problem of the Colorado River remains today very much as G. K. Gilbert stated it nearly 100 years ago: "How much is antecedent and how much is superimposed?" The question must be asked separately for each stretch of the river.

The geologic history of the Colorado River begins with the emergence of the Rocky Mountains and Colorado Plateau from the sea that had flooded them in Cretaceous time. During the early Tertiary (Paleocene and Eocene time, 65–40 million years ago), huge lakes in the northern part of the Colorado Plateau (Flagstaff and Greenriver Lakes) received consequent streams draining the west slope of the newly formed Rocky Mountains. Probably much of the southern part of the Colorado Plateau also drained north to the lakes, because the general dip of the Cretaceous and older rocks on the plateau is north, but the record of that assumed drainage has been lost because of erosion. The Oligocene and Miocene drainage history of much of the southern part of the Colorado Plateau is also obscure because datable deposits there are scarce. During Cretaceous time, the area that later became the Basin and Range province was higher than and drained into the area that later became the Colorado Plateau. This relationship probably continued during early Tertiary time.

By Oligocene time (40–25 million years ago), the lakes in the northern part of the Colorado Plateau had become filled with sediments, and the plateau was being tilted northeast. Filling of the lakes exceeded the rate of tilting, and they overflowed southward. It is assumed that the southward drainage again was ponded temporarily in the Henry Mountains and Kaiparowits basins, which lie south of the Uinta basin. No great amount of water need be involved in this supposed ponding, because the rivers off the west slope of the Rocky Mountains were repeatedly beheaded by the lavas and by the basins and ranges forming there, and because the Green River was still trapped in the Wyoming basin.

Before the end of Oligocene time, the Gunnison River valley, oldest recognizable valley on the western slope of the Rocky Mountains, was eroded down to the Precambrian basement rock, and the eroded sediments were deposited in the lakes to the west. Later, the drainage became interrupted because the valley was tilted eastward and filled with lava and other eruptive materials.

The main stem of the Colorado River in the Rocky Mountains also began with a consequent course that drained westward to the early Tertiary lakes. That original consequent course was different from the present one. Gravel deposits (perhaps 25 million years old) under upper(?) Miocene lavas on the north flank of the White River Plateau show that the Colorado River originally flowed west from about Middle Park across what now is the headwaters of the Yampa River into the headwaters of the present White River that still follows an essentially consequent course down the trough of the Uinta structural basin.

During the Miocene (25–10 million years ago), the west-flowing consequent rivers became interrupted by block faulting that formed basins and ranges across the river courses. Uplift of the Gore Range checked the Colorado River for awhile in Middle Park, and renewed uplift of the White River Plateau further interrupted it west of the Gore Range. Fossiliferous sediments interbedded with the lava downfolded in the basins show that this interruption to the drainage occurred shortly after the middle of Miocene time. Lava in the Gunnison River valley, dated radiometrically, indicates that the drainage there also was interrupted, at least intermittently, during the Miocene.

About the end of Miocene time (about 10 million years ago), the mountain barriers had been fully breached and the present drainage pattern established. The river courses across the structural barriers may have been superimposed in part, as the

Gunnison River seems to have been where it crosses the uplift of Precambrian rocks at the Black Canyon. At other places, the river courses may have been started when the ponded rivers overflowed low places on the rim. At most of the structural barriers, however, uplift was renewed, and the canyons were deepened. Gore Canyon, Glenwood Canyon, Black Canyon of the Gunnison, for example, are in part antecedent.

The history of the Green and Yampa Rivers is similar. They became superimposed across the Uinta Mountains, probably when the mountains were partly buried by the Browns Park Formation of Miocene(?) age. At that time the mountains were lower relative to the adjoining basins than they are today. The Browns Park Formation in that area is much deformed, and the canyons of the rivers through the mountains probably owe much of their depth to late Tertiary and Quaternary uplift of the mountains (or downfolding of the basin); that is, the canyons are in part antecedent.

The San Juan basin probably began to overflow to the west in Oligocene time. Gravel deposits on the Kaibito Plateau south of Navajo Mountain show that the San Juan River had established its course westward across the Monument upwarp and was within 75 miles of the head of the Grand Canyon by late Miocene time. The gravels are regarded as older than earliest Pliocene (pre-Bidahochi Formation) and include pebbles of Miocene volcanic rocks from the San Juan Mountains.

Before middle Miocene time, a large canyon—as wide as the Grand Canyon and half as deep—had been eroded through the southwest rim of the Colorado Plateau. A segment of the canyon, preserved at Peach Springs, Ariz., is partly filled with deposits possibly related to the Muddy Creek Formation and dated radiometrically as 18.3 million years old. A gap at Kingman, Ariz., between the fault blocks of Precambrian rocks forming the Hualapai and Cerbat Mountains, 40 miles southwest of the present rim of the Colorado Plateau, is filled with lavas dated radiometrically as 16–17 million years old; the gap may be a segment of the Miocene canyon at Peach Springs that was faulted off the plateau at a later time. During Miocene and Pliocene time, a considerable area in central Arizona became separated from the Colorado Plateau by faulting and now is part of the relatively low-lying Basin and Range province.

We cannot be sure how much of the Colorado River basin drained off the plateau via the canyon at Peach Springs. Probably the Little Colorado River drainage was first to leave the plateau via that canyon. The Little Colorado River valley looks old. It is broad and open without deep narrow canyons (except at the mouth). Its original course seems to have been south of the Kaibab upwarp, and it may have been joined by the San Juan River. This ancestral course antedates the lavas in the San Francisco volcanic field and could be as old as Oligocene. By middle Miocene time, the canyon at Peach Springs was blocked by uplift and by deposits of volcanic materials and related sediments. Later, ponding of the San Juan and Little Colorado Rivers on the plateau east of the site of the present Grand Canyon seems to be recorded by playa or lake beds in the lower part of the Pliocene Bidahochi Formation.

The lower stretch of the Colorado River valley in the Basin and Range province was an estuary of the Gulf of California at various times during the Miocene and Pliocene. Pliocene marine shells have been found in the estuarine deposits as far north as Parker, Ariz., and very similar deposits without fossils are at The Needles, Ariz. These estuarine deposits and other deposits near the Miocene-Pliocene boundary in the Colorado River delta contain coccoliths and Foraminifera reworked from Cretaceous shale formations on the Colorado Plateau. Certainly there was through drainage from the Colorado Plateau by that time.

In the Lake Mead area, however, the earliest known Colorado River deposits seem to be no older than middle Pliocene and may be younger. During parts of Miocene time, when the river was depositing sediments from the Colorado Plateau in the estuary below The Needles, its course was probably via the canyon at Peach Springs and west from there perhaps via the gap at Kingman, Ariz.

The earliest deposit attributable to the Colorado River in the Lake Mead area is a curious limestone (Hualapai Limestone) that centers about the mouth of the lower Granite Gorge of the Grand Canyon. It was deposited in a lake 1,000 feet deep, yet there is no delta of clastic sediments at the mouth of the gorge. A major source of water was needed just to maintain the lake against evaporation, and the water had to be of a kind that would contribute much calcium carbonate without forming a delta. A possible explanation is that the Pliocene Colorado River, ponded in Grand Canyon above the dry canyon at Peach Springs, lost its water into the cavernous limestone, which is flexed there so that it provides a structural trough with more than 1,000-foot head, plunging from the dry canyon to the mouth of lower Granite Gorge. The first discharge of the Colorado River at the mouth of lower Granite Gorge may have been by big springs of the kind well known in limestone regions.

This lake, ponded in the structural basin immediately west of the Colorado Plateau, apparently overflowed a low place on the rim and cut the canyon at the Black Mountains. Tilted gravels indicate that the Black Mountains were further raised in late Pliocene and Quaternary time. The canyon is therefore partly antecedent.

At the west end of Lake Mead, the Colorado River turns 90° south to join its earlier course in the estuary at The Needles and farther south. This southerly stretch of the Colorado River separates two very different kinds of drainage systems. On the east is a structurally inactive block with the well-integrated Bill Williams and Gila River systems; on the west, the structurally active Mojave block, marked by abundant earthquake epicenters, recent fault scarps, and measurable present-day tilt, has no tributaries worth the name.

Quaternary erosion in the Colorado River basin seems to have been roughly proportional to the time involved, about 2 million years, about 3 percent of the Cenozoic. Throughout much of the Colorado Plateau and Rocky Mountains, about 500 feet of canyon deepening seems to have taken place during the Quaternary. There was greater erosion in the mountains at the valley heads, but radiometric dating of lavas in the bottom of the Grand Canyon suggests that the big canyon was within 50 feet of its present depth 1.2 million years ago.

The present sediment load of the Colorado River represents lowering of the river basin above the Grand Canyon at the rate of 6.5 inches per 1,000 years. Assuming this rate, and further assuming that there has been drainage off the southern part of the Colorado Plateau since middle Oligocene time and drainage from the Rocky Mountains and northern part of the plateau since late Miocene time, the Colorado Plateau and Rocky Mountains could have been lowered about 2 miles by the Colorado River system. This average seems to be about the right order of magnitude.

INTRODUCTION

The Problem

The Colorado River is the river of John Wesley Powell. Not only was he the first to explore and chart the canyons of the Green and the Colorado from Wyoming to the foot of the Grand Canyon, he was first to attempt to explain how they formed. On the basis of their geologic history, Powell distinguished three kinds of valleys in the river system. One type he named **consequent** (Powell, 1875, p. 163); these valleys have courses directly inherited from a bedrock surface formed by folding, tilting, or other type of earth movement. The axis of a newly formed downfold, or **syncline,** becomes a stream course; the axis of a newly formed upfold, or **anticline,** becomes a drainage divide. The radial drainage off the volcanic pile and uplift in the San Juan Mountains in southwestern Colorado (figs. 28, 29) is consequent drainage.

Most of the Colorado River drainage system, though, is not consequent, and Powell distinguished two principal kinds of nonconsequent valleys. One that he called **antecedent** (Powell, 1875, p. 163), persists on a land surface where folds or other displacements form after a consequent drainage system has been formed. Unless the folds or other displacements are produced rapidly, the drainage lines are not diverted, and the streams cut downward vertically as the uplifts are raised athwart their courses.

A second kind of nonconsequent valley Powell called **superimposed** (Powell, 1875, p. 166). This type of valley is formed where previously folded or tilted rocks are buried by younger unconformable sediments on which a consequent drainage then forms. This drainage cuts vertically downward into the buried structures and becomes incised into them.

Powell concluded (1875, p. 166) that the valleys crossing the Uinta Range were antecedent.

Powell's brilliant protégé, G. K. Gilbert, elaborated on Powell's ideas by noting that drainage may become superimposed in several ways (Gilbert, 1877, p. 144):

1. From marine deposits that bury old structures and then become elevated and dissected.
2. From alluvial or other terrestrial deposits that bury old structures and then become dissected.
3. From erosion surfaces truncating older structures.

Gilbert also pointed out that the instability of divides will cause changes in the manner of superposition as downcutting progresses.

Gilbert noted (1877, p. 139–142) that a stream or system of streams belonging to one drainage system

may become diverted to another system by ponding or by deposition of alluvium. In like manner, the shifting of a stream from one system to another may be caused by lateral planation and lateral extension of a flood plain that cuts through a divide, enabling the stream to spill into a neighboring, lower drainage system. Finally, he noted that where strata are inclined, the divides, which are at the brows of the cliffs, retreat as the cliff faces are sapped by erosion. The Pink Cliffs, formed by the southern edge of the Tertiary formations in the High Plateaus in southwestern Utah (fig. 29), are an example. The cliffs face south; the plateau back of them slopes north. As the cliffs retreat northward, the divide between the Colorado River and the drainage to the Great Basin retreats northward. This kind of shift in divide he referred to as monoclinal shifting (Gilbert, 1877, p. 140).

Gilbert also gave us the first clear description of the process we know today as **stream capture.** He wrote (1877, p. 141):

A stream which for any reason is able to corrade its bottom more rapidly than do its neighbors, expands its valley at their expense, and eventually "abstracts" them. And conversely, a stream which for any reason is able to corrade its bottom less rapidly than its neighbor, has its valley contracted by their encroachments and is eventually "abstracted" by one or the other.

The problems of Colorado River history remain today very much as Gilbert described them almost 100 years ago (1876, p. 101), "What is the relation of the drainage system * * * to the system of displacements? How far is it **consequent,** how far **antecedent,** how far **super-imposed**?" Too, how much is due to a combination of those processes or anteposition (Hunt, 1956, p. 65–66), how much is due to capture (for example Bradley, 1936, p. 189), and how much is due to integration resulting from ponding at and overflow of basins as they become filled? All these processes seem to have operated at one place or another.

The question, "How old is the Colorado River?" is oversimplified to the point of being misleading. The structural barriers crossed by the river and its tributaries are of different ages, and most of them involve late Tertiary as well as early Tertiary movements. The canyons through the barriers are of different ages and are the result of different kinds and different combinations of processes. The Colorado River has been evolving ever since the uplift of the Rocky Mountains began (or was resumed) at the end of the Cretaceous period (about 65 million years ago). Some valleys in the river system are as old as Oligocene (40–25 million years ago); other valleys are Quaternary, the last 2 or 3 million years. Not all of the Grand Canyon may be of the

EXPLANATION

River basin boundary

50   0   50   100   150   200 MILES

Contour interval 1000 feet

same age. If the river once discharged from the Colorado Plateau at Peach Springs (Hunt, 1956, p. 30) (figs. 48, 53), the headward part of the Grand Canyon could be very much older than the lower stretches in lower Granite Gorge. Questions about the age and processes of origin must be asked about each part of the river separately, all the way from the headwaters to the mouth.

Other factors besides structure that bear on the geologic history of the river are touched on but lightly in this report. Among these factors are: development of the meander patterns; sculpture of the mountains, plateaus, and canyons; episodes of accelerated weathering, accelerated erosion, and episodes of cut and fill along the river; comparative effects of climatic and of structural change; and changes in river regimen.

Setting

The Colorado River drainage system (figs. 28–31) extends into five physiographic provinces. Its headwaters are in the Southern and Middle Rocky Mountains and it crosses the Wyoming Basin, the Colorado Plateau, and the Basin and Range province. To reach the Gulf of California, the river and most of its tributaries must cross many mountains and high plateaus which are structural barriers of resistant rocks. No other river in the Western Hemisphere crosses so many. Not only does the river cross mountain barriers, it must also cross the Colorado Plateau, a tremendous structural block covering more than half the drainage basin; the plateau has been uplifted and tilted northeast against the river. Grand Canyon, where the Colorado River leaves the plateau, is cut across the highest part of the rim, the highest structurally and one of the highest topographically.

Most valleys in the drainage system are narrow and steep sided; broad alluvial flood plains are uncommon. There are a few small flood plains in the Rocky Mountains and on the Colorado Plateau upstream from some of the structural barriers, but the only extensive ones are in the Basin and Range province—near Needles,

FIGURE 28.—The Colorado River, 1,440 miles long, has a drainage basin of almost 250,000 square miles in five physiographic provinces. In the Southern Rocky Mountains, where the river begins, extensive areas are higher than 10,000 feet in altitude, and peaks are above 14,000 feet. Most of the Colorado Plateau is about 5,000–7,000 feet in altitude, and the river crosses this plateau in deep canyons, culminating in the Grand Canyon. In the Basin and Range province the river is below 2,000 feet; few of the mountains near the Colorado River are as high as 5,000 feet.

Calif., below the Bill Williams River, and along parts of the Gila River. Much of the river's 300-mile course across the Colorado Plateau is in rock-walled canyons, and the river meanders greatly, much more so than most rivers that are not on alluvial flood plains. Surely these meanderings record the difficulties of the river in maintaining its flow across rising folds and against the northeast tilt of the Colorado Plateau. The folding and tilting have continued as repeated, even though minor, movements, while the river has been cutting its canyons, and probably are still going on.

Previous Work

Powell (1875) was first to attempt to explain the many anomalous features of the Colorado River system. He was vague about the age of the river, but according to his interpretation, the Green River is antecedent across the Uinta Mountains. We now know that this interpretation would require an ancient, Paleocene or Late Cretaceous, beginning for the river. Dutton (1882, p. 218–222) was the first to be definite about the age. He concluded that the Colorado River formed by middle Tertiary (Miocene) time as a result of integration, overflow, and drainage of the Eocene lakes. By his (Dutton, 1882, p. 224–226) interpretation, the river was antecedent across the rim of the Colorado Plateau and across the uplifts at Grand Canyon, and the canyon cutting occurred mostly during Miocene and Pliocene time. This seems to have been the history.

Later workers, especially Davis (1901) correctly pointed out that many of the drainage anomalies on the Colorado Plateau are better explained by superposition than by antecedence. Others have assumed capture as a major part of the process, and still others—I for one—have assumed combinations of the processes—anteposition (Hunt, 1956). The river's course, for example, may have been superimposed across an anticline, and then remained in a course antecedent to renewed uplift at the anticline. Table 1 briefly summarizes the principal interpretations about the process and age.

The great differences in ages that have been inferred for the Colorado River—from Eocene to Pleistocene (about 50 million years)—are more apparent than real, because the several authors have not been talking about the same sections of the river. The view that the Colorado is an ancient river considers the river as a whole from the time of the first uplift of the present Rocky Mountains; the view that the river is young is based on particular segments. Most authors have assumed only one process or mode of origin despite the fact that the processes are not mutually exclusive. Some parts of the

EXPLANATION

1. Browns Park
2. Lodore Canyon
3. Yampa River
4. White River
5. Duchesne River
6. Middle Park
7. Park Range
8. Gore Range
9. White River Plateau
10. Grand Mesa
11. Black Canyon of the
     Gunnison River
12. Uncompahgre Plateau
13. La Sal Mts
14. San Rafael Swell
15. Henry Mts
16. Abajo (Blue) Mts
17. Ute Mtn
18. Mesaverde
19. Monument Upwarp
20. Carrizo Mts
21. Navajo Mtn
22. Defiance Upwarp
23. Black Mesa
24. Kaibab Upwarp
25. Vermillion Cliffs
26. White Cliffs
27. Pink Cliffs
28. San Francisco Mts
29. Grand Wash Cliffs
30. Cerbat Mts
31. Hualapai Mts
32. Black Mts
33. Bill Williams River

river system surely are the result of one process, some parts equally surely are the result of another, and still other parts must be the result of several processes. Each part of the river system needs to be looked at separately.

Acknowledgments

The difficulties of interpreting the geologic history of a major river system, the vastness of the area and time to be considered, and the incompleteness of the evidence, leave plenty of room for different interpretations about many phases of the history of the Colorado River. Although a hypothesis for the historical development of the Colorado is offered here, a major purpose of this chapter is to provide a frame of reference into which isolated bits of new evidence can be fitted. If all the widely separated deposits in the river basin could be inventoried and reviewed, a reasonably satisfactory account of the river's history might be indicated; until this is done we must depend on hypothesis. The hypothesis presented in this chapter is summarized in table 2.

Financial support for this study was provided partly by the U.S. Geological Survey and partly by The Johns Hopkins University. The data were assembled during three field seasons. I spent the first season (1964) in the Rocky Mountains, becoming acquainted with the drainage system and the geology of the valleys. A second summer (1965) was spent on the Colorado Plateau and

immediate environs. The stretch below the Grand Canyon was studied during the fall of 1966. The three field seasons involved about 45,000 miles of travel by car.

The area is vast, the geology is highly varied, and the evidence is diffuse. The project would not have been possible without the guidance and assistance of many geologists familiar with details about the various stretches of the rivers. In the Rocky Mountains, much

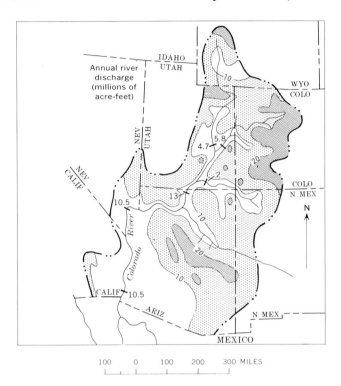

FIGURE 29.—Colorado River drainage basin, showing the principal landforms that distinguish the physiographic provinces crossed by the river and its tributaries.

In the interior of the Wyoming basin, relief along the Green River is only a couple of hundred feet, and in places the valley bottom is wide. Where the resistant formations form escarpments at the turned-up edges of the basin, the relief is as great as 1,000 feet. Because this is a structural basin, the escarpments face outward.

In the Middle and Southern Rocky Mountains, the rivers are in steep-sided valleys 2,000 or 3,000 feet deep where they cross the mountain barriers; there are some small flood plains in the open valleys upstream from these barriers. Escarpments face the mountains, which are uplifts.

On the Colorado Plateau, the rivers characteristically are in canyons cut into very colorful rock formations. Grand Canyon cuts across the high southwest rim of the plateau, which probably still is being uplifted. Broad open valleys like those in the Wyoming Basin occur on the Colorado Plateau in the Uinta basin and along the San Juan and Little Colorado Rivers.

In the Basin and Range province, the Colorado River flows west across the north-trending structural barriers and then turns 90° south and parallels them. Flood plains are extensive along this part of the river.

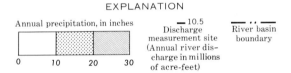

EXPLANATION

Annual precipitation, in inches

0   10   20   30

—10.5
Discharge measurement site (Annual river discharge in millions of acre-feet)

River basin boundary

FIGURE 30.—Average annual precipitation in the Colorado River drainage basin and average annual discharge of the river and of some of its principal tributaries. The annual discharge, usually 10–15 million acre feet, is almost entirely from the Southern and Middle Rocky Mountains. Very little runoff is contributed from the areas where precipitation averages less than 15 inches annually; almost all that water is lost by seepage, evaporation, and transpiration. This dependence on runoff from the Rocky Mountains probably has been true throughout the river's history. Annual runoff from the basin as a whole averages less than 1 inch. Sediment load, however, is one of the highest in the United States; at Grand Canyon this load is about twice the average of other rivers in the United States (load now trapped in Lake Powell) and represents an average lowering of about 6.5 inches per 1,000 years of the basin upstream from Grand Canyon. Most of the erosion is in the shale formations, especially the Cretaceous.

TABLE 1.—*Principal interpretations of process and age for various parts of the Colorado River system*

Publication	Segment of river	Principal process	Age
Newberry (1861)_____	Colorado River below Grand Canyon.	Basin filling and overflow; a form of superposition.	?
Powell (1875)_____	Green and Colorado Rivers_____	Antecedence_____	Not stated; would have to be Paleocene or older.
Gilbert (1876)_____do_____		Consequence, antecedence, and superposition.	Not stated.
Dutton (1882)_____	Grand Canyon_____	Antecedence implied; by basin filling and overflow.	Early Tertiary but younger than the early Tertiary lakes.
Hayden (1862, 1873)_____	Rivers in Rocky Mountains____	Antecedence_____	?
Walcott (1890)_____	Marble Canyon_____	Antecedence; river closely adjusted to local structure during downcutting.	?
Irving (1896)_____	Green River_____	Antecedence?_____	?
Davis (1897)_____	Green River canyons in Uinta Mountains.	Antecedence or superposition depending on what beds overlay the Uinta arch.	?
Emmons (1897)_____do_____		Not antecedence_____	Late Tertiary.
Jefferson (1897)_____	Colorado River_____	At first consequence, then antecedence.	?
Davis (1901)_____do_____		Superposition_____	?
Noble (1914)_____	Grand Canyon_____	Between Bright Angel and Kanab Creeks, river parallels northeast-dipping fissures.	?
Hancock (1915)_____	Yampa River_____	Superposition_____	Late Tertiary.
Longwell (1928)_____	Colorado River from Grand Canyon to Boulder Canyon.	_____do_____	Quaternary.
Sears (1924b)_____	Green and Yampa Rivers_____	_____do_____	Post-Browns Park Formation (that is, middle Pliocene and later).
Moore (1926a, b)_____	Colorado River on the Plateau__	Meanders inherited; size depends on size of river.	Grand Canyon older than canyons upstream.
Blackwelder (1934)_____	Colorado River in Grand Wash and Grand Canyon.	Superposition or piracy as result of basins filling and overflowing.	Pleistocene.
Bradley (1936)_____	Lodore Canyon, Green River___	Capture_____	Post-Browns Park Formation (that is, middle Pliocene and younger).
Longwell (1946)_____	Colorado River, Grand Canyon to Boulder Canyon.	Superposition_____	Post-Hualapai Limestone (that is, late Pliocene and Pleistocene).
Gregory (1947)_____	Colorado River on the Colorado Plateau.	Superposition from a Miocene surface of erosion.	Late Tertiary.
Babenroth and Strahler (1945); Strahler (1948).	Grand Canyon in Kaibab uplift.	Original course could be antecedent; present course superposed from Triassic and adjusted to local structure.	?
Childs (1948)_____	Grand Canyon_____	?	Grand Canyon 2,000 ft deep when lavas reached Black Point 500 ft above Little Colorado River.
Hunt (1946); Hunt and others (1953).	Colorado River on the Colorado Plateau.	Integration by basin fill and overflow; river superposed across folds; antecedent across the plateau.	Early Tertiary but younger than early Tertiary lakes.
Hunt (1956)_____	Colorado River on the Colorado Plateau.	Anteposition across folds; antecedent across plateau.	Middle Miocene.
Sears (1962)_____	Yampa Canyon in Uinta Mountains.	Superposition_____	Post-Browns Park Formation (that is, middle Pliocene and later).
Longwell (1963)_____	Colorado River, Lake Mead to Davis Dam.	_____do_____	Post-Muddy Creek Formation (that is, middle Pliocene and later).
Cooley and Davidson (1963).	Grand Canyon_____	Not stated_____	Late Miocene and Pliocene.
Hansen (1965a)_____	Black Canyon of the Gunnison__	Superposition_____	Younger than the Miocene lavas.
Lohman (1965)_____	Unaweep Canyon and course of Colorado River around Uncompahgre Plateau.	Capture_____	Late Pliocene.
Cater (1966)_____do_____		_____do_____	Late Pliocene or Pleistocene.
McKee and others (1967)___	Grand Canyon_____	Capture by headward erosion of streams draining off Colorado Plateau.	Late Pliocene and Pleistocene.
Metzger (1968)_____	Colorado River below Needles, Calif.	Superposition? following retreat of ancestral Gulf of California embayment.	Pliocene.

TABLE 2.—*Geologic history of the Colorado River*

[Tabular summary of the interpretation, much of it conjectural, presented in this paper. Sequence within time intervals arranged with earliest event at bottom]

Time interval and approximate age of boundaries (in millions of years)	Geographic regions			
	Basin and Range province	Colorado Plateau		Rocky Mountains Colorado and Gunnison Rivers above Grand Junction
		Southern section Below mouth of Green River	Northern section Green and upper Colorado Rivers	
—— 0 —— Quaternary	Colorado River canyon in Black Mountains deepened by renewed uplift (antecedence).	Grand Canyon of Colorado River deepened very little since mid-Pleistocene time. River in Grand Canyon within about 50 feet of present depth about 1.2 million years ago. Uplift and (or) northeast tilting of plateau probably continued intermittently throughout the Quaternary and probably is still continuing.	Canyons of Green and Yampa Rivers deepened about 500 feet.	Main river valleys and canyons deepened about 500 feet in glacial Pleistocene time; headwater stretches deepened 1,000–1,500 feet. Unaweep Canyon abandoned in late Pliocene or earliest Pleistocene time.
—— 2 —— Pliocene	Colorado River discharges to Hualapai Lake and it overflows westward across Black Mountains. Limestone (Hualapai) deposited in fresh-water spring-fed lake centering at mouth of Colorado River canyon in Grand Wash Cliffs. Alluvial and playa beds (Muddy Creek Formation) deposited in Lake Mead area. Colorado River not there. Estuary along lower Colorado River (below The Needles) throughout much of Pliocene time.	Colorado River discharges at mouth of Grand Canyon. Ancestral Colorado River joins the Little Colorado and San Juan Rivers; overflows through arched ancestral Grand Canyon. Uplift and northeast tilting of plateau probably continued intermittently throughout the Pliocene. Renewed uplift at Kaibab Plateau ponds ancestral Colorado and Little Colorado Rivers; begin deposition of Bidahochi Formation (earliest Pliocene). Ancestral drainage, ponded at Peach Springs, discharged at Grand Wash Cliffs as big springs fed by pipes enlarged in the now cavernous limestone formations dipping down axis of present lower Granite Gorge.	Renewed uplift at Uinta Mountains (or downfaulting of adjoining basins) deepens the canyons by perhaps 1,000 feet (antecedence). Green and Yampa Rivers superimposed in southward courses across the Uinta Mountains, probably when the mountains were structurally lower relative to adjacent basins than now and were buried by Browns Park Formation. This superposition probably took place in early Pliocene time, perhaps in the late Miocene.	Canyons of the Colorado River through uplifted blocks such as the Gore Range or White River Plateau deepened 2,000–3,000 feet during Pliocene time (antecedence); Black Canyon of the Gunnison River. Colorado and Gunnison Rivers cross Uncompahgre Plateau and cut Unaweep Canyon.
—— 12 —— Miocene	Estuary along lower Colorado River (below The Needles); Colorado River apparently flowed into it by way of canyon at Peach Springs, Ariz. Accumulation of lavas, dated radiometrically at 16–17 million years old, in gap at Kingman, Ariz., between Hualapai and Cerbat Mountains; the gap may be segment of canyon at Peach Springs, Ariz., faulted off plateau. Deposition of alluvial and playa beds, lower part of Muddy Creek Formation(?), in Lake Mead area; most movement along faults near Grand Wash Cliffs by middle Miocene time.	Canyon at Peach Springs partly filled with deposits dated radiometrically at about 18.3 million years old; renewed uplift at Kaibab Plateau. Gravel deposits on Kaibito Plateau, derived in part from San Juan Mountains, indicate that by late Miocene time, San Juan River flowed across Monument upwarp to within 80 miles of Grand Canyon; probably crossed ancestral Kaibab uplift in canyon and joined ancestral Little Colorado River west of there. By middle Miocene time the Little Colorado River had course south of Kaibab upwarp and left plateau by way of canyon near Peach Springs, Ariz. Plateau uplifted and tilted northeastward intermittently throughout the Miocene.	Doming of laccolithic mountains by intrusions about 25 million years ago caused drainage to be diverted around mountains (La Sal, Ute, Henry, Abajo, Navajo Mountains). White River follows a westward, essentially consequent course down axis of Uinta basin. Ancestral Green and Yampa Rivers discharge into Wyoming basin north of Uinta Mountains. Northern part of main Colorado River drainage is assumed to have ended in playas in Henry Mountains and (or) Kaiparowits basins.	Present course of main stem of Colorado River largely established by overflowing structural barriers by end of Miocene time; Gunnison River superimposed across Precambrian rocks at Black Canyon. Headward part of Colorado River disrupted by formation of structural basins at head of Yampa River, near State Bridge, and in Middle Park; and by uplift of White River Plateau and Gore Range. Ancestral Colorado River continues consequent westward course to Uinta basin; continued outpouring of lava in Gunnison River valley.
—— 26 —— Oligocene	Breakup of highlands into basins and ranges, block faulting; probably faulting began at Grand Wash and at the basins downstream along the Colorado River.	Plateau continues to be uplifted and tilted northeast; San Juan River basin probably overflowed west; drainage history obscure because datable deposits are scarce; probably playas in Henry Mountains and Kaiparowits basins.	Plateau tilted northeast. Filling of playa exceeds rate of tilting, and Uinta basin overflows southward; ancestral Green and Yampa Rivers ponded in Wyoming basin. Lakes filled and converted to playas.	Gunnison River valley tilted eastward and begins to fill with volcanic rocks. Ancestral Colorado River had consequent course at about the position of present White River to Uinta basin; ancestral Gunnison River valley eroded into Precambrian rocks.
—— 38 —— Eocene and Paleocene	Highlands draining eastward and northeastward; folding, faulting.	Plateau uplifted and tilted northeast; drainage probably northward to lakes because of northward tilting.	Area low lying, close to sea level; large lakes (Flagstaff and Green-river Lakes).	Consequent streams flowing west supplied sediment to lakes.
—— 65 —— Cretaceous	Highlands draining eastward and northeastward.	Flooded by seas.	Flooded by seas.	Flooded by seas.

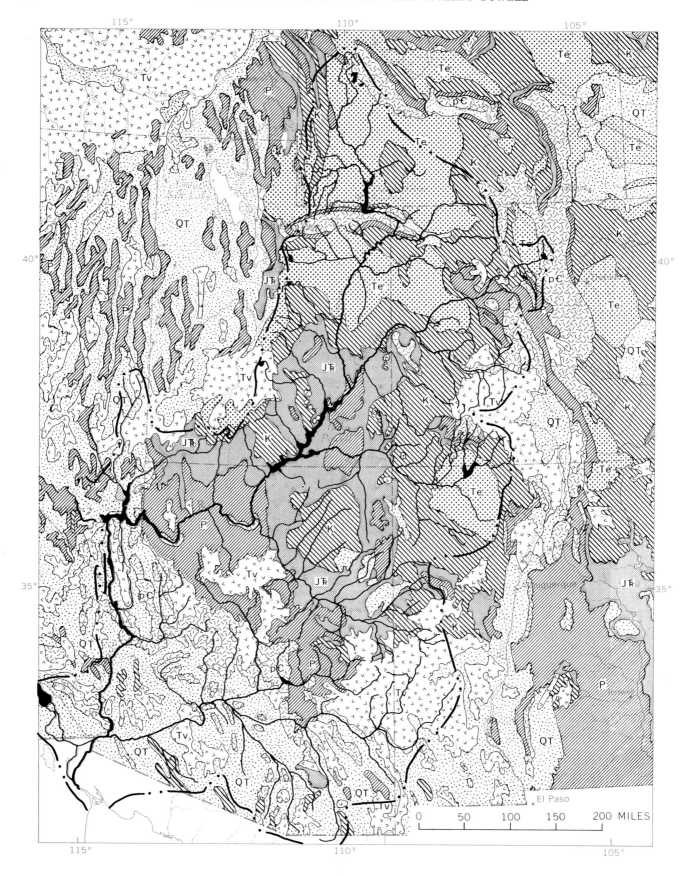

help was provided by Wallace R. Hansen, Stanley W. Lohman, Fred W. Cater, Jr., Thomas S. Lovering, Douglas M. Kinney, and Ogden Tweto, all of the U.S. Geological Survey. Peter Lipman and Robert G. Luedke, U.S. Geological Survey, examined thin sections of gravels that may have been derived from the San Juan Mountains. On the Colorado Plateau, work was aided by Richard A. Young, New York State University College, Geneseo, N.Y.; by Hansen, Lohman, and

EXPLANATION

Quaternary and upper Tertiary
sedimentary deposits

Bidahochi Formation (Pliocene) in the Little Colorado River valley; Muddy Creek Formation (Pliocene?) at the mouth of the Grand Canyon; North Park Formation (Miocene) in Middle Park at the head of the Colorado River

Lower Tertiary formations

Mostly Paleocene and Eocene rocks in Uinta Basin and San Juan Basin

Tertiary volcanic rocks

In the San Juan Mountains, the volcanic rocks are mostly Oligocene to Pliocene; on White River Plateau they are mostly Miocene; elsewhere they are mostly Pliocene. Laccolithic intrusions at the Henry, La Sal, Abajo, Ute, and Carrizo Mountains are mostly lower Miocene. (For locations see fig. 29)

Cretaceous formations

Jurassic and Triassic formations

Paleozoic formations

Precambrian rocks

———————

Contact

——— · · ———

River basin
boundary

Cater, and by John Donnell, Carle H. Dane, and, especially, Maurice E. Cooley, U.S. Geological Survey. Cooley has done intensive and extensive work locating and mapping gravel deposits on the Navajo Reservation and elsewhere on the southern part of the Colorado Plateau; he was more than generous in making his information and ideas available for this study. In the Basin and Range province, guidance was provided by Warren B. Hamilton, D. G. Metzger, and Cooley, U.S. Geological Survey.

The manuscript was reviewed by several of these individuals and by Charles S. Denny and Frank S. Simons, U.S. Geological Survey. Their criticisms and suggestions have greatly improved the presentation. I am grateful for this help and encouragement in making the study, but the reader should be assured that errors in fact or judgment are mine.

Finally, grateful acknowledgment is made to Luna B. Leopold, U.S. Geological Survey, who gave the project necessary administrative support and impetus when it was needed most, at the beginning.

DESCRIPTIVE GEOLOGY

Upper Colorado River Basin—Above the Green River

The upper Colorado River basin is mostly in the Southern Rocky Mountains, but includes the northeast part of the Colorado Plateau. The present course of the main stem of the river (fig. 32) is no older than very late Miocene and may be as young as Pliocene. Before middle Miocene time, the headward part of the Colorado River drained westward at about the position of the White River (fig. 33).

The present drainage pattern here is decidedly askew. All the major tributaries are from the south (fig. 28); the upper 250 miles of the Colorado has no large tributaries from the north. In succession, the Colorado is

———————————

FIGURE 31.—Colorado River basin (from Kinney, 1966). The upper part of the Colorado River system heads in the Middle and Southern Rocky Mountains which consist of uplifted Precambrian, Paleozoic, and Mesozoic rocks and in the mountains in southwestern Colorado (San Juan Mountains), a great pile of volcanic rocks. After leaving the Rocky Mountains, the rivers are in Tertiary formations in the north and eastern parts of the drainage basin, and then, flowing against the northeast dip of the Colorado Plateau, the rivers cross, in succession, Cretaceous, Jurassic, Triassic, Paleozoic, and Precambrian rocks. After leaving the Colorado Plateau at Grand Canyon, the Colorado enters the Basin and Range province, but even there the course is not confined to the basins but cuts through some of the mountain barriers.

joined from the south by the Blue, Eagle, Roaring Fork, and Gunnison Rivers (fig. 32) and the Dolores-San Miguel Rivers. This skewed pattern indicates that this part of the main stem of the river is young.

In Oligocene time, the ancestral headwaters of the Colorado River discharged westward to the Uinta basin across what is now the north-trending structural depression occupied by the headwaters of the Yampa River (figs. 32, 33). The drainage was westward from the Park Range and possibly from the Front Range and across the north flank of what is now the White River Plateau. This course is recorded by river gravels under the tuffaceous beds and lava, thought to be of early Pliocene age, capping that part of the plateau. Samples of the gravels recording the ancestral westward drainage were examined by Ogden Tweto who identified in them Precambrian rock types like those

in the Park Range to the east. The gravels now are at an altitude of 10,400 feet, but part of this high altitude is due to 2,000 feet or more of late Tertiary or Quaternary uplift of the White River Plateau. The course farther west is not known, but probably continued near the present position of the White River, which approximately follows the axis of the Uinta basin. This basin was downfolded during Eocene and Oligocene time as well as later, and its synclinal axis would likely be the location for early consequent drainage westward from the Rocky Mountains.

At present, the Colorado River crosses in succession: Middle Park (fig. 34), a Miocene (and older) basin; the Gore Range (fig. 35), a mountain barrier dating from the early Tertiary but re-uplifted in late Miocene and Pliocene time; a faulted syncline and second uplift immediately west of the Gore Range; another syncline

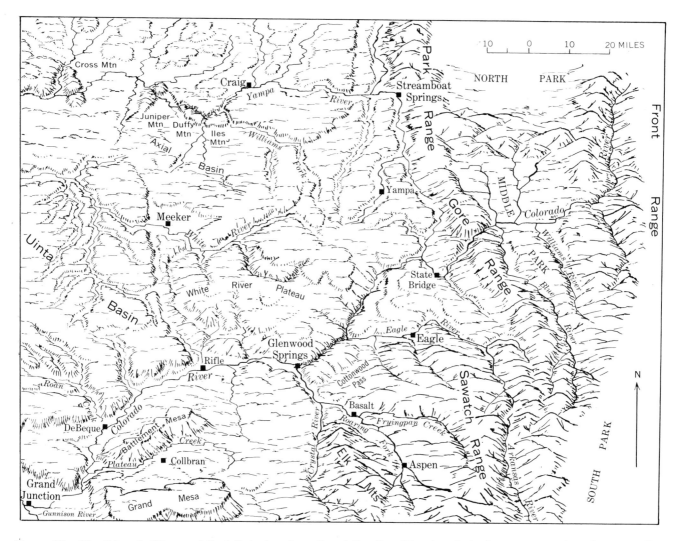

FIGURE 32.—The Colorado River and its tributaries above Grand Junction. The river is in deep canyons where it crosses the uplifted Gore Range and White River Plateau.

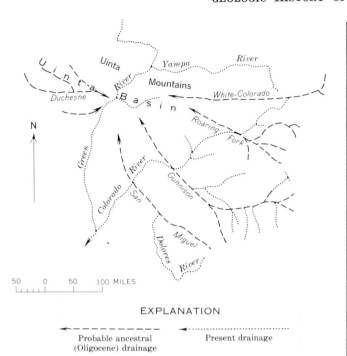

EXPLANATION

← – – – – – – →   ←·············

Probable ancestral   Present drainage
(Oligocene) drainage

FIGURE 33.—Probable ancestral (Oligocene) drainage into the Uinta basin and present drainage. The consequent courses of the ancestral White-Colorado, ancestral Duchesne River, and headward part of the ancestral Gunnison River are reasonably certain; the other ancestral courses indicated are conjectural. The present Colorado River has almost no tributaries from the west, and those above its junction with the Green River are short.

in Miocene lavas and sedimentary rocks at State Bridge (fig. 36); and still another uplift at the White River Plateau (fig. 37), which also was raised in late Tertiary time.

These structures in the Rocky Mountains repeatedly ponded the ancestral Colorado River and turned it southward around the White River Plateau. The present river valley across these basins and ranges is younger than the sedimentary rocks and lava, mostly of Miocene age, downfolded in the basins.

The relationship of the river's course to the mountains and basins is well illustrated by the syncline at State Bridge, between the Gore Range and the White River Plateau (fig. 38). This syncline, which extends north along the headward part of the Yampa River, contains thick deposits of lavas and volcanic ash interbedded with coarse clastic sedimentary rocks that have yielded vertebrate fossils of late Miocene age (fossils from Piney Creek, south of State Bridge; G. E. Lewis, written commun., 1968). The lavas and sedimentary rocks have been downfolded between the uplifted Gore Range and White River Plateau (figs. 36, 37). Lavas in the State Bridge syncline and in the structural de-

pression southeast of Glenwood Springs, rise onto the White River Plateau which is capped by similar lavas and tuffaceous beds. These lavas capping the plateau are assumed to be no younger than those capping Grand Mesa, which have been dated by potassium-argon methods at 9.7 million years±0.5 million years (John Donnell, written commun., 1966).

Structural uplift at the White River Plateau has been about 12,000 feet; most of this occurred before the lava cap was formed, because the lava extends unconformably across at least 8,000 feet of Paleozoic and Mesozoic rocks on the flanks of the uplift (figs. 37, 38). If 10,000 feet of the uplift occurred before the lava cap was formed, and 2,000 feet after that, the main stem of the Colorado River may have been superimposed across the uplift from the lava cap. The canyon above Glenwood Springs was probably cut during Pliocene and later time and is partly antecedent. Dips of the lavas into the State Bridge syncline and into the depression southeast of Glenwood Springs indicate that 2,000 feet or so of Pliocene and later uplift occurred at the plateau. A sixth of the uplift seems to have occurred during the last sixth of Cenozoic time, as if deformation there has progressed linearly with time.

Also, on the east side of the State Bridge syncline, the lavas rise towards the Gore Range (fig. 36). Early uplift of that range is indicated by the overlap of the lavas on the flanks, analogous to those around the White River Plateau; late Tertiary uplift is indicated by the folding of the upper Miocene lavas and sedimentary rocks forming the east flank of the State Bridge syncline. Similar structural history in Middle Park is recorded by Miocene stream and lake deposits there (Troublesome Formation).

The present course of the Colorado River through Middle Park, across the Gore Range, State Bridge syncline, and White River Plateau, clearly is younger than the lavas and sedimentary rocks in the basins and apparently became established by being superimposed across the structures at the very end of Miocene time or the beginning of Pliocene time. The canyons, though, seem to be antecedent.

Lower and middle Tertiary gravel deposits are too scattered to indicate the pattern of the other ancestral drainage. My guess is that when the ancestral Colorado River was north of the early Tertiary dome at the White River Plateau, Eagle River was south of the dome. This interpretation is suggested by the fact that rock types of the kind occurring in the headwaters of the Eagle River have not been found in the gravels interbedded with the lavas in the State Bridge syncline. The ancestral Roaring Fork may have drained westward to join the Gunnison River at Grand Mesa; if so, it prob-

FIGURE 34.—Valley of the Colorado River in Middle Park, a structural basin in the Rocky Mountains, view west. On the skyline is the Gore Range, a block of Precambrian rocks that was repeatedly uplifted across the river's course during middle and late Tertiary time and which repeatedly dammed the river in Middle Park.

ably was turned northward by the uplift recorded by the downstream rise of the Precambrian rocks along the Gunnison River (p. 74).

The amount of canyon deepening along the Colorado River in the Rocky Mountains during the Quaternary seems to have been about 750 feet. At the upper end of Glenwood Canyon, about 300 feet above the Colorado River, is a bed of volcanic ash correlated with the Pearlette Ash Member of the Sappa Formation of Pleistocene age (late Kansan or Yarmouth age; H. A. Powers, cited in Morrison, 1965, p. 36). A similar ash bed at the upper end of the Black Canyon of the Gunnison River and only 200 feet higher than the river suggests even less Quaternary downcutting there. These estimates, of course, assume that uplift and downcutting were both proportional during the early and late Pleistocene. The amount of Quaternary downcutting was probably very much greater near the mountain summits, however (fig. 39). (See for example Wahlstrom, 1947; Richmond, 1962.)

The valleys of the Colorado, Eagle, Fryingpan, and Roaring Fork, and the headward part of the Yampa, are mostly 3,000–4,000 feet deep and have been eroded in the last 10 million years. The amount of valley deepening during the Pliocene and during the Quaternary seems to have been roughly proportional to the time involved. Except in the very heads of the valleys, as in the cirques, the oldest Pleistocene morainal deposits are 500–750 feet above the present drainage, which seems to be about the amount of Pleistocene and Holocene downcutting. In general, therefore, these valleys were deepened about 3,000 feet during the Pliocene and a fifth that amount during the Quaternary. Uplift of the barriers crossed by the rivers has been renewed recently

FIGURE 35.—Canyon of the Colorado River through the uplifted Precambrian rocks of the Gore Range; view upriver toward northeast. Repeated uplift of the range during middle and late Tertiary time slowed or even ponded the Colorado River in Middle Park, the big structural basin upstream from these mountains. This uplift probably occurred as repeated small movements, but each time the river would overflow via the uplifted canyon and cut it deeper. The canyon, therefore, is in part antecedent even though the river initially may have been superimposed across the uplift.

FIGURE 36.—Valley of the Colorado River where it enters the State Bridge syncline. The valley is in this structural basin between the Gore Range and White River Plateau; view is west, downvalley. Miocene lavas forming the near mountains dip downvalley, away from the observer; in the distance the lavas rise again towards the White River Plateau. The axis of the downfold crosses the Colorado River in the distant transverse valley.

enough so that the river gradient is greatly steepened at each barrier (fig. 40), and it seems to have been rapid enough to have caused diversions that have resulted in wind gaps (fig. 41).

In the Gunnison River valley, some parts of the valley are demonstrably old, whereas others are demonstrably young. This is the oldest recognizable valley in the Colorado River basin above Grand Junction. It is a consequent valley in Precambrian rocks (figs. 31, 42), and it illustrates the mixing of processes and ages of valley cutting. The valley is partly filled with Oligocene and Miocene volcanic rocks from the San Juan and West Elk Mountains. The ancestral consequent valley—consequent on the uplift of the Rocky Mountains—predates the volcanic rocks, but the present valley is cut into these rocks and therefore is younger.

In middle and late Tertiary time the Gunnison valley was tilted 1,400 feet or more eastward against the flow of the river, as indicated by the eastward tilt of the synclinal lavas (fig. 43). That some of the tilting is

Quaternary (and perhaps continuing) is suggested by the geomorphology of the valley and habit of the rivers. Near Gunnison, upstream from the Black Canyon, the valleys are in Precambrian rocks as at Black Canyon, but they are wide and bordered by low rounded hills that appear old compared with the steep-walled canyons farther west. Moreover, both Gunnison River and its principal tributary there, Tomichi Creek, meander lazily in a marshy flood plain with gradients only 15 feet per mile. Through Black Canyon, the gradient is more than twice that and for considerable stretches is about 100 feet per mile. Also, according to Hansen (oral, commun., 1966), Quaternary gravels on the northeast side of Black Canyon uplift are tilted.

On Grand Mesa (fig. 47), river gravels at 8,500 feet altitude overlie Eocene lake beds (Green River Formation) and are overlain by basaltic lava dated as earliest Pliocene. Rock types in the gravels are like intrusive rocks in the Elk and West Elk Mountains to the east (Ogden Tweto, written commun., 1968) and probably are Miocene in age. The ancestral Gunnison River in

FIGURE 37.—East flank of the uplift at the White River Plateau, view west. The Colorado River is in the canyon in the middle distance and flows against the dip of the Mesozoic formations underlying the plateau. Lavas, thought to be late Miocene or early Pliocene in age on top of the plateau (skyline), extend unconformably across Cretaceous, lower Mesozoic, and Paleozoic formations. These lavas indicate middle or early Tertiary uplift of the plateau. Upper Miocene lavas in the basins east and south of the plateau have been uplifted 2,000 feet or more as a result of renewed movement in Pliocene and Quaternary time. The river, which crosses the uplift in a deep canyon (Glenwood Canyon), probably was superimposed across the uplift from the lavas or associated deposits, but deepening of the canyon was evidently due to downcutting as uplift continued; that is, the canyon is in part antecedent.

that vicinity at that time could not have been much lower, which suggests that the eastward tilting noted in the Gunnison valley probably extended this far west in late Tertiary and Quaternary time.

Cutting of Black Canyon (about 2,500 ft deep) began in Pliocene time, and about 2,000 feet of downcutting had taken place before the glaciation during Pleistocene time. The bed of volcanic ash (identified as Pearlette Ash Member of the Sappa Formation, Hanson, oral commun., 1966) only 200 feet above the river at the upper end of Black Canyon indicates only about 200 feet of downcutting there in the later Pleistocene. About 400 feet of downcutting seems indicated for the whole of Pleistocene time.

Two quite different kinds of drainage changes that may occur during uplift are illustrated in figures 44–46. In one, the drainage courses shifted during uplift; in the other, the drainage course remained the same during uplift, but the valley was deepened.

In brief, the Black Canyon of the Gunnison is partly the result of the river being superimposed from the volcanic rocks that buried a mountain of Precambrian rocks, and it is partly antecedent, the result of canyon deepening because of renewed doming at Black Canyon. The ancestral valley of the Gunnison is consequent and old—Oligocene. The present valley above the Black Canyon is antecedent across the eastward tilt of the lavas, and it and its southern tributaries, in part deeply incised into Pliocene formations, are young. Still other valley features seem attributable to Quaternary events, and there are examples of quite different kinds of valley adjustments to deformation. The Gunnison River valley provides good examples of how thoroughly different processes and different ages of valley cutting may be combined to produce a river system.

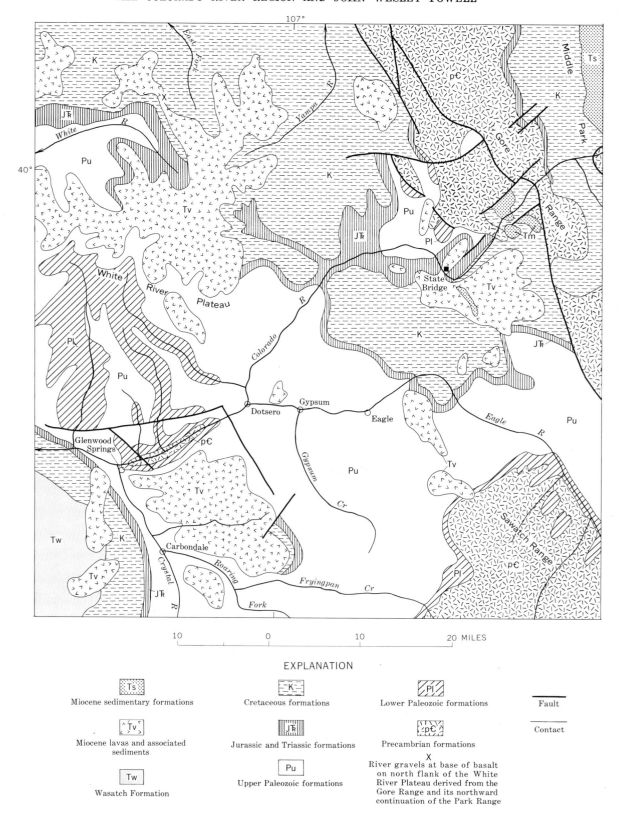

10   0   10   20 MILES

EXPLANATION

Ts — Miocene sedimentary formations

Tv — Miocene lavas and associated sediments

Tw — Wasatch Formation

K — Cretaceous formations

JŦ — Jurassic and Triassic formations

Pu — Upper Paleozoic formations

Pl — Lower Paleozoic formations

pԐ — Precambrian formations

X — River gravels at base of basalt on north flank of the White River Plateau derived from the Gore Range and its northward continuation of the Park Range

Fault

Contact

FIGURE 38.—The upper Colorado River basin in the Rocky Mountains (generalized from Burbank and others, 1935). The river crosses in succession, a basin containing middle Tertiary deposits at Middle Park, uplifted Precambrian rocks in the Gore Range, a second basin containing middle Tertiary sedimentary rocks, uplifted Precambrian rocks overlain by lavas which form the east flank of the State Bridge syncline and the east flank of the White River Plateau; then the river flows in a canyon to Glenwood Springs.

FIGURE 39.—U-shaped glaciated valley at the head of Roaring Fork. Valleys as large as this (1,300 ft. deep) at the heads of rivers in the Rocky Mountains are generally interpreted as having been eroded during the Pleistocene. Valley deepening downstream during the Pleistocene, however, was only half as much or less. View along highway below Independence Pass.

Similar drainage changes on a larger scale seem indicated along the Uncompahgre River. Where it emerges from the San Juan Mountains above Ridgeway (fig. 47), volcanic rocks rise 2,000 feet east and west above the valley floor. In part this may be an old valley, like that of the Gunnison, partly filled with volcanic rocks, but the valley is also in part a structural depression.

The original drainage seems to have been northwest past Horsefly Peak on the Uncompahgre Plateau (fig. 47), where gravel deposits derived from volcanic rocks

in the San Juan Mountains are at 10,000 feet altitude. These gravels are 2,000 feet higher than the base of the volcanic rocks along the Uncompahgre River, and most of this difference (about 1,500 ft) seems attributable to the late Pliocene and Quaternary uplift of the Uncompahgre Plateau described by Cater (1966). The gravels may be as old as Miocene. Similar but lower gravels northwest of Horsefly Peak probably represent progressive monoclinal shifting of the Uncompahgre River

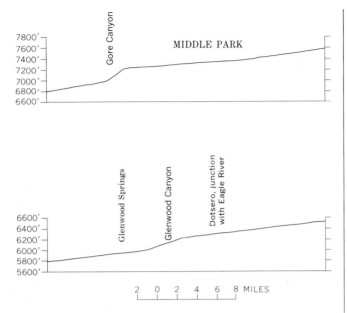

FIGURE 40.—Profiles of the Colorado River in the Southern Rocky Mountains, showing the steepened gradients where the river is in canyons crossing the structural barriers.

northeast down the flank of the plateau to its present valley.

In the vicinity of Grand Junction is the most spectacular example of drainage diversion in the whole drainage basin, a diversion caused by uplift and abandonment of a large canyon (fig. 48). Unaweep Canyon, 2,000 feet deep, as much as 4 miles wide at the rim, and having a floor a mile wide in gneissic Precambrian rocks, is an elevated nearly dry canyon that extends across the Uncompahgre Plateau (figs. 47, 49). Two small streams now drain to the opposite ends of the canyon, but they are much too small to have carved the big valley in such resistant rocks. They are excellent examples of underfit streams. The divide between their heads is 2,000 feet higher than the nearby stretches of the Colorado and Dolores Rivers. The canyon was cut by a major river, certainly the Gunnison and probably also the Colorado, that discharged southwestward across the Uncompahgre Plateau when it was lower than it is now. The structural and drainage changes there (fig. 50) have recently been described by Lohman (1965) and Cater (1966).

Gravels deposited by the Gunnison River when it flowed westward through the canyon have been found at both ends (Cater, 1966). Those at the southwest end are 1,400 feet lower than the floor of Unaweep Canyon in the center of the plateau and indicate that the southwest flank of the plateau has been uplifted this amount since Unaweep Canyon was abandoned (Cater, 1966,

p. C91). Moreover, those gravels are within 200 feet of the present level of the Dolores River and indicate that the river has cut downward no more than that since the gravels were deposited. Thus, it follows that the amount of downcutting by the Dolores River since Unaweep Canyon was abandoned probably is only about 100 feet, because part of the difference in altitude probably is due to uplift of the gravels when that flank of the Uncompahgre Plateau was folded (Cater, 1966, p. C91). As a result of correlating these gravels with deposits in the La Sal Mountains, Cater (1966, p. 90–91) infers that Unaweep Canyon was abandoned in late Pliocene, or possibly earliest Pleistocene time.

During the early history of Unaweep Canyon, the Colorado may still have been ponded, at least intermittently, in the structural basins above the White River Plateau and Gore Range. The stretch of river above Grand Junction may have originally headed near Rifle. This may have been the situation at one time because this section (Grand Junction to Rifle) is the only stretch of the Colorado River above its junction with the Green where the tributaries are symmetrically arranged on both sides (fig. 32). This drainage pattern above Grand Junction would be younger than the lavas on Grand Mesa, presumably early Pliocene, which is about the time suggested for the Colorado, Eagle, and Roaring Fork to have been turned into their present courses. Midway between Grand Junction and Rifle the old drainage would have been roughly 3,000 feet above the present river level.

Evidence has already been presented indicating that the Gunnison is at least twice as old as this stretch of the Colorado River upstream from Grand Junction, and it looks it, for it is as deep and twice as wide (figs. 51, 52). The fact that the bigger stream, the Colorado, has the smaller valley probably reflects the difference in age because both are in easily eroded rocks.

Late Tertiary and Quaternary structural deformation took place south of the Uncompahgre Plateau near the La Sal Mountains. These mountains were domed by intrusions (laccoliths) in middle Tertiary time; they have been dated by potassium-argon methods at 25 million years (Stern and others, 1965). The Dolores River swings in a wide arc around the mountains and, in doing so, must cross, nearly at right angles, a series of faulted anticlines underlain by salt beds in the Pennsylvanian Paradox Formation (fig. 53). The Colorado River after being joined by the Dolores, crosses the faulted anticlines west of the La Sal Mountains. The downfaulted crests of the anticlines contain conglomerate (Hunt, 1958, p. 314; Carter and Gualtieri, 1965) that probably

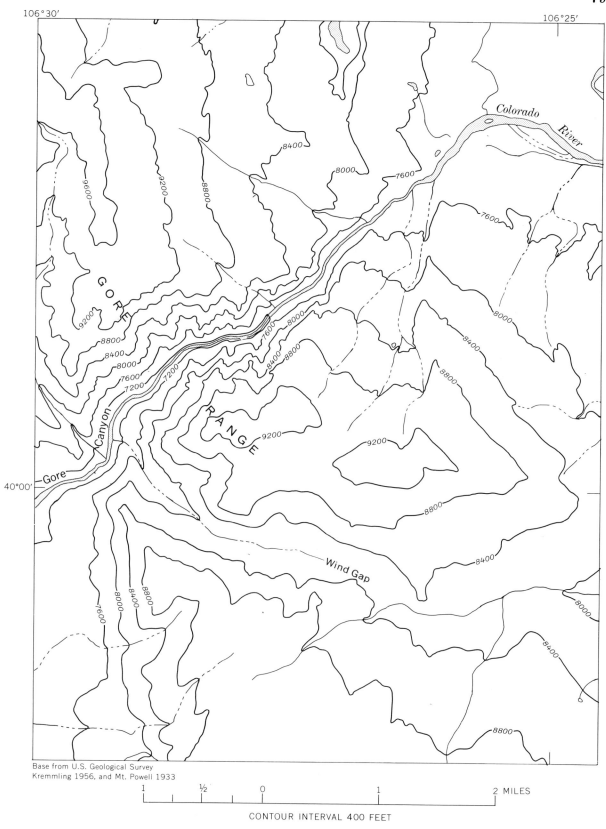

Base from U.S. Geological Survey
Kremmling 1956, and Mt. Powell 1933

CONTOUR INTERVAL 400 FEET

FIGURE 41.—Wind gap in the Gore Range south of Gore Canyon. East of the range is a wide valley (Blue River) which joins the Colorado about 3 miles east of Gore Canyon. The wind gap probably represents a former course of Blue River (or possibly even of the Colorado River) prior to late Tertiary uplift of the Gore Range.

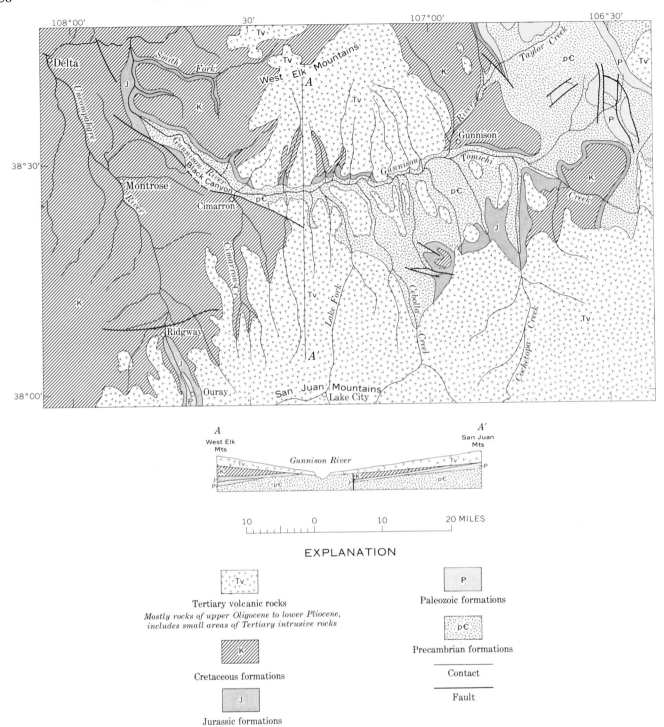

EXPLANATION

Tertiary volcanic rocks

*Mostly rocks of upper Oligocene to lower Pliocene,
includes small areas of Tertiary intrusive rocks*

Cretaceous formations

Jurassic formations

May include some Triassic rocks

Paleozoic formations

Precambrian formations

Contact

Fault

FIGURE 42.—Gunnison River valley, Colorado (generalized from Burbank and others, 1935). The river cut into Precambrian rocks before eruption of the volcanic material that poured into the valley from the San Juan Mountains and West Elk Mountains. The eruptions began in Oligocene time and continued through the Miocene and into the Pliocene. The valley of the Gunnison River dates from the Oligocene (about 35 million years) ; some of its tributaries from the San Juan Mountains are incised into Pliocene lavas and occupy young valleys (about 5 million years).

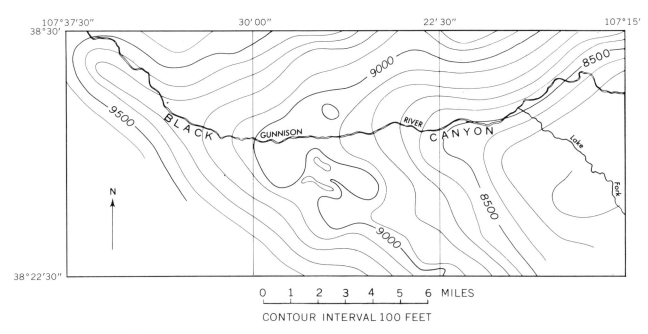

FIGURE 43.—Structure contours drawn at the base of lavas and related eruptive rocks filling the Gunnison River valley; the lavas occupy a trough coinciding with the river valley and inclined more than 1,400 feet upstream (to the right). Much or most of this warping of the lavas occurred in late Tertiary time. (From Hansen, 1965a, fig. 23.)

is Pliocene in age. The conglomerates are younger than the intrusive rocks and contain gravels derived from them; in Castle Valley, conglomerate 1,000 feet thick is vertical and is unconformably overlain by two or more boulder deposits, till, and glacial outwash of pre-Wisconsin age (Hunt, 1958, p. 314; Richmond, 1962, p. 93–94). The deformation presumably is due to movement of the salt, perhaps attributable to accelerated solution during the Pleistocene when melt waters discharged from the snowfields and glaciers on the La Sal Mountains.

Before the oldest till overlying the tilted Pliocene(?) conglomerate was deposited, the Colorado River already was deep in its canyon where it crosses the faulted anticlines; no more than 500 feet of downcutting there is attributable to the Quaternary, although in the La Sal Mountains, 1,000 feet or more of valley deepening is attributed to the Quaternary (Richmond, 1962, p. 93–94).

On the west slope of the San Juan Mountains, at Glade Park, Shawe (1968) found deposits clearly derived from the San Juan Mountains, now isolated by erosion from their source; valleys there have cut 1,000 feet into Mancos Shale since the deposits were formed, which is like the deep erosion in the La Sal Mountains and along tributaries of the Gunnison River on the north flank of the San Juan Mountains (p. 75). The

headward parts of valleys in the mountains of the Colorado River drainage basin were greatly deepened during Quaternary time, but along the main stems, maximum cutting during the Quaternary does not seem to have exceeded about 500–750 feet.

The Dolores River provides another example of stream diversion, canyon deepening by antecedence, and a means of estimating the amount of lowering by erosion of the Colorado Plateau in southeastern Utah during late Tertiary and Quaternary time. The river begins with a consequent southwesterly course off the San Juan Mountains (fig. 54). In this consequent course, the valley is 2,500 feet deep in southwest-dipping Jurassic and Triassic formations and has a gradient averaging about 50 feet per mile. Where it turns sharply northward, the canyon is about 200 feet deep in the Morrison Formation, and the gradient is less than 25 feet per mile. The drainage arrangement suggests that the Dolores originally continued its consequent southwesterly course to join the San Juan River and that it was turned northward when the laccolithic intrusions domed Ute Mountain. I assume that the intrusions at Ute Mountain are early Miocene, like those at the La Sal Mountains (p. 78).

After turning the bend, the Dolores River takes a northerly course across the broad northwest-trending Dolores anticline (fig. 54). Where the river crosses the

FIGURE 44.—Black Canyon of the Gunnison River (foreground), in Precambrian rock, is 2,500 feet deep. View is northeast to the West Elk Mountains (on skyline). Uplift of the Precambrian rocks, while the canyon was being eroded, diverted drainage that formerly came to Black Canyon from the West Elk Mountains; the abandoned valley has been left hanging.

crest of the fold, rock units are 1,000 feet structurally higher than at the bend, and the river gradient on the southern flank of the fold is about 20 feet per mile. At the crest, where the river again has cut into Triassic rocks, it meanders widely and then plunges 40 feet per mile down the north flank of the fold. Almost certainly this canyon has been arched by the same kind of uplift that led to abandonment of Unaweep Canyon; if there had been resistant rocks in the canyon across this fold, like the Precambrian rocks at Unaweep Canyon, the Dolores River might have turned to a new course.

Warped Pleistocene gravel terraces along Disappointment Creek (Shawe, 1968) show that some of the deformation in this area is Quaternary.

Evidence bearing on erosion of the plateau surface in southeastern Utah in late Tertiary and Quaternary time is provided by a deposit of Dolores River gravel along the west rim of the Dolores River canyon, where it enters the south flank of the Dolores anticline. The deposit forms the divide at the head of drainage to Cross Canyon and the San Juan River (fig. 54). When that gravel was deposited there must have been hills of

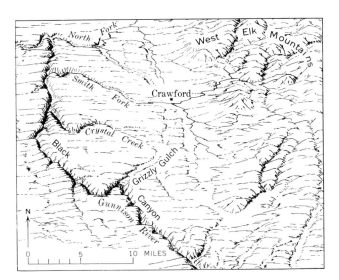

FIGURE 45.—Example of drainage changes during uplift at Black Canyon. Grizzly Gulch and Crystal Creek, that flowed to the Gunnison River across the hard-rock core of the uplift, were captured by more rapidly eroding streams that flowed to Smith Fork through soft rocks. Grizzly Gulch now is a hanging valley and contains Quaternary gravels tilted northeast (Hansen, 1966). Tributaries of the North Fork of the Gunnison are about to capture Smith Fork and turn it northward at the vicinity of Crawford, where a divide of soft rocks, about 50 feet high, holds the stream on a course about 1,000 feet higher than the North Fork only 8 miles away.

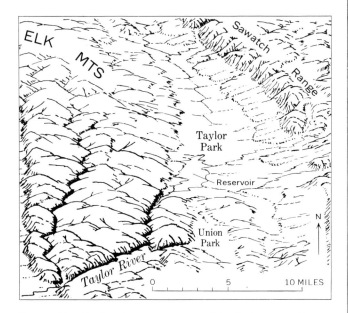

FIGURE 46.—Taylor Park, a structural basin between the uplifted Elk Mountains and Sawatch Range, is drained by way of Taylor River canyon. The Elk Mountains, which are crossed by the canyon, are a block of Precambrian and Paleozoic rocks raised structurally many thousands of feet above Cretaceous formations in the valley immediately to the west. The surface of the uplifted block plunges eastward under Taylor Park.

Mancos Shale on what is now a stripped plain on resistant sandstone (Dakota Sandstone); the sandstone and the plain formed on it slope 2,000 feet southwest to the bluffs overlooking the San Juan River. Between the anticline and the San Juan River the structural relief is 4,000 feet.

Southeastern Utah and southwestern Colorado must have been largely covered by Cretaceous formations when the laccolithic mountains formed in early Miocene time because Cretaceous shale, intruded by laccoliths, is still preserved at all of the mountains, even including the Abajo Mountains, which are on top of an upwarp. Also, there are reasons for supposing that in Miocene time, southeastern Utah was structurally lower than it is now (p. 99). The Dolores anticline forms the southern boundary of the salt anticlines and probably is related to the parallel Uncompahgre Plateau which forms the north boundary. It is assumed, therefore, that there was renewed uplift on this fold in late Tertiary and Quaternary time, that the Dolores River deepened its canyon across the fold as the uplift continued (antecedence), and that at least 2,000 feet of the structural relief between the anticline and the San Juan River is due to late Tertiary or Quaternary earth movement.

By this interpretation, Cross Canyon and the other streams draining southward to the San Juan River are consequent streams and largely of late Tertiary and Quaternary age. The stripped surface now is blanketed by a loess deposit that, judging by its intensive weathering and burial by fan gravels at the foot of the Abajo Mountains, is probably middle glacial Pleistocene in age (about 500,000 years ago). The Mancos Shale had been stripped from the plain before this loess was deposited. The assumption of late Tertiary and Quaternary uplift at the Dolores anticline also helps explain why the Dolores River did not take a consequent northwesterly course at the position of Hatch Wash (fig. 54). The northward course would be along an older north-trending syncline west of the San Juan Mountains and east of the Monument upwarp and domes at the Abajo and La Sal Mountains; the northwesterly structural features are attributed to late Tertiary and Quaternary deformation, and the Dolores River has maintained an antecedent course across them. The same might apply to the Colorado River, which crosses the structural features west of the La Sal Mountains.

At Moab, the Colorado River begins a meandering course southwestward against the regional northward dip (figs. 55, 62) and has a gradient of only about 1 foot per mile. The canyon, cut into Jurassic, Triassic, and upper Paleozoic rocks, consists of an outer rim of Jurassic and Triassic strata and an inner gorge in

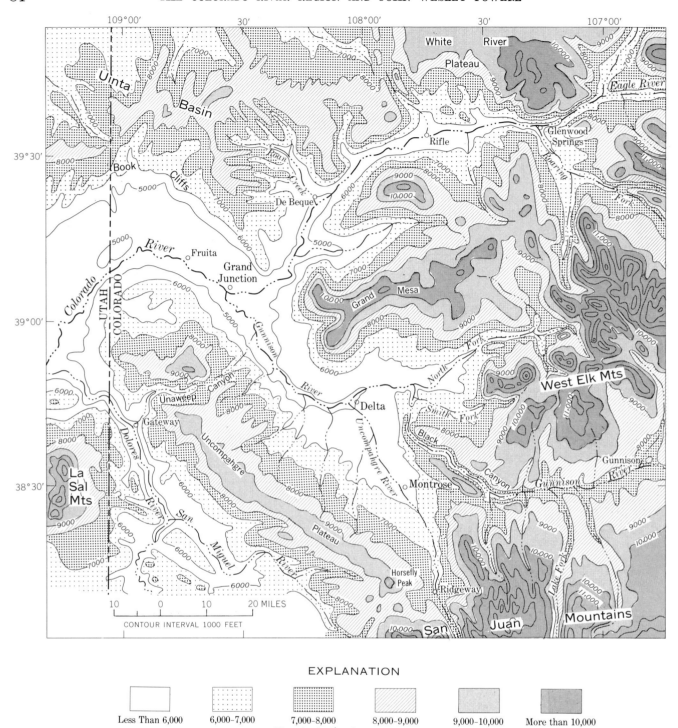

EXPLANATION

| Less Than 6,000 | 6,000–7,000 | 7,000–8,000 | 8,000–9,000 | 9,000–10,000 | More than 10,000 |

Elevation, in feet above mean sea level

FIGURE 47.—Altitudes in the Grand Junction area, where the Gunnison joins the Colorado River.

FIGURE 48.—Unaweep Canyon, the abandoned canyon of the Gunnison River, and probably of the Colorado River, across the uplift at the Uncompahgre Plateau. The mile-wide canyon is in Precambrian gneissic rocks (lower cliff) overlain by Triassic rocks (form slope on skyline) and Jurassic sandstones (cliff on skyline). The uplift that elevated this canyon and diverted its drainage occurred in very late Pliocene or early Pleistocene time.

Paleozoic strata (fig. 56). The outer rims are 8–10 miles apart; the inner gorge is 1–2 miles wide. River gravels were not found more than about 500 feet above the river and only in the inner gorge. No river gravels were found on the broad stripped bench back from the inner gorge; gravel deposits there are locally derived fan gravels from the outer rim. The river gravels surely are Quaternary, and most of the cutting of the inner gorge probably occurred during the late Pliocene and Quaternary while uplift continued in southeastern Utah.

Green and Yampa Rivers

Green River did not join the Colorado River system until after the Miocene(?) Browns Park Formation was deposited. The river entered Browns Park valley at the north foot of the Uinta Mountains after the uppermost beds of the Browns Park Formation there had been deposited, and supposedly the river continued eastward, but where it went is uncertain. Subsequently, it turned southward into Lodore Canyon across the

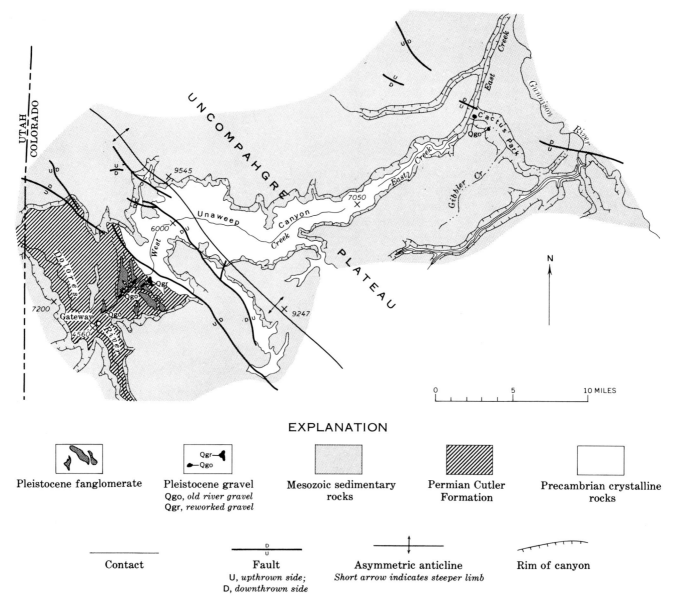

FIGURE 49.—Unaweep Canyon and part of the Uncompahgre Plateau. (From Cater, 1966, p. C87.)

EXPLANATION

Pleistocene fanglomerate

Pleistocene gravel
Qgo, *old river gravel*
Qgr, *reworked gravel*

Mesozoic sedimentary rocks

Permian Cutler Formation

Precambrian crystalline rocks

Contact

Fault
U, *upthrown side;*
D, *downthrown side*

Asymmetric anticline
Short arrow indicates steeper limb

Rim of canyon

Precambrian rocks uplifted in the Uinta arch (fig. 57, 58). This diversion occurred no earlier than late Miocene time. Green River is the type example for Powell's antecedent stream, but the age relations do not allow this stretch of Green River to be older than the Uinta Mountains, the earliest uplift of which antedates the Eocene Green River Formation. Powell's theory of antecedence was dismissed in favor of the theory that Lodore Canyon resulted from the river being superimposed from beds of the Browns Park Formation that extended across the uplifted Precambrian rocks.

Antecedence also was dismissed as an explanation for the several canyons by which the Yampa River crosses uplifts. Yampa River joins the Green River in a canyon within the Uinta Mountains rather than in the open country to the north or south.

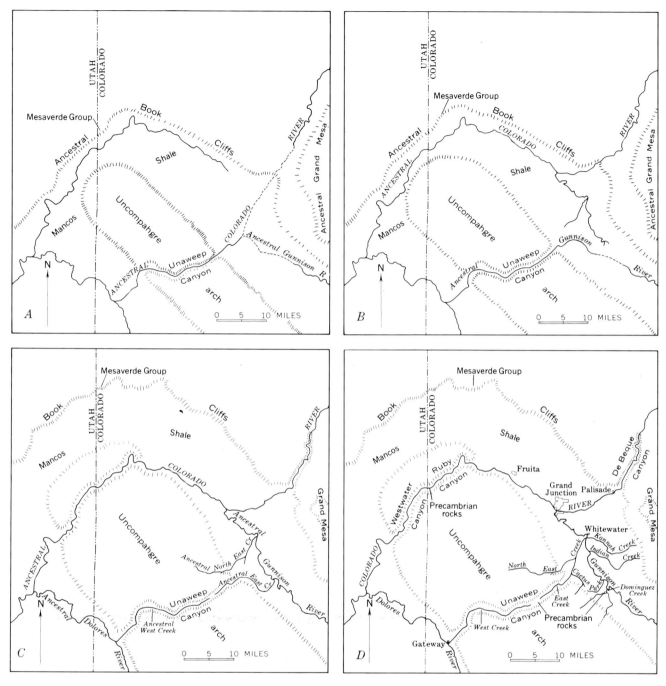

FIGURE 50.—Probable sequence of drainage changes where the Colorado River crosses the Uncompahgre Plateau (from Lohman, 1965, p. 71). *A*, earliest stage, Pliocene; *B*, *C*, latest Pliocene and earliest Pleistocene; *D*, present.

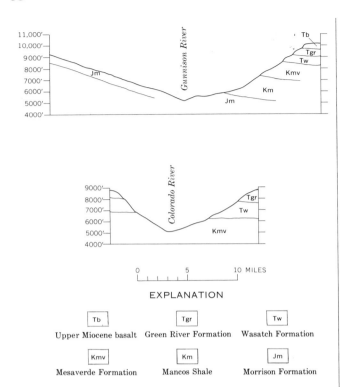

FIGURE 51.—Cross profiles illustrating contrast in valleys of the Gunnison and Colorado Rivers. Each profile is about 25 miles above the junction of the two rivers. Both rivers flow across nonresistant rocks.

Superposition by itself, however, seems untenable. This theory first requires that the Browns Park Formation cover the eastern 50 miles of the Uinta Mountains and the adjoining lower parts of northeastern Utah, northwestern Colorado, and part of southern Wyoming. It further requires the removal of that cover. However, there was not enough time to remove such deep fill completely over that vast area. As that area is only about 5 percent of the Colorado River drainage basin, the volume is also excessive in terms of the amount of material in the Pliocene and younger sediments of the delta.

The conflicting interpretations however, become reconciled by assuming that the river's course was determined by superposition before the last movements of uplift at the Uinta Mountains (or the last downwarping of the adjoining basins). The canyon could have been deepened during and after that final uplift, and thus be in part antecedent. In my view this is the probable sequence of events, and, if so, Powell was as right as his later critics.

The Yampa River heads in the volcanic rocks and interbedded sedimentary rocks of probable middle and late Miocene age, downfolded in the structural trough extending northward from the State Bridge syncline along the west foot of the Gore and Park Ranges (figs. 32, 38). This headward part, therefore, is no earlier than late Miocene or early Pliocene time.

After turning westward near Steamboat Springs (fig. 32), the Yampa River enters a broad strike valley in Upper Cretaceous shale. The river gradient is about 10 feet per mile. This stretch of valley probably originated at least as early as Miocene time, and perhaps in the Oligocene, as a strike valley along the southern edge of the Eocene rocks on the northeast flank of the White River Plateau. Part of the tilting here is Pliocene, however, resulting from the later stages of uplift at the White River Plateau, and the position of the river in the strike valley very likely has monoclinally shifted northward down the dip as downcutting and tilting progressed.

Farther west (fig. 32), the strike valley is filled with the Miocene(?) Browns Park Foundation (fig. 29), which consists of conglomerate, sandstone, and silt from the surrounding uplands mixed with considerable material of volcanic origin. The Browns Park Formation is similar in age and rather like the Miocene fill along the headward part of the Yampa River and in the State Bridge syncline, but it contains less lava.

Just west of Craig (fig. 32), the Yampa River turns southwest from the open strike valley and enters a canyon in tilted beds of Cretaceous sandstone that rise southward towards the White River Plateau. The position of this canyon probably was determined by superposition from the Browns Park Formation, but it is unnecessary to assume that the fill was as high as the present canyon rims (about 7,000 ft.) If 500 feet of uplift on this part of the north flank of the White River Plateau is post-Browns Park, the beds from which superposition occurred need not have been any higher than the top of the present fill west of Craig (about 6,600 ft.) This kind and amount of displacement in Pliocene and Quaternary time is quite consistent with the dips in the Browns Park Formation just west of Craig (fig. 58) and with what is known in general about late Cenozoic uplift at the White River Plateau.

This canyon of the Yampa River across the tilted beds has a wildly meandering course with a gradient of only about 5 feet per river mile. This gradient probably reflects the difficulty the river had in maintaining its way while uplift progressed. Similar relationships in the canyons south of the Uinta basin are similarly interpreted (p. 83).

FIGURE 52.—Valley of the Colorado River where it crosses the east end of the Uinta basin. After leaving the Southern Rocky Mountains, the Colorado River enters the Colorado Plateau and crosses the eastern end of the Uinta basin in this deep valley carved in the Green River Formation (Eocene), upper two-thirds of the cliff, and the Wasatch Formation (Paleocene and Eocene), base of the cliff. Locally there are lavas on the plateau surface above the Green River Formation; these have been dated radiometrically as early Pliocene (about 10 million years old). In places, the lavas overlie river gravels. View is northwest, about 20 miles west of Rifle, Colo. Mount Logan (peak at left) is at an altitude of 8,444 feet; the river (marked by trees) at the base of the mountain is about 5,000 feet in altitude.

A few miles farther west, at Juniper Mountain, the Yampa has cut another gorge about 600 feet deep through a structural dome of Paleozoic rocks protruding through the Miocene cover (fig. 58). The downcutting here has occurred since earliest Pliocene time.

For 25 miles west of Juniper Mountain, the Yampa River is in the Browns Park Formation until it is again in a canyon through an isolated structural dome, this one at Cross Mountain (fig. 59). This canyon is 1,000 feet deep. Structural relief on the Paleozoic formations is at least 10,000 feet, and there is no problem superimposing the Yampa River across this upfold, as Hancock (1915) suggested, if 500 feet (5 percent) of the doming is due to the Pliocene and younger downfolding of the Browns Park Formation in the adjoining structural basin. By this interpretation the river course was superimposed, but half or more of the depth of the canyon through Cross Mountain is due to antecedence. Seven miles west of Cross Mountain, the Yampa River enters the Uinta Mountains to follow a canyon course for about 25 miles to its junction with Green River.

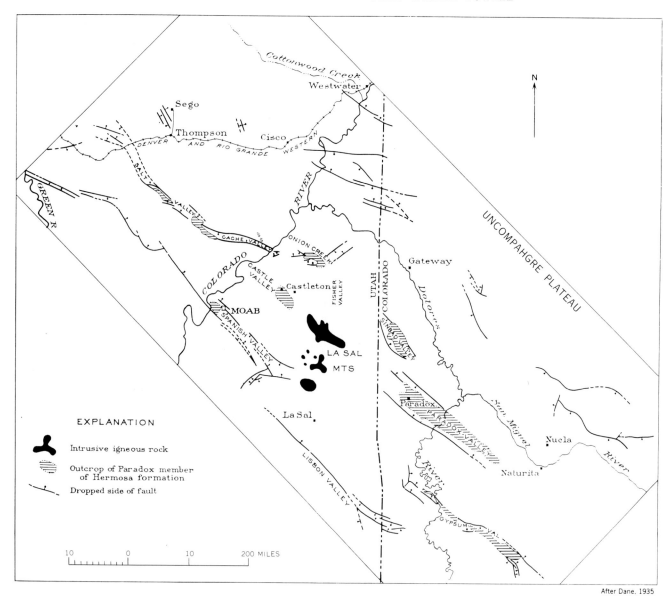

FIGURE 53.—Relation of the Dolores and Colorado Rivers to the northwest-trending faulted anticlines southwest of the Uncompahgre Plateau (from Dane, 1935).

As already noted, the theory that the canyons of the Green and the Yampa are solely antecedent is untenable because it requires that the rivers and their canyons be older than the initial uplift of the Uinta Mountains, which is earliest Tertiary or possibly even Late Cretaceous. The alternative, that the rivers and the canyons are entirely the result of superposition, however, also seems untenable because it means that the structural basins north, south, and east of the mountains were filled to the height of the canyon rims (present altitudes about 6,000–7,500 ft) and that this vast depth of fill was then eroded. Bradley (1936) recognized this difficulty and suggested that part of the canyon cutting might be attributed to headward erosion by a stream draining south; by his interpretation, the fill in Browns Park need have been only as high as the wind gap at the head of the south-draining stream. Both hypotheses, superposition and capture, assume that the east end of the Uinta Mountains was structurally stable during late Tertiary and Quaternary time and escaped the folding and warping known to have occurred only a little way to the east.

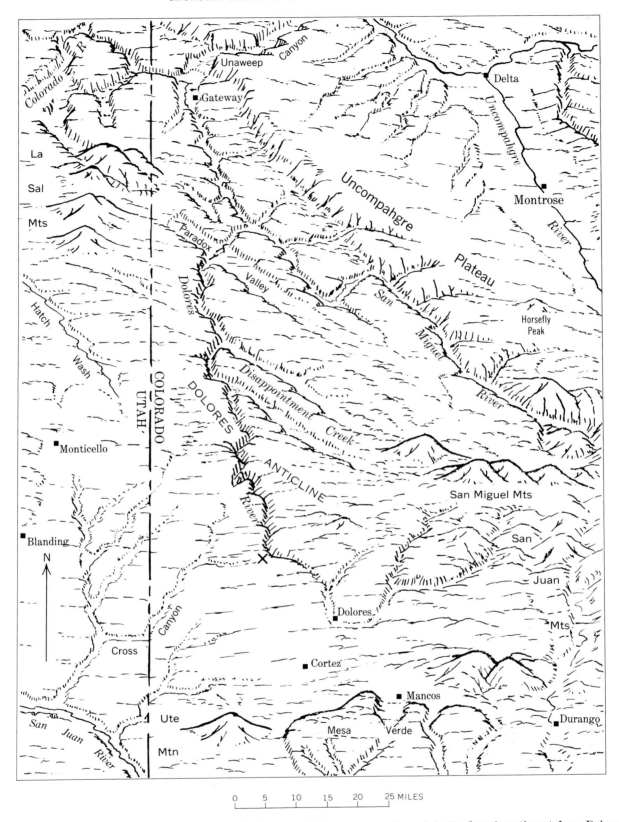

FIGURE 54.—Dolores River drainage basin. The headwaters of the river probably originally flowed southwest from Dolores to join the San Juan River; they may have been turned northward by the early Miocene doming at Ute Mountain. A gravel deposit (X), on the west rim of the north-trending canyon, forms the divide between the Dolores River and drainage to the southwest. When the Dolores River deposited the gravel there must have been hills of Cretaceous shale at the site of Cross Canyon and the canyons northwest of it.

FIGURE 55.—Crossing the Canyonlands section of the Colorado Plateau, the Colorado and Green Rivers are in deep colorful canyons in Jurassic, Triassic, Permian, and Pennsylvanian rocks. This view of the Colorado is northeast (upstream) at The Loop about 6 miles above the junction with the Green River. The gorge is about 500 feet deep; the broad bench (most of photograph) is underlain by the Permian (Cutler Formation), and no river gravels were found on it. In the distance, about 8 miles away, are the cliffs of the Triassic and Jurassic rocks, about 1,200 feet high (compare with fig. 56). In early Miocene time (about 25 million years ago) much or most of the canyonlands still were covered by Cretaceous shale (Mancos Shale). River deposits correlated with glacial deposits in the La Sal Mountains indicate about 500 feet of canyon deepening during Quaternary time (the last 2–3 million years).

There has been considerable post-Browns Park deformation in the eastern part of the Uinta Mountains and eastward nearly to Craig (Sears, 1924a, pl. 35; Bradley, 1936, p. 185; Hansen, 1965b, p. 162–166, 171–172). Hansen (1965b, p. 172) notes that a large segment of the eastern Uinta Mountains was tilted northward

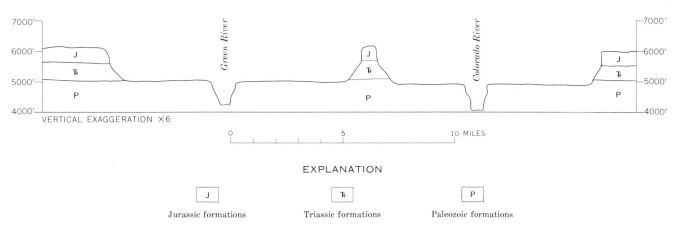

VERTICAL EXAGGERATION ×6

EXPLANATION

J	Tʀ	P
Jurassic formations	Triassic formations	Paleozoic formations

FIGURE 56.—Generalized profile across the canyons of the Colorado and Green Rivers, about 15 miles above their junction. The rivers are in an inner gorge carved in upper Paleozoic rocks that form broad benches. River gravels were not found on the benches, only fan deposits (derived from the outer cliffs which are composed of Triassic and Jurassic rocks).

FIGURE 57.—Gates of Lodore, where the Green River leaves its open valley in Browns Park (foreground) and flows in a canyon that crosses the Uinta Mountains. Powell (1875) believed that the canyon was antecedent. Critics pointed out that the mountains date from early Tertiary time and that the river could not be that old because it is flowing on upper Tertiary strata. They assumed that the river must have been superimposed from upper Tertiary sediments that filled Browns Park and extended across the tops of the mountains. The interpretation offered in this report assumes that both Powell and his critics are partly right, that the river course was determined by superposition when the mountains were not much, if at all, higher than Browns Park, and that renewed uplift of the mountains (or downwarping of Browns Park) enabled the canyon to be deepened (antecedent).

and eastward after deposition of the Browns Park Formation. Much of the canyon deepening probably occurred because the river was antecedent to this late de-

formation, and a little evidence that this is what happened is found by comparing the mountains with the Uinta basin to the south.

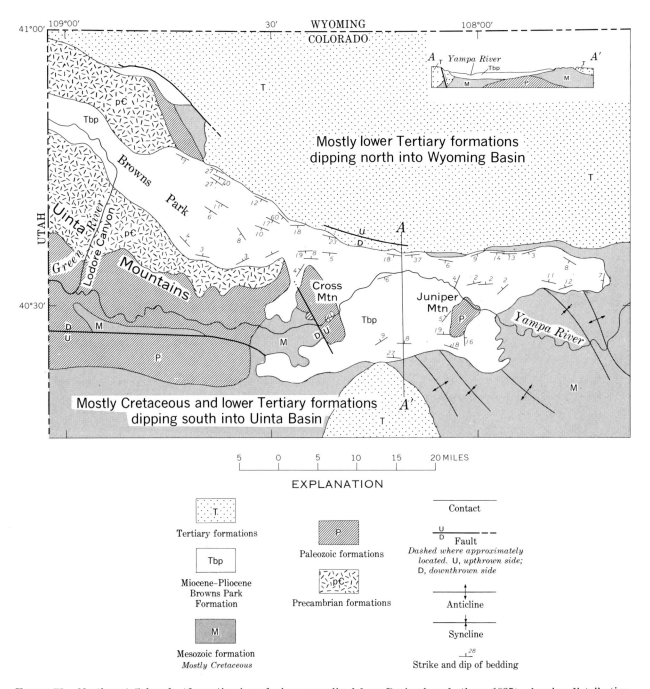

FIGURE 58.—Northwest Colorado (formation boundaries generalized from Burbank and others, 1935), showing distribution of the Miocene(?) Browns Park Formation along the Yampa River and in Browns Park (strike and dip symbols in Browns Park Formation and cross section generalized from Sears, 1924a, pl. 35). The Browns Park Formation occupies a structural depression that lies along the structural arch forming the Uinta Mountains. Precambrian, Paleozoic, Mesozoic (mostly Cretaceous), and lower Tertiary formation are anticlinally folded under the arch.

In the Uinta basin the uppermost formation is the Duchesne River (fig. 60), classed by some as Oligocene (Wilmarth, 1938, p. 637) and by others as uppermost Eocene (Wood and others, 1941, p. 19, pl. 1). Uinta basin was the site of a lake that gradually was filled with sediment and evolved to a playa and, finally, while the uppermost beds of the Duchesne River Formation were deposited, into an alluvial plain (Warner, 1966, p. 949–950). In all probability, the Duchesne River Formation is the youngest deposit laid down in the Uinta basin, and drainage was southward out of the basin from that time on.

FIGURE 59.—Yampa River where it emerges from its canyon through Cross Mountain, an uplift involving Paleozoic and Precambrian rocks. The gorge is 1,000 feet deep, yet upstream from it the Yampa River valley is broad and open and 1,000 feet
lower than the top of Cross Mountain. In the canyon, Yampa River has a gradient of 60 feet per mile; below the canyon
(seen here) the gradient averages 4 feet per mile.

Opinions differ, and probably will continue to differ, about whether the Browns Park Formation ever formed much of a cover across the Uinta basin. I doubt if there ever was much Browns Park Formation deposited there. In the first place, where Green River crosses the Uinta basin, the beds at the surface are playa and fluviatile mudstone (Duchesne River Formation). These beds form a flat upland underlying more than 700 square miles and extending 30 miles east and west from the Green River. The area is smooth except for the valleys cut 100–300 feet into it. The beds are easily eroded and the surface looks like a dissected and slightly lowered playa or flood plain. To me it seems unlikely that such easily eroded beds could have been buried and then exhumed with so flat a surface from under a cover such as the Browns Park Formation. Such could happen to a resistant formation, but hardly likely to easily eroded mudstones. Too, why should the master stream, the Green, be coincidently located in that low part of the Uinta basin where the Duchesne River Formation becomes fluviatile?

Yet, immediately to the north, in the Uinta Mountains, there are thick gravel deposits of the Browns Park Formation on the plateau at Diamond Mountain (altitude 7,500 ft) (fig. 61). According to D. M. Kinney (written commun., 1966), these deposits were laid down in ancient dendritic stream channels that extended eastward towards the present Green River. On the plateau east of the Green River, the same Miocene surface and remnants of the Browns Park Formation are at 8,000 feet altitude. At these present altitudes, the Miocene surface and Browns Park Formation project about 1,500 feet higher than the Duchesne River Formation, where it is turned up against the south side of the mountains. This difference in altitude surely is not an accident of erosion, for it would be strange to have had the Browns Park Formation eroded from the low Uinta basin while it was preserved on the mountains.

The difference in altitude between the Browns Park Formation on Diamond Mountain and Yampa Plateau and the Duchesne River Formation in the Uinta basin can be explained by assuming relatively little erosion

FIGURE 60.—Diagrammatic cross section of the Uinta basin north from the Book Cliffs, Utah. The southward rise of the lower Tertiary formations indicates middle or late Tertiary folding. About one-fourth of the folding is assumed to have occurred in late Tertiary time (modified slightly after Rocky Mountain Assoc. Petroleum Geologists and others, 1951, fig. 61).

in the Uinta Basin and about 1,000 feet of post-Browns Park displacement along the steep fold separating the two formations. This is only 5 percent of the total structural relief on that Cenozoic fold, and about 20 percent of Cenozoic time is available for the displacement. It seems unlikely that this part of the Colorado River basin remained stable during late Tertiary and Quaternary time when there was so much deformation in virtually every other part, including areas nearby.

The Miocene surface at Diamond Mountain and adjoining parts of the eastern end of the Uinta Mountains rise northward to a maturely eroded surface having rounded knobs (formed by the Uinta Mountain Group) between broad open valleys floored in part by the Browns Park Formation (fig. 61). These valleys head at wind gaps overlooking the western end of Browns Park and the canyon of Green River farther west. Some of these, notably Cart Creek, formerly drained south, but their drainage now is reversed, as indicated by the barbed tributaries that converge southward. Green River may have first crossed the Uinta arch at Cart Creek, for this underfit stream is cut into a broad valley in the quartzite, almost opposite the place where Green River first bumps into the Uinta Mountains.

In summary, by my interpretation, which assumes 1,000 feet of Pliocene and later displacement of the Uinta basin relative to the mountains, Pliocene and later erosion along the Green and Yampa Rivers would involve: (1) about 500 feet of general lowering by erosion of the Uinta basin at the hogback of the Duchesne River Formation and farther south; (2) about 500 feet of valley deepening by the Green River across the Uinta basin; and (3) about 1,500 feet of downcutting in the canyons of the Green and Yampa Rivers in the Uinta Mountains. This interpretation combines both superposition and antecedence.

FIGURE 62.—Top of the Kaibab Limestone in the Colorado Plateau (from Hunt, 1956, p. 52). The map shows that the southwest rim of the plateau is structurally high (the Kaibab Limestone there is at an altitude of more than 7,000 feet) and that the north part is structurally low (the Kaibab Limestone there is at 8,000 ft below sea level). Strata dip north, and the Colorado River flows southwest against the dip. The map also shows the dimensions of the big upwarps that are crossed by the drainage: the Uncompahgre, Monument, and Kaibab. Originally, the Kaibab upwarp was like the others and had a long smooth west-dipping flank; in middle and late Tertiary time this was faulted, and the fault blocks were raised. The formations there are once more nearly horizontal, but they now are highly elevated. (See also fig. 75.)

Canyons South of the Uinta Basin

The increasingly fluviatile sedimentation in the upper part of the Duchesne River Formation and the geomorphology there have been used as the basis for inferring that exterior drainage from the Uinta basin began shortly after the Duchesne River Formation was deposited, that is, in Oligocene or Eocene time. Probably the drainage went to the next basin southward, the Henry Mountains structural basin (fig. 62), but the record has been destroyed by erosion. The Henry Mountains basin had begun to form in earliest Tertiary time because the Waterpocket fold, which forms the west flank of the basin, is overlapped by lower Tertiary formations (Smith and others, 1963, p. 61; see also Gregory and Moore, 1931, p. 116). To reach the Henry Mountains structural basin, the drainage had to cross an uplift that now is structurally 10,000 feet higher than the playa in Uinta basin (fig. 62). In order for the drainage to go south, the surface at the uplift must have been lower than the playa; the difference of 10,000 feet can be attributed partly to deposition in Uinta basin, partly to Oligocene and earlier erosion in the south, and partly to renewed late Tertiary uplift at the south.

The southward rise of the Duchesne River Formation onto the south flank of the Uinta basin indicates Oligocene or later uplift of the Canyonlands relative to the basin. The south rim of the basin along the Book Cliffs is now 8,000 feet or so in altitude, and there had to be gaps in the rim lower than the top of the Duchesne River Formation, which is presently about 5,500 feet in altitude. In the absence of any direct evidence, in order to rationalize the few facts that are available, it is here assumed that at least 25 percent of the tilt of the south flank of the Uinta basin occurred during the second half of the Cenozoic, that is, since the end of Oligocene time.

By this assumption, the structural surface at the Book Cliffs would have been 3,000 feet lower relative to the Uinta basin than now, and the structural surface where Green River joins the Colorado would have been about 6,000 feet lower (fig. 62). Whatever the position of the ancestral Book Cliffs, there would have been a plain on the Cretaceous shale formations extending southward from them. If the ancestral cliffs were as far south as the junction of the Green and Colorado Rivers, the plains would have been about the same level as the surface of the Duchesne River Formation. From here, the structural surface slopes westward into the Henry Mountains structural basin, and probably the topographic surface did also.

Evidence that the parts of the Colorado Plateau in Utah and Colorado still were largely covered by Cretaceous rocks in early Miocene time is found at the laccolithic mountains, nearly all of which intrude Cretaceous rocks (p. 78). The northward course of the Dolores River was established before the Cretaceous was eroded, because river gravels on the west rim of the Dolores River canyon form the divide between the Dolores and the distant San Juan River (p. 82). Cretaceous rocks had to be present when those gravels were deposited. Probably the Cretaceous had been eroded from most of the south part of the plateau by Miocene time.

If, however, the Cretaceous were restored in the northern part of the plateau with the structure as it is now (fig. 62), southeastern Utah would be several thousand feet higher than the Uinta basin. This hypothesis would also require that deposition continued in the Uinta basin until the later Cenozoic. The paleogeography seems to require that about half the northward tilt of the Colorado Plateau and about half the folding localized at the upwarps and basins occurred during the second half of Cenozoic time.

The original drainage that overflowed southward from the Uinta basin consisted only of the Duchesne and White River drainage basins (fig. 63), the latter possibly joined by an ancestral Yampa River south of the Uinta Mountains (Sears, in Hansen, 1965b, p. 173). The Green River did not reach the Canyonlands until late Miocene or early Pliocene time, and the headward

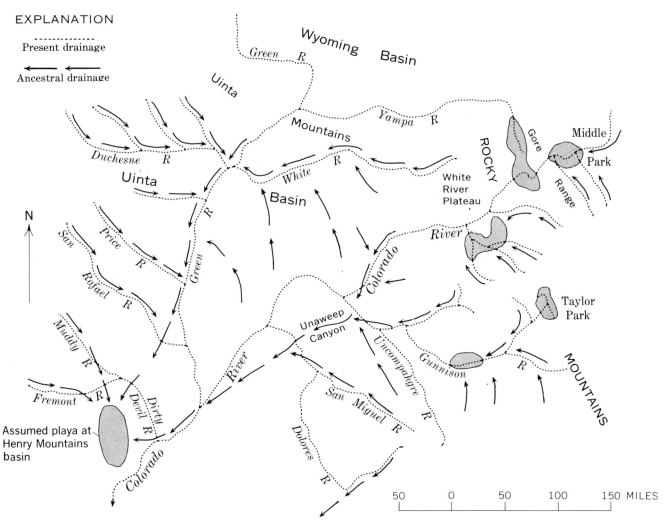

FIGURE 63.—Possible drainage system in the upper Colorado River basin at the beginning of Miocene time, before intrusions formed the laccolithic mountains. Structural basins that may have contained sluggish drainage, playas, or lakes, are patterned. The Uinta basin drainage is assumed to have overflowed southward to the Henry Mountains basin. The Green and Yampa Rivers were still within the Wyoming basin north of the Uinta Mountains. The courses of most of the rivers in the Rocky Mountains were interrupted, at least intermittently, by the basins and ranges that formed there during middle and late Tertiary time.

part of the Colorado River was repeatedly interrupted by deepening of the late Tertiary basins there. The Gunnison, joined by the San Miguel and later by the Dolores, probably reached the Canyonlands before middle Miocene time.

No evidence has been found that indicates when the Henry Mountains basin filled and overflowed southward, but interpretations of the history of the lower stretches of the Colorado River are easier if drainage from the north is delayed as late as possible (p. 113). Partly to relieve problems downstream, it is here assumed that the ancestral Duchesne-White-Gunnison drainage was ponded in the Henry Mountains basin and the next one south of there, the Kaiparowits basin, until Pliocene time, when that drainage was enlarged by addition of the Green River and steady discharge by the main stem of the Colorado.

It has already been noted (p. 83; fig. 55) that the canyon of the Colorado River meanders greatly upstream from its junction with the Green, and that the Green also meanders (fig. 64). The rivers are here flowing against the structural dip of the rocks. After the rivers join, they turn downdip into the Henry Mountains basin in a canyon, Cataract Canyon (fig. 65), that is much straighter than the canyons above the junction.

The meandering courses of all the valleys have been maintained during the last thousand feet or so of downcutting. Moreover, many meanders have steep walls on the inside as well as on the outside of the bends; the meander belt has changed very little during canyon cutting. At only two places are there large cutoff meanders of the inner gorge; both are in Glen Canyon, and both are about 500 feet above the river. I assume they are at least as old as early Pleistocene. One is at the mouth of White Canyon, opposite old Hite, 6 miles below the mouth of the Dirty Devil; the other, known as The Rincon, is where the Colorado River crosses the Waterpocket fold (fig. 66).

The meandering of the inner canyons where the rivers flow against the dip of the rocks suggests that the northward tilting in this part of the Colorado Plateau has continued while the last thousand feet of canyon was being cut. If these stretches of the canyons are partly antecedent, as seems probable, about three-quarters of the depth of the inner canyons might be attributed to downcutting during the Quaternary; cutting of the inner canyon probably began no longer ago than late Pliocene. The wide valley above the stripped Paleozoic formations (fig. 56) involves very much more erosion, and by my interpretation, this erosion would have taken place when the drainage basin and streams were small. I infer that cutting of the outer canyon began at least as long ago as the Miocene, but after intrusion of the

laccoliths, because southeastern Utah probably still was largely blanketed by Cretaceous formations (p. 83). This allows about 20 million years for erosion of the outer canyons in the vicinity of the junction of the Green and Colorado Rivers.

As the meander pattern differs above and below the junction of the Green and Colorado Rivers, so do the stream gradients. In 70 river miles above the junction, both rivers have gradients of only about 1.3 feet per mile; in 40 river miles below the junction, along Cataract Canyon, the gradient is 10 feet per mile. Along Glen Canyon, next below Cataract Canyon, the geologic structure is nearly flat except for broad warps (fig. 67); Glen Canyon meanders more than Cataract Canyon but less than the canyons above the junction. The gradient in 180 miles of Glen Canyon is about 1.5 feet per mile. In all three stretches of the canyons, the rocks differ little in their resistance to erosion; the differences in gradient and meander pattern probably reflect responses of the streams to continuing deformation. The relationships are rather like the smaller scale model of the Dolores River where it crosses the Dolores anticline (p. 81).

The higher and outer canyon walls are set far back from the rim of the meandering inner gorge (figs. 27, 55, 56), and only locally derived fan gravels, not river gravels, were found on the bench between them. The retreat of these cliffs is the result of mass wasting and other erosion along washes and is not attributable to lateral cutting by the rivers. Gravel is resistant compared with much of the bedrock along the canyons, and it is surprising not to find at least some remnants of high-level river gravel along these canyons. Such gravels were sought by air reconnaissance as well as by some ground work and were not found. River gravels are found 1,600 feet above the Dirty Devil River (fig. 64), and there are equally high gravels between the Colorado and San Juan Rivers and farther south. The absence, or at least scarcity of such gravels on the benches bordering the Green and Colorado Rivers near their junctions may reflect the small size of the streams that began the canyon cutting; the tremendous contrast in abundance and extent of gravels in the inner and outer canyons must indicate some kind of change or discontinuity in the river history.

We have noted that when the Uinta basin began to overflow, even though the ancestral Book Cliffs were as far south as the mouth of the Green River, there would have been a plain in Cretaceous shale south of the cliffs at about the altitude of the surface of the Duchesne River Formation. The Henry Mountains basin is 5,000 feet structurally lower than that and could have contained the entire section of Upper Cretaceous beds and

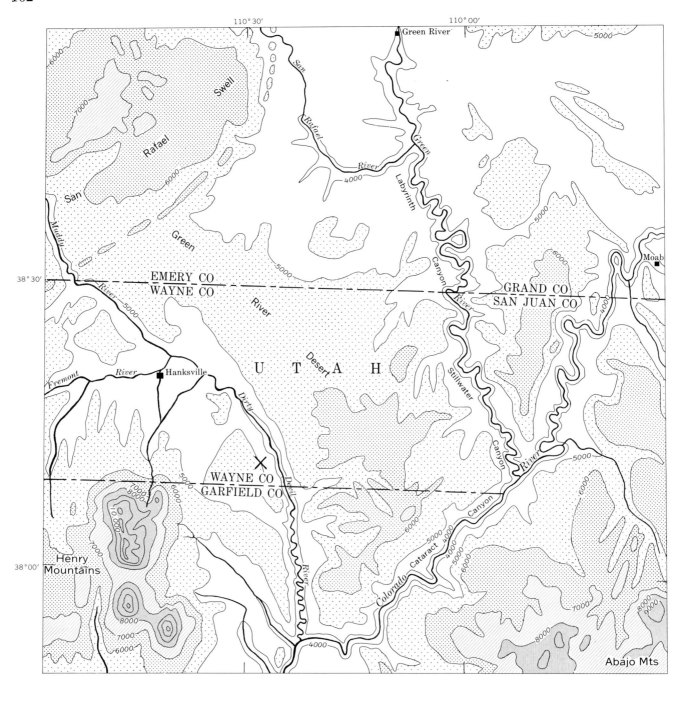

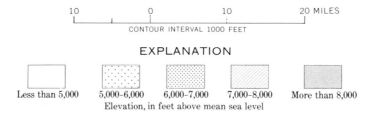

CONTOUR INTERVAL 1000 FEET

EXPLANATION

| Less than 5,000 | 5,000–6,000 | 6,000–7,000 | 7,000–8,000 | More than 8,000 |

Elevation, in feet above mean sea level

1,000 or 2,000 feet of Tertiary beds. This is about the thickness of beds that Gilbert (1876, p. 94) estimated to have been in the basin when the laccoliths were intruded, and an estimate that I was unable to improve in my survey of the mountains (Hunt and others, 1953, p. 147). The three very different approaches give about the same thickness of beds, which is encouraging in view of the numerous and tenuous assumptions that have to be made in order to interpret drainage history in this part of the Canyonlands.

The basin at the Henry Mountains became smaller when the laccolithic mountains formed, presumably about the same time as the similar La Sal Mountains (25 million years, p. 78), that is, early Miocene. This doming, together with the influx of sediments into the basin, which is small compared with the Uinta basin, could have raised the surface and caused it to overflow around the south end of the Circle Cliffs upwarp into the Kaiparowits basin (fig. 62).

Generally, on the Colorado Plateau the drainage is well adjusted to the laccolithic mountains. The arcuate course of the Fremont and Dirty Devil Rivers around the north end of the Henry Mountains probably reflects drainage adjustment to the doming and to the debris that must have been shed radially off the newly formed mountains. The lower course of the Dolores River also swings in a wide arc around the north side of the La Sal Mountains (fig. 54). San Juan River and the Colorado River, near their junction, swing with the strike of the formations around the northwest side of Navajo Mountain (fig. 29). San Juan River follows the trough of the syncline between the domes at Ute Mountain and Carrizo Mountain (fig. 29). Such adjustment of the drainage to the igneous structures contrasts strikingly with the lack of adjustment to the other folds.

The principal tributaries from the west side of the Green and Colorado Rivers rise in the High Plateaus where uplift occurred in late Tertiary and Quaternary

time as well as earlier (Callaghan, 1938, 1939; Gardner, 1941; Averitt, 1964a, b). There is evidence for three major stages of deformation separated by two periods of comparative stability and considerable denudation (Averitt, 1964b, p. 44). Late Cretaceous or early Tertiary folds were bevelled by erosion and overlapped by Eocene strata, as the Circle Cliffs. The second episode of deformation involved faulting on a major scale beginning in middle Tertiary time; Eocene rocks formed cliffs along the faults. During a subsequent period of comparative stability, the cliffs retreated 8 miles from the faults (Averitt, 1964b, p. 44). The third episode of deformation was represented by renewed faulting in late Tertiary and Quaternary time. Potassium-argon dates suggest an early Pliocene age for some of the volcanic rocks involved in this later faulting (Bassett and others, 1963). The amount of Quaternary uplift may be about 2,000 feet (Hunt, 1956, p. 61); this deformation may be continuing, for there have been seismic epicenters along the west edge of the High Plateaus. Smith and others (1963, p. 61) report displacement during late Wisconsin or Holocene time of at least 160 feet, and probably more, on Thousand Lake fault that crosses the Fremont River near Bicknell. Late Pleistocene deformation in the High Plateaus also has been reported by Hardy and Muessig (1952) and by Spieker and Billings (1940, p. 1192–1193).

Three of the streams draining from the High Plateaus cross the San Rafael Swell, where folding almost certainly began in early Tertiary time (Gilluly, 1929, p. 126–127), but later uplift at the Swell is indicated by the arching of the lower Tertiary formations around the north end of the fold. Three rivers that cross the Swell—the Price, San Rafael, and Muddy—were originally cited as antecedent streams (Dutton, 1882, p. 63), but probably they were superimposed across the Swell from lower Tertiary formations (Davis, 1901, p. 140; Gilluly, 1929, p. 126). All three rivers have steepened gradients where they cross the Swell. These relationships resemble those along the Dolores River and would be expected if the San Rafael River valley had been arched by the late uplift of the Swell.

At several places on the Colorado Plateau, there is evidence that canyon cutting was interrupted and that the streams became superimposed on geologic structures outside their former valleys. The valley of Halls Creek, a strike valley 35 miles long, on the east side of the Waterpocket fold (between the Henry Mountains basin and Circle Cliffs upwarp, fig. 62) is an example. At two places, Halls Creek leaves its strike valley and meanders into canyons cut 500 feet deep in resistant

FIGURE 64.—Meander pattern of the Colorado and Green Rivers above their junction, where the rivers are flowing against the dip of the bedrock. The meandering reaches have gradients averaging less than 1.5 feet per mile. Below the junction, in Cataract Canyon, the Colorado River is flowing down the dip; its course there is much straighter, and the gradient averages 10 feet per mile; × indicates location of gravel deposit, 1,600 feet above the Dirty Devil River. This gravel deposit contains cobbles derived from lava flows (lower Pliocene) in the High Plateaus (to the west) and cobbles of diorite porphyry (probably lower Miocene) from the Henry Mountains. This canyon and the inner gorge of the Colorado River, where it is joined by the Dirty Devil, are no older than middle Pliocene.

FIGURE 65.—View down Cataract Canyon, where the Colorado River flows down the west flank of the Monument upwarp in a series of cataracts, one of the roughest stretches of water along the Colorado River.

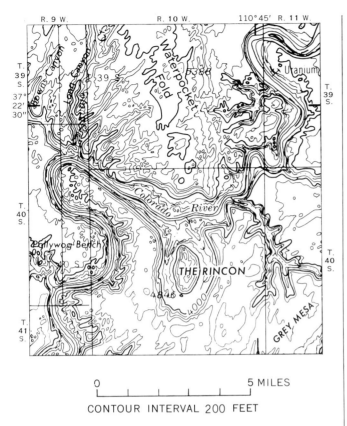

FIGURE 66.—The Rincon, a cutoff meander in Glen Canyon where the Colorado River crosses the Waterpocket fold. This is an exceptional feature; in general the meanders have not changed greatly while the river has cut downward 1,000 feet.

sandstone of the fold. Probably Halls Creek was superimposed on the fold from a shale formation or valley fill, presumably when streamflow was checked, either by regional northeast tilting of the Colorado Plateau or by local folding or warping. On the basis of height above present drainage, the age of the event is estimated as late Pliocene or early Pleistocene.

Some features of Pleistocene age in this part of the Colorado River drainage basin include the natural bridges (Gregory, 1938; Baker, 1936) and the alcoves and arches (Hunt and others, 1953, p. 171) in the inner canyons. Probably the alcoves containing the prehistoric dwellings at Mesaverde and in the Navajo Country also are Pleistocene features. In late Pleistocene time there must have been snowfields on many of the north-facing cliffs, several of which contain ancient debris avalanches. Two locations of note are about 20 miles southwest of the Abajo (Blue) Mountains (at the Bears Ears) (fig. 29) and about 20 miles farther west (at Fry Canyon). These deposits are deeply dissected and deeply weathered, but they record a middle or late Pleistocene

episode when the climate was more moist than now and the canyon walls were mantled with the weathering products of this period.

San Juan and Little Colorado Rivers

The hypothesis formulated thus far assumes that drainage from the northern part of the present Colorado River basin did not discharge southward beyond the Henry Mountains or Kaiparowits basins until the end of Miocene time. Until then, the discharge to these basins probably was small because much of the drainage from the Southern Rocky Mountains was repeatedly ponded within the mountains, and Green River was contained somewhere north of the Uinta Mountains. At present rates of discharge, we might suppose that about 3 million acre feet annually reached the Henry Mountains basin (about one-third present discharge; see fig. 30). This amount was divided between two small streams, one from the Uinta basin and the other from the Southern Rocky Mountains. Such a small volume—and there is no reason to suppose it was ever very much greater—might be contained for a long time in a fairly small basin. Natural lakes at middle Tertiary basins may have been extensive enough to dissipate the entire river flow by evaporation.

Stratigraphic evidence on the history of the rivers is found again in the San Juan River drainage basin. This evidence includes a gravel deposit at an altitude of 6,800 feet on White Mesa and other deposits nearby on the Kaibito Plateau south of Navajo Mountain (fig. 68) (Cooley, 1960a; Cooley and Davidson, 1963; this report, fig. 32; Cooley and others, 1969). The gravels include several kinds of Precambrian rocks, volcanic rocks, chert like that contained in Paleozoic formations, locally derived sandstone and conglomerate from Jurassic formations, and fossil shells reworked from basal Upper Cretaceous formations.

That the gravel was deposited by a stream flowing southwest is indicated by (1) the crossbeds that dip southwest, (2) the occurrence of reworked fossils (*Gryphaea newberryi*) from the sandstone (Dakota Sandstone) at the base of the Upper Cretaceous which is east and not west of the gravel, and (3) the occurrence of conglomerate from a Jurassic formation (Morrison Formation) that also is east of the gravel. The deposit has been correlated (Cooley, oral commun. 1965) with erosion surfaces that are older than the Bidahochi Formation, considered to be early and middle Pliocene in age (Lance, 1954). The gravel appears to be of late Miocene age.

FIGURE 67.—Glen Canyon (left), now flooded by Lake Powell, is cut into nearly horizontal shale and sandstone (mostly Triassic and Jurassic). At lower right are the incised meanders of the Dirty Devil River just above its junction with the Colorado. The mountains are the two southernmost peaks of the Henry Mountains, Mount Holmes (right) and Mount Ellsworth (left). The distant skyline is formed by the Waterpocket fold.

The gravels include several kinds of rocks that can be matched in the southwestern part of the San Juan Mountains—pink granite like that in the Precambrian rocks on the south side of the San Juan Mountains (Needle Mountains) and welded tuffs like those in the volcanic rocks of Oligocene and early Miocene age in the central and southwestern part of the San Juan Mountains. The occurrence of these Oligocene and lower Miocene volcanic rocks in the gravels and the apparent absence of younger rock types lends support to Cooley's estimate of the age of the gravel (about middle Miocene), which is based on geomorphology.

Some of the less well rounded Precambrian quartzite, chert, and quartz clasts also could have come from the Precambrian in the San Juan Mountains, but the very well rounded clasts probably are reworked from conglomerates of Permian, Triassic, and Jurassic age. These younger rocks also are exposed in the San Juan Mountains and nearby. Rocks that might have come from a

southern or western source were not found. The evidence indicates that the San Juan River flowed across the Monument upwarp (figs. 62, 68) by late Miocene time.

Very similar gravels on the northwest corner of Black Mesa at an altitude of 7,000–7,200 feet (M. E. Cooley, written commun., 1968) probably correlate with those on the Kaibito Plateau.

Marble Canyon, only 40 miles west of the Kaibito Plateau, has been deepened about 3,800 feet since the gravels on the plateau were deposited, for the gravels are that much higher than the Colorado River in Marble Canyon. Stream gravels about the same height above the rivers have also been reported on the plateau west of the head of Marble Canyon, but these gravels are composed only of quartzite (Phoenix, 1963) and probably are from nearby Mesozoic formations. On the rim of Glen Canyon at about the Utah-Arizona State line (just west of the mouth of Wahweap Creek), Phoenix (1963) also found stream gravels consisting of 85 percent quartzite, 13 per-

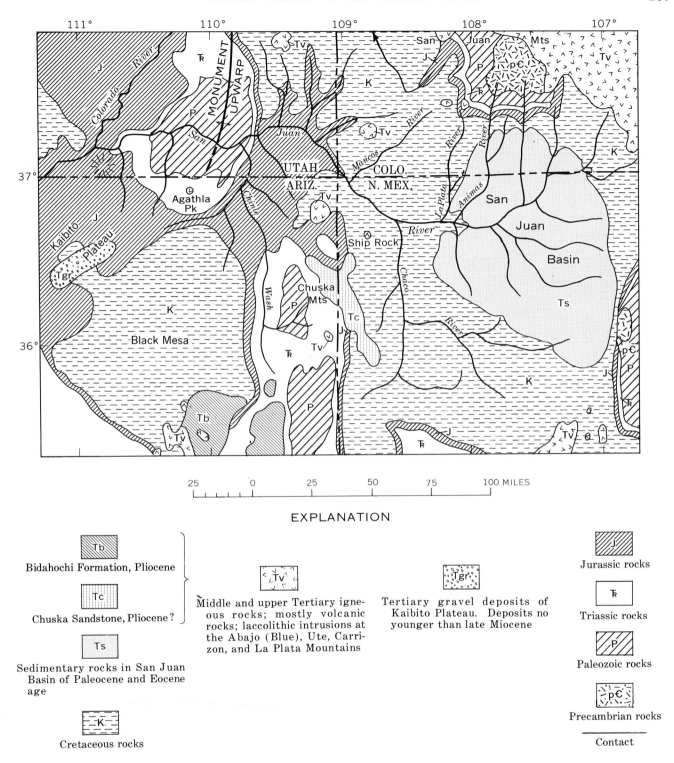

EXPLANATION

Tb

Bidahochi Formation, Pliocene

Tc

Chuska Sandstone, Pliocene?

Ts

Sedimentary rocks in San Juan Basin of Paleocene and Eocene age

K

Cretaceous rocks

Tv

Middle and upper Tertiary igneous rocks; mostly volcanic rocks; laccolithic intrusions at the Abajo (Blue), Ute, Carrizon, and La Plata Mountains

Tgr

Tertiary gravel deposits of Kaibito Plateau. Deposits no younger than late Miocene

J

Jurassic rocks

Ŧ

Triassic rocks

P

Paleozoic rocks

pС

Precambrian rocks

Contact

FIGURE 68.—Four Corners area (from U.S. Geol. Survey, 1932) showing the geologic setting of the gravels of the Kaibito Plateau. The gravels, almost certainly derived from the San Juan Mountains and deposited by a stream flowing southwest, are considered no younger than late Miocene. The San Juan River was across the Monument upwarp and within 75 miles of the Grand Canyon when they were deposited. San Juan basin was a playa during the early Tertiary (Paleocene and Eocene, 65–40 million years ago); discharge from the basin probably began during the Oligocene, perhaps first towards the southwest and then west.

cent greenish-gray andesite porphyry, and 2 percent various cherts. These gravels probably were reworked from the Wasatch Formation to the west.

The Kaibito Plateau gravels are about 800 feet higher than the rim of the canyon of the San Juan River where it crosses the Monument upwarp; the gravels on Black Mesa are 1,000–1,200 feet higher than the canyon rim. The highest part of the rim is about 6,000 feet in altitude; the fold, where it is crossed by the San Juan River, is only about 5,000 feet high structurally, and some of this structural relief may be due to late Tertiary upwarping. The chances are that in early Miocene time, the fold, like the rest of southeastern Utah, still was covered by Cretaceous formations, and perhaps the river was superimposed across the upwarp from an erosion surface in the thick and easily eroded Cretaceous shale.

The late Miocene drainage lines in the Four Corners area, as inferred by Cooley and Davidson (1963, fig. 10), are given in figure 69. The absence on the Kaibito Pla-

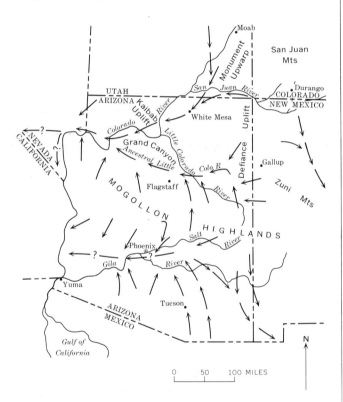

FIGURE 69.—Drainage directions in Arizona during late Tertiary (late Miocene and early Pliocene) time, as interpreted by Cooley and Davidson (1963, fig. 10). My interpretation of the drainage changes on the Colorado Plateau (the area north of the Mogollon Highlands) is similar except: (1) the headward part of San Juan River (at least as far east as Durango) probably drained southwest rather than southeast; and (2) the Colorado River and its tributaries above the San Juan may have been ponded in the north part of the Colorado River basin until Pliocene time.

teau of gravels derived from the north may be attributed to possible ponding of the ancestral northern drainage, first in the Henry Mountains basin and later in Kaiparowits basin, or possibly the ancestral drainage already was at the position of Marble Canyon; with this modification, the interpretation by Cooley and Davidson seems more probable than my previous interpretation (Hunt, 1956, figs. 59–61).

The gradient of the San Juan River steepens where it crosses the Monument upwarp. In 15 miles upstream from Comb Ridge, the river course is straight and its gradient is about 13 feet per mile. In the eastern part of the fold, the river and its canyon meander, and in 15 river miles, the gradient continues about 13 feet per mile. As the river descends the west flank of the fold, the meandering course continues, but beginning near the Goosenecks, the gradient steepens to about 20 feet per river mile. After about 10 miles, the gradient flattens again to about 8 feet per mile, and a comparably low gradient continues to the junction of the San Juan with the Colorado River. Part of this change in river gradient probably is attributable to late Tertiary uplift at the Monument upwarp.

It has been suggested (p. 81) that the ancestral course of the Dolores River, before the intrusion of laccoliths at Ute Mountain, probably was southwest. Possibly the original drainage across the Monument upwarp was by the ancestral Dolores River, and the San Juan may have joined the Dolores as a result of capture. Certainly the drainage pattern suggests that. In Paleocene and Eocene time, drainage off the south side of the San Juan Mountains ended in the San Juan basin and filled it with sediments. When the basin overflowed, the ancestral San Juan River was turned out of it, probably to the west and probably as early as Oligocene time. Whatever its early drainage history, by late Miocene time the San Juan River had established its course across the Monument upwarp.

One of the stratigraphic keys to drainage history in the southern part of the Colorado Plateau is the Chuska Sandstone, but it unfortunately still is a poorly known formation. The sandstone has been correlated with part of the Datil Formation (Wrucke, 1961; also Cooley and Davidson, 1963, p. 24) on the basis of lithologic similarities, particularly the occurrence of heulandite cement and of eolian and fluvial structures that resemble those in the upper part of the Datil. A Pliocene(?) age of the sandstone is indicated.

The sandstone caps the north end of the Defiance upwarp and unconformably overlies the folded Mesozoic formations (figs. 62, 70). Its altitude is 7,650–8,200 feet, which is about 2,500 feet higher topographically

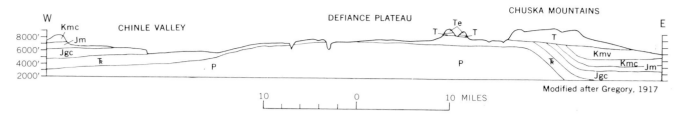

Te, late Tertiary lavas; T, Chuska sandstone; Kmv, Mesaverde group; Kmc, Mancos shale; Jm, Morrison formation and San Rafael group; Jgc, Glen Canyon group; ⱦ, Triassic formations; P, Permian formations

FIGURE 70.—Cross section of the Defiance upwarp. (From Hunt, 1956, fig. 21, modified from Gregory, 1917.)

than Chinle Wash and about 2,000 feet higher structurally. Some of the difference in structural position probably is due to late Tertiary deformation, but the wide valley of Chinle Wash seems to have been lowered about 2,000 feet since early Miocene time. The ancestral San Juan River may have been superimposed across the Monument upwarp from the equivalent of the Chuska Sandstone in that area. In any event, the course of the San Juan River seems to be younger than the sandstone.

The fact that the Chuska Sandstone is preserved on the top of an uplift, rather than in the adjoining basins, yet is nearly horizontal suggests that it was deposited in an anticlinal valley along the crest of that uplift. If so, the topography has become inverted.

Farther east, where the San Juan River crosses an east-dipping hogback of Cretaceous sandstone (Mesa Verde Group), it is joined by the Chaco River which crosses the hogback at another place (fig. 71). Relationships are similar where Chinle Wash joins the San Juan River. Probably the stream courses were superimposed from a level a few hundreds of feet above the present streams (Hunt, 1956, p. 70). The episodes causing the superimposed valleys at Chaco River, Chinle Wash, and Halls Creek are assumed to have been contemporaneous or nearly so. Accordingly, in the central part of the Colorado Plateau, I infer a late Pliocene or early Pleistocene surface of aggradation or planation about 500 feet above the present drainage and downcutting of about 2,000 feet below the Pliocene(?) Chuska Sandstone on the Defiance upwarp. Volcanic necks south of the San Juan River are 1,500 feet higher than the present surface around them (for example Ship Rock, N. Mex.; Agathla Peak, Ariz., fig. 68) and have been considered of Pliocene age (Williams, 1936). They may be older than Pliocene because neighboring intrusions that probably are related have been dated radiometrically as Miocene or older (biotite 25 million years; sanidine 40 million years; Akers and others, 1969).

The southernmost valley on the Colorado Plateau, that of the Little Colorado River, is unusual in the

337–429 O—69——9

Colorado River system because it is broad, open, and demonstrably old. It is a strike valley in north-dipping Triassic rocks (fig. 31) and is joined nearly at right angles by long parallel tributaries. Those from the

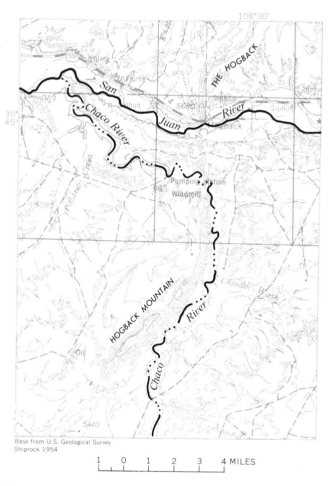

FIGURE 71.—Junction of Chaco and San Juan Rivers. The Chaco, flowing north to join the San Juan, follows a course along the east side of Hogback Mountain formed by east-dipping Cretaceous sandstones. Two miles south of the San Juan River, the Chaco turns through the hogback and the rivers join about 7 miles northwest of the turn.

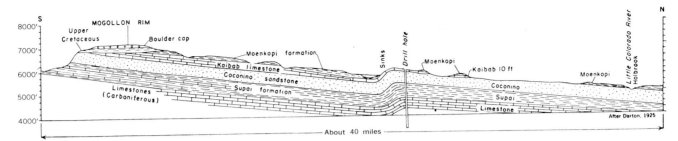

FIGURE 72.—Cross section showing the stripped surface on Paleozoic formations that rise to the Mogollon Rim south of the Little Colorado River. The Cretaceous rocks overlap Triassic and Permian rocks on the rim, showing that the stripping of the Triassic in this area began in Mesozoic time. The erosion of the Cretaceous rocks was accomplished by the end of Miocene time because lower Pliocene deposits (Bidahochi Formation, not shown in cross section) occur in the valley of the Little Colorado where they are only 500 feet higher than the river. For a more detailed section, see Finnell (1966a, b).

south flow with the dip of the rocks, those from the north flow against the dip, yet the stream patterns are alike.

In the eastern part of the Little Colorado River valley are widespread deposits of limy sand and clay mixed with beds of volcanic ash and some lava, known as the Bidahochi Formation (Hack, 1942; Akers, 1964). The deposits, about 1,000 feet thick, are mostly of fluviatile origin, but the lower part includes some playa and lake beds. They were laid down by streams flowing westward ('Hack, 1942; Repenning and Irwin, 1954; McKee and others, 1967). The formation contains vertebrate fossils of Pliocene age (Williams, 1936), the oldest of which are regarded as early Pliocene (Lance, 1954; J. H. Irwin and others, unpub. data). The valley of the Little Colorado River has been deepened a maximum of only about 500 feet since the Bidahochi Formation was deposited. Clearly, at the end of the Miocene, the Little Colorado River was in a west-draining valley very much like the present one.

Downstream the strike valley skirts the northeast edge of the San Francisco volcanic field, and early lava of the San Francisco field extends into the valley at an altitude of 4,700 feet and only 500 feet higher than the Little Colorado River (Robinson, 1913, pl. 3; Gregory, 1917, pl. 2; Childs, 1948; Colton, 1950, p. 15).

South of the Little Colorado River is a stripped surface on Paleozoic formations that rise to the Mogollon Rim (fig. 72). Much of the stripping occurred during the Mesozoic because the Cretaceous rocks overlap the Triassic and extend onto the Paleozoic. Moreover, the stripping had largely been completed by the beginning of Pliocene time because there has been a maximum of only 500 feet of downcutting since then.

The altitude of the rim of the Colorado Plateau south of the Little Colorado River is about 7,500 feet, about the same as the rim of the Grand Canyon (fig. 28). The stripped surface has gravels derived from mountains of

crystalline rocks to the south. These mountains no longer exist; they have been faulted away from the south edge of the plateau and now are part of the Basin and Range province. At the time those gravels were deposited, their source was higher than the rim of Grand Canyon, and the gravels are 2,000 feet higher than the Little Colorado River towards which they were headed. The gravels clearly were derived from the south and when deposited were in transit northward to the Little Colorado River (McKee, 1951, p. 498; Mears, 1950; Lehner, 1958; Twenter, 1961). Some of these gravels have been correlated with the Bidahochi Formation (Cooley and Davidson, 1963, p. 25) and provide the basis for the drainage positions and directions indicated in figure 69.

The gravels are not well dated but probably are of middle and late Tertiary age. Whatever their age, the topographic relationships in this part of the Colorado Plateau at the end of Miocene time must have been very much as today. It has been suggested that the ancestral Colorado River once flowed southeast along the valley of the Little Colorado and that the drainage became reversed by tilting (McKee and others, 1967). Uplift at the Kaibab upwarp could have ponded the ancestral drainage at the time the Bidahochi Formation was deposited, and this might account for the gravels on the Kaibito Plateau if they are a remnant of a once broad fan. Other gravel deposits south and west of the present Little Colorado River indicate westward drainage before the eruptions at the San Francisco volcanic field; most probably the valley of the Little Colorado River has drained west since middle Tertiary time.

In brief, by middle Miocene time, at least two rivers had reached the head of the Grand Canyon—the Little Colorado River and the ancestral San Juan. If drainage from the north, the ancestral Colorado, also reached there, its course was west of the Kaibito Plateau and probably near the position of the present Marble Canyon.

Originally, the Little Colorado River passed south of the Kaibab uplift (fig. 69) through a gap now having an altitude of 6,800 feet (fig. 73). The upper end of the Grand Canyon is 20 miles north, and the rims there are 1,000 feet higher than the gap. The surface under the Bidahochi Formation slopes eastward (fig. 73). There seem to be three ways in which the Little Colorado River might have crossed the Kaibab uplift: (1) As a result of capture by the San Juan River when the San Juan was already incised across the plateau; (2) as a result of the deposition of 1,000 feet of fill east of the Kaibab uplift, and subsequent removal of this fill; or (3) as a result of 1,000 feet of uplift during and since deposition of the Bidahochi Formation. Probably all three possibilities were factors. Capture seems probable. Post-Bidahochi uplift of the Kaibab Plateau also seems probable. This is suggested by the many faults that displace lava in the north part of the San Francisco volcanic field, (Robinson, 1913, p. 36–37; Cooley, 1960b), and such uplift could cause ponding that would lead to deposition of sediments east of the Kaibab.

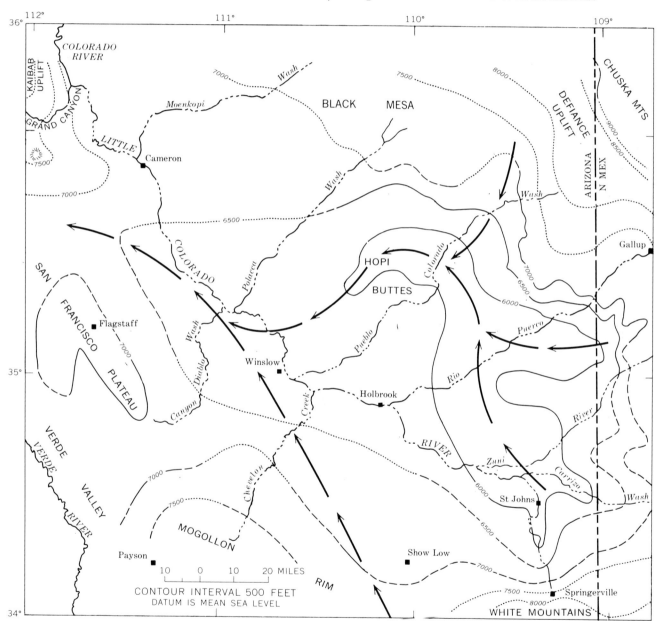

FIGURE 73.—Base of the Bidahochi Formation and probable course (arrows) of the ancestral Little Colorado River and its tributaries. Generalized from Cooley and Akers, 1961, p. C247. The high altitude (more than 6,500 ft) of the indicated course through the gap south of the Kaibab uplift is almost certainly due to 1,000 feet or more of uplift at the gap during and since deposition of the Bidahochi Formation.

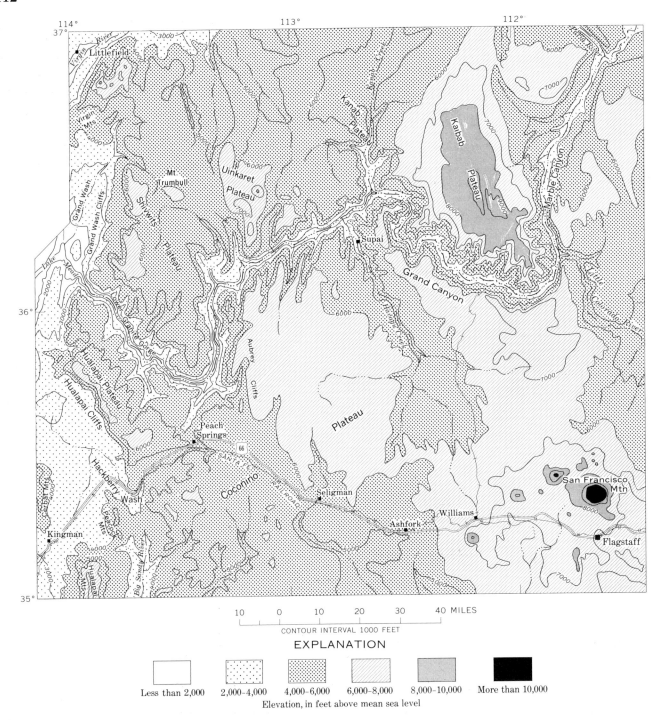

EXPLANATION

Less than 2,000   2,000–4,000   4,000–6,000   6,000–8,000   8,000–10,000   More than 10,000

Elevation, in feet above mean sea level

FIGURE 74.—Grand Canyon region. About half the difference in altitude between the plateaus and the basins to the west and south is attributed to late Cenozoic uplift of the Colorado Plateau.

The gravels on the Kaibito Plateau (altitude 6,800 ft) are 1,000 feet lower than the present rim of the Grand Canyon, and they project about 1,500 feet lower. The ancestral middle Miocene San Juan River that deposited these gravels may have joined the ancestral Little Colorado River around the south end of the Kaibab uplift, but if so, still another 1,000 feet of fill would be required for the drainages to be superimposed across the Kaibab, again, unless there was later uplift. Because the fill east of the Kaibab would have to be as young as the upper beds of the Bidahochi Formation, differential uplift of the Kaibab Plateau is indicated.

The probabilities are that in middle Miocene time, the Kaibab Plateau—now formed of Kaibab Limestone—was 1,000–1,500 feet lower structurally than it is now. How much Triassic shale persisted above the limestone is unknown. The San Juan River, and questionably the main stem of the Colorado, probably crossed the plateau in a canyon at least hundreds of feet deep. The Little Colorado River, which was in an open valley south of the uplift, could have joined the main drainage west of the Kaibab as a hanging valley, with a waterfall like there is near the mouth of the Little Colorado River today.

Grand Canyon—Grand Problem

This brings us to the grand problem of the Colorado River, the history of the Grand Canyon (figs. 74, 75). If the interpretations of the structural and drainage histories upstream are approximately correct, Grand Canyon at the Kaibab Plateau was started by the ancestral San Juan River, perhaps in early Miocene time. West of the Kaibab upwarp, the San Juan River joined the ancestral Little Colorado, apparently an older stream that may have eroded canyons west of the Kaibab. At what time they were joined by the drainage passing the Kaiparowits and Henry Mountains basins and by the Green River and headward part of the Colorado is not known, but surely by the beginning of the Pliocene. According to this interpretation, the streams that began cutting Grand Canyon, perhaps in the early Miocene, had a discharge only about one-fifth of the whole river-basin capacity, at present rates of discharge only 2 or 3 million acre feet annually (fig. 30).

The foot of the Grand Canyon provides good evidence that no large river discharged there until middle or late Pliocene time. Somewhere between the head and foot of the Grand Canyon we lose 10 or 15 million years of river history, and as it is easier to lose the record of a small river than that of a large one, I favor the interpretation that the streams from the north were held back by ponding in the northern basins until middle Pliocene time.

The evidence for a young date for the Colorado River at the foot of the Grand Canyon has recently been summarized by Ivo Lucchitta (McKee and others, 1967, p. 4, 5). Grand Wash trough was formed by downfaulting of the blocks in and west of the Wash; the Grand Wash Cliffs (fig. 76) mark the western edge of the Colorado Plateau. The displacement by the fault is at least 1 mile and may be as great as 3 miles, depending upon the structures buried by the fill in Grand Wash. Most of the faulting occurred before an upper Miocene fill, the lower part of the Muddy Creek Formation (?), was deposited in Grand Wash. The structural separation of the Colorado Plateau and the Basin and Range province in that area dates from the beginning of that faulting. The lower part of the Muddy Creek Formation in Grand Wash has been correlated, although with considerable uncertainty, with volcanic deposits farther west that are given latest Miocene or earliest Pliocene dates (11.8±0.7 million years, 10.6±1.1 million years; McKee and others, 1967, p. 5).

The Muddy Creek Formation in Grand Wash was derived mostly from the mountains to the west; it was derived in part from the Grand Wash Cliffs. No Colorado River deposits are known there, and the Colorado River did not discharge into Grand Wash while the Muddy Creek Formation was being deposited (Blackwelder, 1934; Longwell, 1936).

Unconformably overlying the Muddy Creek Formation is a limestone formation (Hualapai Limestone, Longwell, 1936, p. 1429). This is a quiet-water deposit containing very little clastic material and centering near the mouth of the Grand Canyon. The water body probably was a lake but might have been the headward part of an estuary connected with the Gulf of California. (See p. 120.) The Hualapai Limestone is more than 1,000 feet thick (Longwell, 1936, p. 1430), but this thickness may be misleading because the limestone, being an embankment deposit, is confined to the sides of the lake basin. Similar limestone is reported 500 feet or more above the river on both sides of the Grand Canyon near its mouth (Lee, 1908, p. 30, 31), as if the lower few miles of the Grand Canyon antedate the Hualapai Limestone. The limestone has been involved in some of the latest structural movements in Hualapai Wash, but is much less deformed than the underlying Muddy Creek Formation, which in turn is much less deformed than the underlying Paleozoic formations.

The age of the Hualapai Limestone is not known except that it is younger than the Muddy Creek Formation. Post-Hualapai folding and faulting is slight enough to give the impression that the deposit cannot be much older than the earliest Colorado River gravel deposits which are within a few hundred feet of the

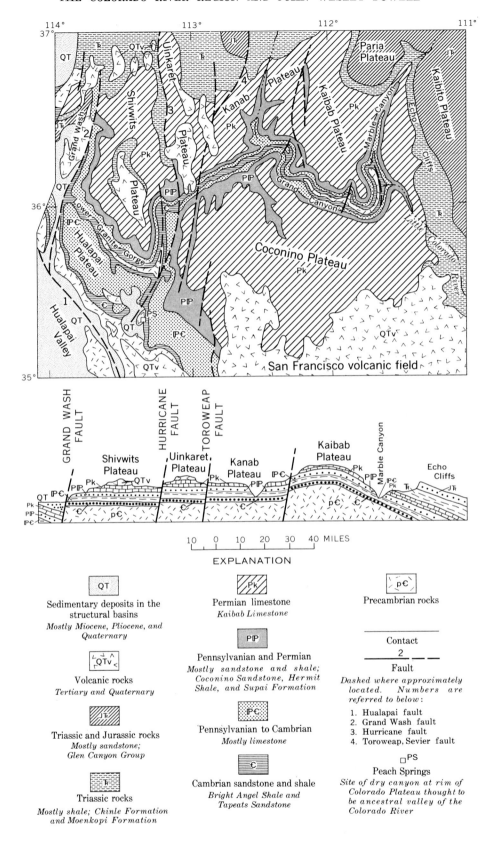

EXPLANATION

QT

Sedimentary deposits in the structural basins
Mostly Miocene, Pliocene, and Quaternary

QTv

Volcanic rocks
Tertiary and Quaternary

J℞

Triassic and Jurassic rocks
Mostly sandstone; Glen Canyon Group

℞

Triassic rocks
Mostly shale; Chinle Formation and Moenkopi Formation

Pk

Permian limestone
Kaibab Limestone

ℙℙ

Pennsylvanian and Permian
Mostly sandstone and shale; Coconino Sandstone, Hermit Shale, and Supai Formation

ℙ€

Pennsylvanian to Cambrian
Mostly limestone

€

Cambrian sandstone and shale
Bright Angel Shale and Tapeats Sandstone

p€

Precambrian rocks

——————
Contact

———2———
Fault
Dashed where approximately located. Numbers are referred to below:

1. Hualapai fault
2. Grand Wash fault
3. Hurricane fault
4. Toroweap, Sevier fault

□PS

Peach Springs
Site of dry canyon at rim of Colorado Plateau thought to be ancestral valley of the Colorado River

present river level and also are locally tilted and faulted. Longwell (1936, p. 1475) first inferred that the limestone, which antedates the Colorado River in Grand Wash, was very late Pliocene or even Pleistocene in age; later he supposed (1946, p. 829) that the river there might be as old as late Miocene. I prefer his earlier estimate because the limestone is so much less deformed than the underlying Muddy Creek Formation.

The Hualapai Limestone poses problems. The lake in which it was deposited was at least three times larger than Lake Mead; substantial recharge would be required to maintain the lake against evaporation. If the lake covered 450,000 acres and evaporated 75 inches annually, which probably are conservative estimates, the water surface would lose about 2,750,000 acre feet of water annually, a quantity greater than the combined flow of the present San Juan and Little Colorado Rivers (fig. 30). What was the source of so much water? And what was the source of so much calcium carbonate? If there was a canyon at the lower Granite Gorge, why is there no delta where it discharged into the lake? Even Lake Mead has one! These questions will be considered after looking at the geology of another part of Grand Canyon.

At the upper end of the lower Granite Gorge, where Grand Canyon crosses the Hurricane fault (fig. 75), there is an anomalously wide and deep dry canyon extending southwestward at Peach Springs and breaching the southwest rim of the Colorado Plateau (fig. 77). The dry canyon is alined with the stretch of Grand Canyon that is along the Hurricane fault zone. Its rims average farther apart than do the rims of Grand Canyon in the stretch along the Hurricane fault, and it is half as deep. The valley is filled with gravel, locally derived fanglomerate, lavas, and tuffs, quite like the Muddy Creek Formation.

The area has been geologically mapped and described by Twenter (1962) and more recently by Young (1966; summary in McKee and others, 1967, p. 6–9). The sequence of events recorded by the dry canyon and by the fills in it begins with regional tilting of 3°–5° northeast, possibly concurrent with movement along the Hurricane

FIGURE 75.—Grand Canyon region showing the several plateaus. In Eocene time, the Kaibab Plateau was an upwarp with steep east flank and long evenly dipping west flank, similar to the San Rafael Swell, Circle Cliffs, and other upwarps on the Colorado Plateau (fig. 62). In middle Tertiary time, the west flank was broken by several faults. Subsequently, the area between the Kaibab Plateau and the Grand Wash fault was raised; strata in the fault blocks west of the Kaibab Plateau are now nearly horizontal but greatly elevated.

and Grand Wash faults. The canyon was cut by earlier streams that drained south through the now dry canyon. According to Young (1966, p. 7), "Data from wells reveal a deep Cenozoic valley fill (pre-volcanic) near Truxton, Arizona. When corrected for post-volcanic fault movements, the relationship between channel segments suggests, but does not prove, that a Cenozoic stream may have flowed southwest down the ancestral Peach Springs Canyon." (See also Twenter, 1962.) This canyon antedates the Muddy Creek Formation and appears to be older than the mouth of Grand Canyon.

The oldest of the fills in the dry valley and valleys tributary to it are arkosic gravels as much as 400 feet thick. These gravels were derived from the Basin and Range province (fig. 80) and transported northeast onto the plateau (Young, 1966; see also Koons, 1948, p. 59; Koons, in McKee and others, 1967, p. 10; and Krieger, in McKee and others, 1967, p. 15); the drainage then turned southwest off the plateau via the Peach Springs dry valley. After this, according to Young (1966), the valleys became blocked by 300 feet of locally derived talus, fanglomerate, and colluvium. Limestone and limy shale were deposited in valleys where ponding occurred. Some of the fanglomerate seems to have come from the Shivwits Plateau side of the lower Granite Gorge, and if so, this provides evidence that there was no Colorado River in the lower Granite Gorge at that time.

The next higher unit found by Young in the canyon at Peach Springs is a gravel 300–400 feet thick containing crystalline and volcanic pebbles; this suggests reestablishment of northeasterly drainage from elevated Precambrian rocks that later were faulted off that edge of the Colorado Plateau. After this gravel was deposited, volcanism caused lava and volcanic tuff to spread northeast into the dry canyon. A sample of tuff from one of the canyons has yielded a radiometric date of 18.3 ± 0.6 million years before present, that is, middle Miocene (McKee and others, 1967, p. 8). These volcanic deposits blocked southward drainage from the plateau after middle Miocene time.

No undoubted Colorado River gravels have been found in the fill in Peach Springs dry valley, yet a large stream and considerable time were needed to erode so wide a canyon. The absence of Colorado River gravels could be due in part to ponding of the ancestral river at various fault blocks, especially the Kaibab Plateau. Ponding could settle out much or most of the coarse sediment and provide water as clear as that discharging at present at Glen Canyon dam. Further, gravels that could be diagnostic of the San Juan Mountains would be pretty small by the time they were transported as far

FIGURE 76.—Grand Wash Cliffs, which form the southwest rim of the Colorado Plateau, near the mouth of the Grand Canyon; one of the highest parts of the Colorado Plateau, both structurally and topographically. Precambrian rocks are exposed at the base of the cliffs; above them are lower Paleozoic strata, mostly limestone.

as the dry valley at Peach Springs, and they may be obscured by the coarse cobble gravels from nearby sources. At present, 95 percent of the gravel being transported by the Colorado River in the Grand Canyon consists of locally derived materials; only 5 percent has upstream sources (M. E. Cooley, unpub. data, 1967). I postulate that the ancestral Colorado River (that is, the ancestral San Juan and Little Colorado) left the Colorado Plateau via the dry canyon at Peach Springs.

The course here postulated for the Colorado River would provide an explanation for the curious Hualapai Limestone at the mouth of Grand Canyon, which required a body of water vastly larger than Lake Mead, highly charged with calcium carbonate and without a source that would deposit clastic sediments. At the Peach Springs depression the river would have been in a canyon in limestone (Redwall, Martin, and Muav Limestones), and the structure of these rocks is such that they are more than 1,000 feet higher at Peach Springs than at the mouth of Grand Canyon. Lower Granite Gorge coincides with a synclinal flexure trending and plunging west-northwest. Water from ponded segments of the river upstream would have been dammed by the fill at Peach Springs and could have discharged through the cavernous limestone to supply springs at the low point of the structure, which is the mouth of Grand Canyon where the maximum deposition of the Hualapai Limestone is centered. Such a

mechanism involves piping on a truly grand scale. Some may believe that the scale is outrageous, yet a comparably distant source (50 miles) seems indicated for some of the large springs farther west, in Death Valley (Hunt and Robinson, in Hunt and others, 1966, p. B39–B40). The requirements are fully met along the lower Granite Gorge—an adequate water source with an adequate head over fissured limestone. The postulated piping would provide the large quantity of water required for the lake and the limestone deposited in it and would explain the absence of deltaic deposits in the lake.

The interpretation offered here is that the Grand Canyon at the Kaibab Plateau is pre-middle Miocene and that the canyon cutting there was started by the ancestral San Juan River as the result of superposition before the last 1,500 feet of uplift at the Kaibab Plateau. The older Little Colorado River is postulated to have begun the erosion of the canyons west of the Kaibab Plateau (fig. 69).

This early drainage supposedly left the Colorado Plateau by way of the dry canyon at Peach Springs. According to my interpretation, by middle Miocene time, Grand Canyon was more than 1,000 feet deep and extended from the east side of the Kaibab to somewhere southwest of Peach Springs. Deepening of the canyon was repeatedly interrupted by uplifts of the fault blocks crossing it. By late Miocene time the drainage was blocked from discharging at Peach Springs by uplift

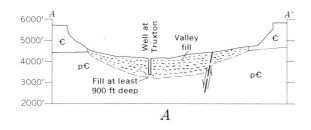

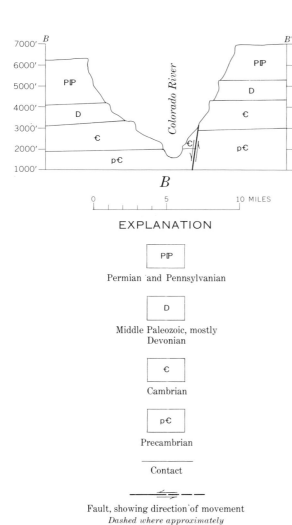

EXPLANATION

PℙP

Permian and Pennsylvanian

D

Middle Paleozoic, mostly
Devonian

Є

Cambrian

pЄ

Precambrian

———
Contact

———
Fault, showing direction of movement
*Dashed where approximately
located*

FIGURE 77.—*A*, Cross section of the dry canyon breaking
the rim of the Colorado Plateau along the Hurricane
fault zone. The cross section is at Truxton, which is
about 8 miles southwest of Peach Springs. The well
at Truxton, 900 feet deep, may have reached the
granitic bedrock, *B*, Cross section of the Grand
Canyon in the stretch along the Hurricane fault, 25
miles northeast of *A*. The formations rise roughly
2,500 feet from *B* to *A*, and much of this is probably
due to late Tertiary deformation. See figure 79 for
location of sections.

of the now dry canyon and by volcanic materials which
came into it from the Basin and Range province. The
ponded drainage began escaping along fissures in the
limestone at the position of the lower Granite Gorge.
When the drainage was joined by the Green and Colorado Rivers, the increased discharge could have opened
the lower end of Grand Canyon through the limestone.
By my interpretation, the Colorado River did not discharge as surface water through the whole length of
lower Granite Gorge until after the limestone was
deposited.

Downcutting in Grand Canyon during the last half
of the Pleistocene has been minimal. At the mouth of
Toroweap Valley, lava flows extended into the canyon
from the north when the river was within 50 feet of
its present position. The lavas, which formed a dam in
the inner gorge 600 feet high, are dated at 1.2±0.6 million years before present (Damon, 1965, p. 42, also
cited in McKee and others, 1967, p. 14; see also Koons,
1945; Maxson, 1950). If this date is correct, there has
been even less downcutting in Grand Canyon during the
Quaternary than has been indicated for the canyons
upstream.

Ponding of the rivers upstream from the Kaibab upwarp could be attributed to combinations of four factors, all known to have been operative: (1) Overloading
of streams by some climatic event or by volcanic eruptions during late Miocene and Pliocene time; (2) development of the rain shadow east of the High Plateaus
(fig. 30) as a result of elevation of the plateaus in Pliocene time; (3) local uplift at the individual folds and
at the fault blocks; and (4) northeast tilting of the
Colorado Plateau.

Reasons have been given for assuming that about
half of the northeast tilting of the Colorado Plateau
occurred during the second half of the Cenozoic (p.
99). The southwest rim of the plateau is 20,000 feet
higher structurally than the northeast edge (fig. 62).
Precise leveling in the Lake Mead area has indicated
sinking, apparently because of the load of water in the
reservoir, and southwestward tilting of the lake basin
(Longwell, 1960, p. 36), as if uplift of the southwest
rim of the Colorado Plateau is continuing. Farther
north, the Hurricane fault still seems to be active
(Averitt, 1964a, table 1). About a quarter (5,000 ft)
of the tilting upstream against the direction of flow of
the rivers may have occurred during the late Miocene
and Pliocene. It does seem that a combination of factors on the Colorado Plateau during Pliocene time could
have contributed to greatly diminishing the drainage
discharge.

What are some alternative explanations for the Grand Canyon? The possibility that the Colorado River discharged from Grand Canyon before deposition of the Muddy Creek Formation in Grand Wash cannot be completely dismissed simply because no Colorado River gravels have been found beneath the Muddy Creek Formation. A drill hole at any time could reveal them even though the possibility seems unlikely. If the gravels are there, the river must have been ponded on the Colorado Plateau upstream from the Kaibab upwarp while the Muddy Creek Formation was being deposited.

Blackwelder (1934) and Longwell (1936, 1946) assumed that the data for the river across Grand Wash had to apply to the whole river system, and "* * * the river came into existence as a result of the latest great uplift of the Rocky Mountain-Colorado Plateau region, in late Pliocene or early Pleistocene time * * *" (Longwell, 1936, p. 1471). Longwell interpreted the Colorado River as "following essentially its original consequent course" (1936, p. 1471). Later he elaborated on this (1946, p. 833), "If the uplifted Plateau surface was essentially a peneplane, superposition of the new drainage channel across the beveled East Kaibab monocline and other structural features must have started from this surface, along a consequent course determined by topographic irregularities." We know now that there was no "peneplane," that the canyons are at least as old as middle Miocene, and that the south rim of the plateau was substantially higher than the valley of the Little Colorado River at the end of the Miocene.

Another interpretation of the river history, developed at a symposium in 1964 under auspices of the Museum of Northern Arizona, assumes an ancestral (Miocene?) Colorado River east of the Kaibab Plateau but continuing southeastward along the valley of the Little Colorado River (McKee and others, 1967, p. 52). The reversed drainage in the Little Colorado River valley, according to this interpretation "may possibly have connected with an ancestral Rio Grande * * *" (McKee and others, 1967, p. 54). This ancestral drainage to the southeast then was captured by headward erosion of a stream system heading on the west side of the Kaibab Plateau ("Hualapai drainage system" of McKee and others). According to this theory, the diversion occurred while the drainage was in the easily eroded Triassic formations; increased discharge after diversion enabled entrenchment of the drainage into the more resistant, older rocks forming the present Grand Canyon. In latest Miocene and earliest Pliocene time, according to this theory, the ancestral Colorado River was ponded in the Little Colorado River valley where it contributed to the lake and playa deposits in the lower part of the

Bidahochi Formation (fig. 78). This seems likely under either interpretation. Subsequently the west-flowing Hualapai drainage eroded headward across the Triassic formations on the Kaibab upwarp to capture the ponded drainage (McKee and others, 1967, p. 61).

The capture hypothesis does not seem to offer advantages over the assumption of an ancient Colorado River having segments that were repeatedly ponded. The assumption of reversed drainage in the Little Colorado valley is unlikely and unnecessary. All the evidence, and there is a lot of it, on the south rim of the Colorado Plateau indicates drainage northward into the valley of the Little Colorado River and into the Grand Canyon. The base of the Bidahochi Formation is 2,000 feet lower than the rim of the Grand Canyon at the Kaibab Plateau, and although this difference could readily be attributed to renewed, late uplift of the Kaibab Plateau, such uplift is against the assumed reversal of the Little Colorado River. To assume no Pliocene uplift at the Kaibab Plateau would require the erosion of a canyon at least 1,500 feet deep to capture the big rivers in the low country east of the plateau. There seems to be no climatic, topographic, or structural reason for the drainage rising west of the Kaibab upwarp to be so precocious. The original course of the Little Colorado River probably was west around the south end of the Kaibab Plateau, as suggested by Cooley (Cooley and Akers, 1961; this report, fig. 47).

No large volume of water could have been discharged at Grand Wash because, as already noted, there was no drainage out of the lower Granite Gorge of the Grand Canyon when the Muddy Creek Formation was being deposited there. The drainage from the plateau could have discharged by way of the canyon at Peach Springs, but that canyon was dammed while the fill in it, which surely is correlative with the Muddy Creek Formation in Grand Wash, was being deposited. Whether by headward erosion of drainage west of the Kaibab, or by the ancient Colorado, the canyon at Peach Springs had already been cut. It is, therefore, older than the valley of the Little Colorado River where filled by the Bidahochi Formation, and it seems to be older than the mouth of the Grand Canyon.

The directions of the early Pliocene drainage postulated by the symposium (McKee and others, 1967) and shown in figure 78 are quite like the pattern I would postulate for that stage of river history. My hypothesis, however, assumes a canyon that had been cut by the ancestral Colorado (San Juan) River across the Kaibab Plateau as the plateau was uplifted (a situation similar to that of Unaweep Canyon where it crosses the Uncompahgre Plateau). At this time, the ancestral drain-

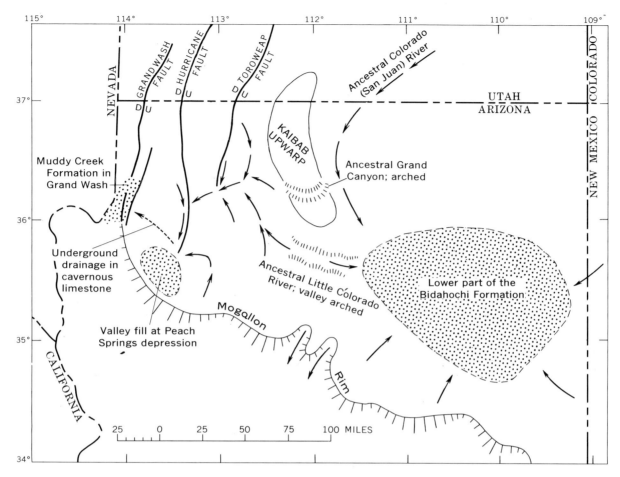

FIGURE 78.—Inferred drainage pattern in northern Arizona when the lower part of the Bidahochi Formation was deposited at the beginning of Pliocene time. Drainage directions largely as interpreted by McKee and others (1967). Arched ancestral valley of the Little Colorado River south of Kaibab upwarp as interpreted by Cooley and Akers (1961). Arched ancestral valley at Kaibab upwarp and underground drainage to Grand Wash are interpretations added in this report.

age discharged from the plateau at Peach Springs. This canyon system that had been cut by the ancestral Colorado River became segmented by the renewed uplift at the Kaibab upwarp, and the lower part was ponded by Miocene and early Pliocene fill in the canyons there.

Grand Canyon to the Gulf of California

In crossing the Basin and Range province from the Colorado Plateau to the Gulf of California, the whole aspect of the Colorado River valley changes. Alternately, the river flows in unconsolidated gravels and sand that fill broad open structural valleys and in deep, narrow, rock-walled canyons through block-faulted mountains separating the valleys.

During early Tertiary time when the surface of the Colorado Plateau remained near sea level, except perhaps at the upwarps, the Basin and Range province was subjected to intensive deformation, including folding,

thrust faulting, and both intrusive and eruptive igneous activity. Drainage off the Colorado Plateau became disrupted by structural depressions in the Basin and Range province. When drainage from the Colorado Plateau first began discharging to the Basin and Range province is problematical.

The geology at the Peach Springs dry canyon indicates clearly that a sizable river was discharging there from the plateau more than 18 million years ago, and it had been discharging long enough before that to have eroded a canyon 1,000 feet deep. The drainage course must be as old as early Miocene and could be late Oligocene. By my interpretation, this canyon first was cut by the Little Colorado River and enlarged later by the ancestral San Juan River.

Whatever river carved the canyon at Peach Springs, it antedates the volcanic and gravel deposits that partly fill the canyon, and all traces of the river are lost in the Basin and Range province. Some of the possible early

Miocene river courses in that part of the Colorado River basin are suggested by reconstructing the early Miocene landscape there.

The probability is that in early Miocene time, the Hualapai, Cerbat, and Virgin Mountains (fig. 79), which are composed largely of Precambrian rocks, still were attached to and part of the Colorado Plateau, or had just begun to be faulted away from it. This is more than idle conjecture, because on the Colorado Plateau is evidence that mountains of Precambrian rocks in this area shed sediments northeastward onto the plateau; these old gravels antedate some of the lavas on the southwest rim of the plateau. Further, much of the faulting is later than the lavas that are in fault blocks broken away from the rim.

It is tempting to turn the early Miocene drainage from the dry canyon at Peach Springs southward into the valley of the Big Sandy River, but if the Big Sandy was in existence in early Miocene time, its valley was probably a broad open strike valley on a fault block just beginning to separate from the Colorado Plateau, like the present Chino Valley at the head of the Verde River (fig. 80). The Big Sandy River valley in its present form appears to be a late Tertiary structural valley.

At Kingman, Ariz., between the block of Precambrian rocks forming the Hualapai and Cerbat Mountains is a gap (fig. 79) partly filled with volcanic rocks that resemble the other middle Tertiary volcanic rocks in that region. The lava seems to have flowed into the gap rather than being faulted into it; if so, the gap is old and may very well be a segment of the ancient valley that extended west from Peach Springs. I looked for river gravels under the lava but found none.

Both the geomorphology and the structural geology provide a little support for inferring that the ancient drainage was west at right angles to the present basins and ranges. Beyond the gap at Kingman is an even thicker series of volcanic rocks in the south end of the Black Mountains; this may have been the eruptive center that supplied the Miocene volcanic material that spread eastward into the canyon at Peach Springs.

This volcanic center is near what may have been the mouth of the ancestral Miocene drainage. As will be noted shortly, the Colorado River valley downstream from here was an estuary of the Gulf of California, at least in early Pliocene time. Before considering that part of the river's history, though, the modern river valley below Grand Canyon should be briefly described.

After leaving the Colorado Plateau, the course of the modern river, like the presumed course of its predecessor, is westward, at right angles to the basins and ranges. At Hoover Dam, the river turns south approximately parallel with the grain of the topography. We have inferred that the Colorado River reached the Lake Mead area by underground drainage in middle or late Pliocene time when the Hualapai Limestone was deposited. The area was and still is tectonically active. Angular unconformities in the Muddy Creek Formation show that the basins and ranges were being formed while that fill was accumulating in the basins (see for example Longwell, 1936, p. 1420; Hunt, McKelvey, and Wiese, 1942, p. 301). Early Colorado River gravels that possibly are as old as late Pliocene are turned up steeply along the northwest foot of the Black Mountains (Longwell, 1936, p. 1466) and show that the downfolding and downfaulting of the basins continued in Pleistocene time. Younger sand and gravel deposits (Chemehuevi Formation), in part lake beds and regarded as Pleistocene but not well dated (Longwell, 1963, p. E12–E15), are little deformed. The river was superimposed across the south end of the Virgin Mountains and probably across the Black Mountains (fig. 81), but subsequent uplift of the ranges almost certainly means that the canyons are antecedent. Each time a range like the Black Mountains was uplifted, the elevated canyon bottom would become the spillway for overflow of the river ponded above it, and the canyon would be deepened to drain the ponded waters. If the episodes of uplift were slow enough, there need not have been much ponding, and the downcutting would keep pace with the uplift.

The Colorado River turns 90° south near Hoover Dam. From there to the head of the delta near Yuma, three valley forms are found (fig. 82): (1) Gorges through bedrock barriers; (2) open but narrow valleys between bluffs cut into locally derived gravel fans (fig. 83); and (3) wide flood plains on Colorado River deposits overlapping the gravel fans. Drilling records indicate the fan gravels may in places be 2,000 feet thick (Metzger, 1965).

Unconformably overlying the fan gravels, and extending under the Colorado River gravels, Metzger found beds of limestone, clay, and sand containing Foraminifera indicative of brackish water· (Metzger, in McKee and others, 1967, p. 3; Metzger, 1968.) With the Foraminifera are algae, barnacles, pelecypods, and ostracods (Hamilton, 1960, p. 276). Also found with these fossils are coccoliths from Cretaceous formations (Patsy J. Smith, written commun., May 1968); presumably the coccoliths were derived from the Colorado Plateau.

The estuarine deposits first were regarded as upper Miocene or lower Pliocene (Mckee and others, 1967, p. 3) on the basis of probable correlation with the

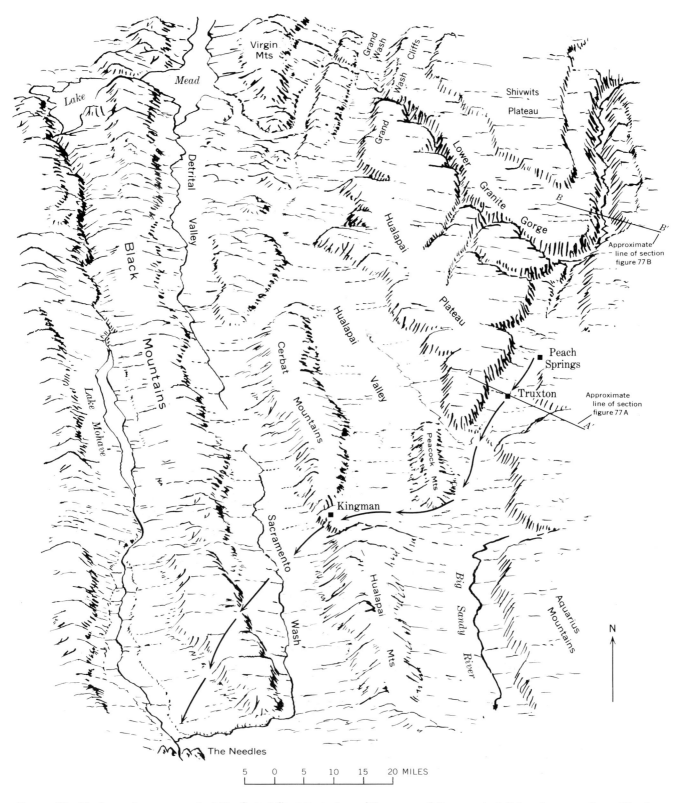

FIGURE 79.—Basins and ranges west of the Grand Canyon, and possible course of the ancestral Colorado across them. The dry
canyon at Peach Springs is pre-middle Miocene in age. The ancestral Colorado River probably discharged southwest through
it and perhaps continued southwest through the gap at Kingman between the blocks of Precambrian rocks forming the
Hualapai and Cerbat Mountains. The gap is filled with volcanic rocks, probably of Miocene age. The south end of the
Black Mountains is a major volcanic center and may have contributed the volcanic deposits at Kingman and at Peach
Springs. In Pliocene time, an estuary of the Gulf of California extended northward to The Needles.

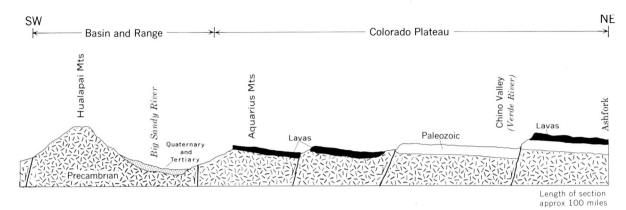

FIGURE 80.—Diagrammatic section northeast from the Hualapai Mountains to Ashfork, Ariz., to show contrast in the strike valleys occupied by the Big Sandy River and by the head of the Verde River (Chino Valley). The more southwesterly faults have the greater displacement and probably are older. (See also Twenter, 1961, fig. 205.3.) In early Miocene time, the strike valley at Big Sandy River was probably just beginning to form and was similar to the present strike valley at Chino Valley. Under the lavas, at many places on the Colorado Plateau, are stream gravels derived from the mountains of Precambrian rocks that have been separated by faulting from the Colorado Plateau.

FIGURE 81.—Canyon of the Colorado River through the Black Mountains, view down valley. The river was superimposed across this fault block of Precambrian rocks at a time when the fault block was substantially lower than it is now. Subsequently, as the block continued to rise, the river deepened its canyon.

Imperial Formation (see also Wilson, 1931, 1933; Woodring, 1931; MacNeil, 1965, p. 8) which also contains fossils (Foraminifera) identified as being reworked from Cretaceous shale on the Colorado Plateau (Merriam and Bandy, 1965). Later work suggests that the deposits along the Colorado River are Pliocene (Metzger, 1968). The marine (or brakish-water) fauna in these deposits has been found as far north as Parker, and similar deposits without the fossils are reported in the basins upstream and near the big volcanic center at the south end of the Black Mountains, possibly the mouth of the ancestral drainage westward from the Colorado Plateau at Peach Springs.

On the Riverside Mountains (west side of the river, below Parker) the estuarine deposits are at least 800 feet in altitude (Hamilton, 1960, 1964), 500 feet higher than the present Colorado River; near the mountains the beds are tilted as much as 19° (Metzger, 1963, p. 15). In The Needles region, similar deposits are 1,500–1,800 feet above sea level (D.G., Metzger, written commun. 1968). There must have been this much uplift since the Gulf of California extended into and flooded the lower 200 miles of the Colorado River valley. As already noted, the fanglomerates that underlie the estuarine beds are presently at least 2,000 feet thick; at the time of the estuary, therefore, the basins must have been downwarped at least 3,000 feet.

As uplift progressed and the estuary drained, the Colorado River discharged along the basins. Metzger (in McKee and others, 1967, p. 3) notes that river deposits occur as deep as 600 feet below and as high as 450 feet above the present flood plain. The oldest river deposits are younger than the ancestral drainage westward from Peach Springs; that is, they probably are no older than middle Pliocene.

The Colorado River from Hoover Dam to the mouth separates two very different kinds of drainage systems (fig. 84). On the east, the river is joined by through-flowing drainage of the Gila and Bill Williams river systems. The Gila and its tributaries are in long longitudinal valleys between the mountain ranges, and they cross the mountains in deep gorges. The base of the fills in many of the longitudinal valleys is lower than the bedrock in the gorges across the ranges. The streams may have been ponded by uplift at the mountain barriers and maintained their courses by overflowing and cutting downward at the gorges; along the lower Gila, the basin fills may include estuarine deposits like those along the Colorado River (Metzger, 1968). This is a tectonically stable area with few earthquake epicenters (fig. 85).

On the west side, the Colorado River has no tributaries worth the name. The theory is that the Colorado River once was joined by the Mojave River draining via Bristol, Cadiz, and Danby dry lakes, and that this drainage became disintegrated by the earth movements. This is a tectonically active area with many earthquake epicenters. The evidence that the Mojave Desert drainage once connected with the Colorado River is provided by the fishes now isolated at springs in the desert, for they are species related to those in the Colorado River (Hubbs and Miller, 1948).

Also, Foraminifera like those in the estuarine beds along the Colorado River have been discovered recently in drill cores at Danby and Cadiz Lakes (Smith, 1960). This strongly suggests that the estuarine beds extended at least as far northwest as Cadiz Lake, but the same species have also been found in cores at Panamint Valley, the valley west of Death Valley. It is difficult to visualize a water connection extending that far (Smith, 1960), although if the Foraminifera are as old as early Pliocene, a very different terrain might make a connection conceivable. Judging by inferred rates of speciation of the fishes, Hubbs and Miller (1948, p. 94) suggested that the Colorado River was well integrated, hydrographically and faunistically, as recently as late Pleistocene time. This may be so, although a greater age for the integrated drainage and slower rate of speciation seems indicated.

The former outlet of the Mojave River may have been at the Big Maria Mountains (at the pass south of Quien Sabe Peak). The fanglomerate east of the mountains contains very well rounded pebbles mixed with the subangular and subrounded locally derived fanglomerate (Hamilton, 1964). The rounded pebbles, constituting perhaps one part in a million of the fanglomerate, are evidently reworked from a still unidentified gravel bed. The gravels do not look like the Colorado River gravels derived from the northeast; they include rocks like those in the Mojave Desert—quartzite like the upper Precambrian quartzite and dark chert like that occurring abundantly in the Paleozoic limestones.

SOME CONCLUSIONS

A principal conclusion of this study is that Powell was in large part right in his interpretation of the history of the Colorado River—at least, he was less wrong than his later critics implied. Powell recognized the intimate dependence of river history on structural history. He believed that the canyons were antecedent. Their most striking feature—great depth—does indeed seem best explained by his hypothesis. Powell's interpretation needs to be modified, however, because the locations of the canyons, at least of most of them, seem best explained by superposition from an alluvial cover or from erosion surfaces in the shale formations.

In crossing the Colorado Plateau, the Colorado River crosses about 20,000 feet of strata inclined northeastward against the river's course. About half this tilting took place before Cenozoic time and antedates the formation of the Colorado River system. Half the tilting

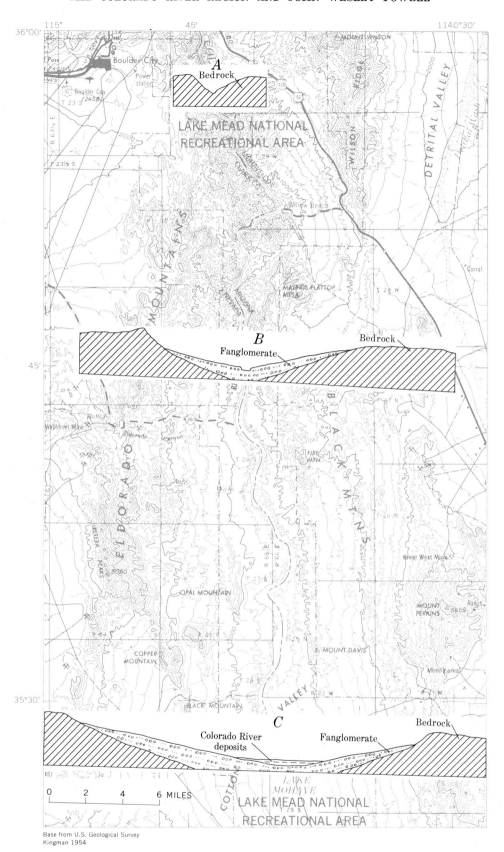

Base from U.S. Geological Survey
Kingman 1954

occurred during the Cenozoic while the river system was developing. Throughout their courses, the major streams go from one structural basin to another and must cross the structural barriers between the basins.

The gradients of the streams steepen greatly where they cross the structural barriers. In other drainage basins, such steepened gradients, called knickpoints, have been attributed to lowered base level and retreat of the knickpoint upstream, or to the streambed being held up by resistant rocks. In the Colorado River system, the steepened gradients coincide with the structural barriers, some of which do not involve differences in rock resistance, and these steepened gradients seem best explained by arching of the streambeds. One example is the steep gradient of Cataract Canyon down the east flank of the Henry Mountains structural basin compared with the much flatter gradients of the Green and Colorado Rivers flowing against the dip of the rocks above the junction of the rivers. Other examples are where the Dolores River crosses the Dolores anticline and where the Colorado River crosses the Waterpocket fold. At none of these places is there much difference in rock resistance along the riverbed.

The amount of deformation during Tertiary and Quaternary time in the Colorado River basin seems to have been roughly proportional to the time involved. Geologists profess not to be catastrophists, yet geological literature is replete with "great upheavals" (technically called orogenies). The geologic history of the Colorado River raises grave doubts whether there was any period of time as long as the Quaternary (2–3 million years) without major earth movement somewhere in the river basin.

My hypotheses for explaining various stretches of the rivers rest heavily on late Cenozoic structural movements, some of them demonstrable, some assumed. The most striking examples of the effect of earth movements on river history are the late Tertiary drainage changes along the main stem of the Colorado River in the Rocky Mountains, the abandonment and uplift of Unaweep Canyon, the abandonment and uplift of the dry canyon at Peach Springs, and the disrupted drainage that coincides with known present-day earth movements west of the lower stretch of the Colorado River. Although many of the structural features began form-

ing in early Tertiary time, in the so-called Laramide orogeny, much of the deformation continued into late Tertiary and even Quaternary time; there does not seem to have been any end to that orogeny.

Evidence of late Cenozoic earth movements is not always present at particular stretches of the river where such movement has been assumed. One of my major assumptions concerns dating the mile or so of uplift of the 1,000-mile-wide structural arch of which the Rocky Mountains and northern part of the Colorado Plateau are part. This regional uplift probably began in Oligocene time after the early Tertiary lakes had been filled with sediment, because middle Tertiary deposits are restricted to structural basins in the Rocky Mountains and Basin and Range province; they are generally lacking on the plateau. The southern part of the plateau has been raised considerably higher than the northern part (fig. 62). In the absence of evidence for a sudden jarring uplift, I assume the Rocky Mountains and Colorado Plateau were raised gradually during the last 35 million years, a rate of uplift of 150 feet per million years, less than 6 inches since the time of Christ. Continued activity on the Hurricane fault and the results of precise leveling in the Lake Mead area can be interpreted to suggest that uplift is still continuing (p. 117). The evidence for late Cenozoic earth movement that is available at some of the local structures has been emphasized because this evidence has been omitted in previous hypotheses, yet these late earth movements can account for most of the apparent conflicts in earlier hypotheses.

Although the streams are inconsequent across the structural basins and barriers, they are very well adjusted to the structural domes at the laccolithic mountains and detour around them. (See Hunt, 1956, p. 82.) The stream courses apparently antedate the laccolithic intrusions. This fact suggests either that the river system was well developed by early Miocene time or that some of the laccolithic mountains are younger than the single age determination (25 million years) made at the La Sal Mountains.

Meanders are deeply incised along the rivers on the Colorado Plateau, and the meander belt changed very little while the canyons were being deepened the last 1,000 feet. Cutoff meanders are scarce. Indeed the greatest incidence of cutoff meanders in the Canyonlands is on the west flank of the Monument upwarp. In addition to the two examples cited along the Colorado River, several in White Canyon produced the natural bridges there. These cutoff meanders could be attributed to renewed uplift at the Monument upwarp which caused the meanders to migrate westward while the canyons were being deepened.

FIGURE 82.—Colorado River valley between Hoover Dam and Davis Dam. Cross sections show: A, gorge through area of bedrock uplift; B, narrow valley between fanglomerate bluffs immediately downstream from the area of bedrock uplift; C, broad flood plain of Colorado River deposits that bury the lower ends of the fans. This flood plain ends downstream at the next uplift. These three valley forms are repeated several times between Hoover Dam and the Gulf of California.

FIGURE 83.—The open valley of the Colorado River below the bedrock gorge at Parker Dam; view downstream. Fanglomerate in river bluffs. Bluffs become farther apart downstream and are separated by a broad flood plain of Colorado River deposits.

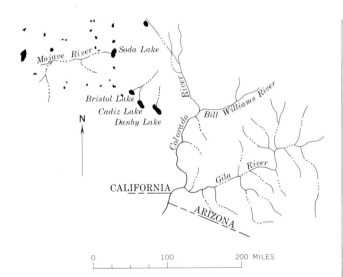

FIGURE 84.—Contrast in drainage east and west of the Colorado River where it flows south between Arizona and California. On the east is an integrated system of tributaries; on the west the tributaries have been interrupted by late Tertiary and Quaternary earth movements, and the drainage that formerly was tributary to the Colorado is now ponded in a series of playas.

Amounts of erosion seem to have been roughly proportional to the amount of time involved. Some evidence for this is available along the west edge of the Colorado Plateau where cliff retreat has been correlated with faulting (Averitt, 1964a, b). At times, the faulting was accelerated, but between these episodes the maximum amount of cliff retreat was only a few miles. The faulting progressed in repeated small increments without any "great upheaval," and erosion progressed at about the same rate as the deformation. In the river basin as a whole there is no evidence for any long period of crustal stability during the Cenozoic, and there does not seem to have been any "great denudation."

There are, of course, evident changes in kind and rate of weathering and erosion attributable to short-range climatic change, such as occurred during the Quaternary. During periods as brief as this (2–3 million years), episodes of accelerated weathering and erosion have alternated with episodes when rates were slowed, but total erosion during the Quaternary seems to have been roughly equal to the erosion that took place during comparable intervals of time during the Tertiary.

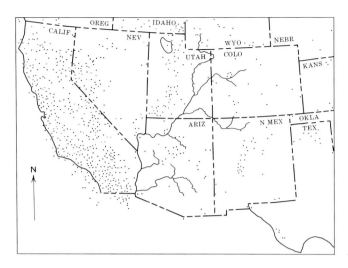

FIGURE 85.—Earthquake epicenters in southwestern United States (from Childs and Beebe, 1963, p. 131). The southerly course of the river between Arizona and California separates a structurally stable area on the east that has dendritic drainage from a structurally unstable area on the west that has interrupted drainage. Structural instability of the area west of the Colorado River is indicated by recent fault scarps and measurable earth tilt as well as by the many earthquake epicenters.

Present erosion above the Grand Canyon, as indicated by the sediment load of the Colorado River, averages about 6.5 inches per 1,000 years (Ritter, 1967). My reconstruction of the history of the river system suggests that rivers in the southern part of the Colorado Plateau began draining to the Basin and Range province before the end of the Oligocene (that is, more than 25 million years ago) and that the whole drainage system has formed since latest Miocene time (about 12 million years ago). At present rates of erosion, the Rocky Mountains and Colorado Plateau would have been lowered, on the average, about a mile in the last 10 million years. Perhaps the erosion averaged no more than that in the preceding 20 million years when most of the drainage was ponded at various places in the north. The amounts are about the right order of magnitude. Even the amount of canyon deepening attributable to the Quaternary, averaging about 500 feet, seems about right, considering the time involved.

This erosion has been differential. The shales, especially the Cretaceous shales, erode readily and must make up by far the greatest proportion of the present sediment in the rivers. Even within the shale formations the erosion is differential, being greatest on badland slopes and along arroyos and least on pediments, which are chiefly surfaces of transportation. The occurrence of Cretaceous shale at all the laccolithic

mountains implies that when those intrusions formed, presumably in early Miocene time, the Cretaceous formations were essentially continuous across the Colorado Plateau north of the Black Mesa and San Juan basins. Superposition of the river system across the structural barriers may have been from erosion surfaces in the Cretaceous formations. The Colorado Plateau was lower then, but erosion may have been rapid because of the great extent of the easily eroded shales.

Another effect of the differential erosion is to increase the topographic relief at the laccolithic mountains. The mountains are formed of resistant rocks, and the surrounding terrain erodes more rapidly than they do. As a result, these mountains are becoming higher and more rugged as erosion progresses; in effect, as they become older they appear younger.

As a body of water, the Colorado River is small. Its flow is only 5–10 percent of that of other great rivers in the United States, such as the Columbia, Snake, Missouri, Ohio, and St. Lawrence. But the Colorado River is a major geographic force in the American Southwest. The river crosses the arid lands that need its water, some of the arid lands about which Powell concerned himself. Because of its physiographic setting and geologic history, the Colorado River basin is spectacularly scenic. Nearly half our national parks and monuments are within the basin. Even after 100 years, however, the explanation of this landscape still defies us.

BIBLIOGRAPHY

Akers, J. P., 1964, Geology and ground water in the central part of Apache County, Arizona: U.S. Geol. Survey Water-Supply Paper 1771, 107 p.

Akers, J. P., Shorty, J. C., and Stevens, P. R., 1969, Hydrogeology of the Cenozoic igneous rocks, Navajo and Hopi Indians Reservations: U.S. Geol. Survey Prof. Paper 521–D. (In press.)

Averitt, P. A., 1964a, Table of post-Cretaceous geologic events along the Hurricane fault, near Cedar City, Iron County, Utah: Geol. Soc. America Bull., v. 75, no. 9, p. 901–908.

———— 1964b, Upper Tertiary surficial deposits near Cedar City, Iron County, Utah: Geol. Soc. America Bull., v. 75, no. 1, p. 37–44.

Babenroth, D. L., and Strahler, A. N., 1945, Geomorphology and structure of the East Kaibab monocline, Arizona and Utah: Geol. Soc. America Bull., v. 56, no. 2, p. 107–150.

Baker, A. A., 1936, Geology of the Monument Valley-Navajo Mountain region, San Juan County, Utah: U.S. Geol. Survey Bull. 865, 106 p.

Bassett, W. A., Kerr, P. F., Schaeffer, O. A., and Stoenner, R. W., 1963, Potassium-argon dating of the late Tertiary volcanic rocks and mineralization of Marysvile, Utah: Geol. Soc. America Bull., v. 74, no. 2, p. 213–220.

Blackwelder, Eliot, 1934, Origin of the Colorado River: Geol. Soc. America Bull., v. 45, no. 3, p. 551–566.

Bradley, W. H., 1936, Geomorphology of the north flank of the Uinta Mountains: U.S. Geol. Survey Prof. Paper 185–I, p. 163–199.

Burbank, W. S., and others, compilers, 1935, Geologic map of Colorado: Washington, D.C., U.S. Geol. Survey, scale 1 : 500,000.

Callaghan, Eugene, 1938, Preliminary report on the alunite deposits of the Marysvale region, Utah: U.S. Geol. Survey Bull. 886–D, p. 91–134.

———— 1939, Volcanic sequence in the Marysvale region in southwest-central Utah: Am. Geophys. Union Trans., 20th Ann. Mtg., pt. 3, p. 438–452.

Carter, W. D., and Gualtieri, J. L., 1965, Geyser Creek Fanglomerate (Tertiary), La Sal Mountains, eastern Utah: U.S. Geol. Survey Bull. 1224–E, p. E1–E11.

Cater, F. W., 1966, Age of the Uncompahgre uplift and Unaweep Canyon, west-central Colorado: U.S. Geol. Survey Prof. Paper 550–C, p. C86–C92.

Childs, O. E., 1948, Geomorphology of the valley of the Little Colorado River, Arizona: Geol. Soc. America Bull., v. 59, no. 4, p. 353–388.

Childs, O. E., and Beebe, B. W., eds., 1963, Backbone of the Americas—Tectonic history from pole to pole, a symposium: Am. Assoc. Petroleum Geologists Mem. 2, 320 p.

Colton, H. S., 1950, The basaltic cinder cones and lava flows of the San Francisco Mountain volcanic field, Arizona: Mus. Northern Arizona Bull. 10, 50 p.

Cooley, M. E., 1960a, Analysis of gravel in Glen-San Juan Canyon region, Utah and Arizona: Arizona Geol. Soc. Digest, v. 3, p. 19–30.

———— 1960b, Physiographic map of the San Francisco Plateau-lower Little Colorado River area, Arizona: Arizona Univ., Geochronology Lab.

Cooley, M. E., and Akers, J. P., 1961, Ancient erosional cycles of the Little Colorado River, Arizona and New Mexico: U.S. Geol. Survey Prof. Paper 424–C, p. C244–C248.

Cooley, M. E., and Davidson, E. S., 1963, The Mogollon Highlands—Their influence on Mesozoic and Cenozoic erosion and sedimentation: Arizona Geol. Soc. Digest, v. 6, p. 7–35.

Cooley, M. E., Harshbarger, J. W., Akers, J. P., and Hardt, W. F., 1969, Regional hydrogeology of the Navajo and Hopi Indian Reservations, Arizona, New Mexico, and Utah: U.S. Geol. Survey Prof. Paper 521–A, 61 p.

Damon, P. E., 1965, Correlation and chronology of ore deposits and volcanic rocks: Arizona Univ., Geochronology Labs., Ann. Prog. Rept. C00–689–50, Contract AT (11–1)–689, to Research Div., U.S. Atomic Energy Comm., 157 p.

Dane, C. H., 1935, Geology of the Salt Valley anticline and adjacent areas, Grand County, Utah: U.S. Geol. Survey Bull. 863, 184 p.

Darton, N. H., 1925, A résumé of Arizona geology: Arizona Bur. Mines Bull. 119, 298 p.

Davis, W. M., 1897, Current notes on physiography: Science, new ser., v. 5, p. 647–649.

———— 1901, An excursion to the Grand Canyon of the Colorado: Harvard Coll. Mus. Comp Zoology Bull. 38, p. 107–201.

Dutton, C. E., 1882, The Tertiary history of the Grand Canyon district: U.S. Geol. Survey Mon. 2, 264 p., atlas.

Emmons, S. F., 1897, The origin of Green River: Science, new ser., v. 6, p. 19–21.

Finnell, T. L., 1966a, Geologic map of the Cibecue quadrangle, Navajo County, Arizona: U.S. Geol. Survey Geol. Quad. Map GQ–545.

———— 1966b, Geologic map of the Chediski Peak quadrangle, Navajo County, Arizona: U.S. Geol. Survey Geol. Quad. Map GQ–544.

Forrester, J. D., 1937, Structure of the Uinta Mountains: Geol. Soc. America Bull. v. 48, no. 5, p. 631–666.

Gardner, L. S., 1941, The Hurricane fault in southwestern Utah and northwestern Arizona: Am. Jour. Sci., v. 239, no. 4, p. 241–260.

Gilbert, G. K., 1876, The Colorado Plateau province as a field for geological study: Am. Jour. Sci., 3d ser., v. 12, no. 67, p. 16–24, no. 68, p. 85–103.

———— 1877, Report on the geology of the Henry Mountains: U.S. Geog. and Geol. Survey Rocky Mt. Region (Powell), 160 p.

Gilluly, James, 1929, Geology and oil and gas prospects of part of the San Rafael Swell, Utah: U.S. Geol. Survey Bull. 806–C, p. 69–130.

Gregory, H. E., 1917, Geology of the Navajo country; a reconnaissance of parts of Arizona, New Mexico, and Utah: U.S. Geol. Survey Prof. Paper 93, 161 p.

———— 1938, The San Juan country, a geographic and geologic reconnaissance of southeastern Utah: U.S. Geol. Survey Prof. Paper 188, 123 p.

———— 1947, Colorado drainage basin: Am. Jour. Sci., v. 245, no. 11, p. 694–705.

Gregory, H. E., and Moore, R. C., 1931, The Kaiparowits region, a geographic and geologic reconnaissance of parts of Utah and Arizona: U.S. Geol. Survey Prof. Paper 164, 161 p.

Hack, J. T., 1942, Sedimentation and volcanism in the Hopi Buttes, Arizona: Geol. Soc. America Bull. v. 53, no. 2, p. 335–372.

Hamilton, W. B., 1960, Pliocene(?) sediments of salt water origin near Blythe, southeastern California: U.S. Geol. Survey Prof. Paper 400–B, p. B276–B277.

———— 1964, Geologic map of the Big Maria Mountains NE quadrangle, Riverside County, California, and Yuma County, Arizona: U.S. Geol. Survey Geol. Quad. Map GQ–350.

Hancock, E. T., 1915, The history of a portion of Yampa River, Colorado, and its possible bearing on that of Green River: U.S. Geol. Survey Prof. Paper 90–K, p. 183–189.

Hansen, W. R., 1965a, The Black Canyon of the Gunnison, today and yesterday: U.S. Geol. Survey Bull. 1191, 76 p.

———— 1965b, Geology of the Flaming Gorge area, Utah-Colorado-Wyoming: U.S. Geol. Survey Prof. Paper 490, 196 p.

———— 1966, Stream piracy on the Gunnison, in Geological Survey Research 1966: U.S. Geol. Survey Prof. Paper 550–A, p. 81.

Hansen, W. R., Kinney, D. M., and Good, J. M., 1960, Distribution and physiographic significance of the Browns Park Formation, Flaming Gorge and Red Canyon areas, Utah-Colorado: U.S. Geol. Survey Prof. Paper 400–B, p. B257–B259.

Hardy, C. T., and Muessig, S. J., 1952, Glaciation and drainage changes in the Fish Lake Plateau, Utah: Geol. Soc. America Bull., v. 63, no. 11, p. 1109–1116.

Hayden, F. V., 1862, Some remarks in regard to the period of elevation of those ranges of the Rocky Mountains near the sources of the Missouri River and its tributaries: Am. Jour. Sci., 2d ser., v. 33, p. 305–313.

———— 1873, Sixth annual report of the United States Geological Survey of the Territories * * * for the year 1872: Washington, D.C., 844 p.

Hubbs, C. L., and Miller, R. R., 1948, The Great Basin, with emphasis on glacial and postglacial times; 2, The zoological evidence; Correlation between fish distribution and hydrographic history in the desert basins of western United States: Utah Univ. Bull., v. 38, no. 20, p. 18–166.

Hunt, C. B., 1946, Guidebook to the geology and geography of the Henry Mountains region: Utah Geol. Soc. Guidebook, 1, 51 p.

—— 1956, Cenozoic geology of the Colorado Plateau: U.S. Geol. Survey Prof. Paper 279, 99 p.

—— 1958, Structural and igneous geology of the La Sal Mountains, Utah: U.S. Geol. Survey Prof. Paper 294–I, p. 305–364.

Hunt, C. B., assisted by Averitt, Paul, and Miller, R. L., 1953, Geology and geography of the Henry Mountains region, Utah: U.S. Geol. Survey Prof. Paper 228, 234 p.

Hunt, C. B., and Mabey, D. R., 1966, Stratigraphy and structure, Death Valley, California: U.S. Geol. Survey Prof. Paper 494–A, 162 p.

Hunt, C. B., McKelvey, V. E., and Wiese, J. H., 1942, The Three Kids manganese district, Clark County, Nevada: U.S. Geol. Survey Bull. 936–L, p. 297–319.

Hunt, C. B., Robinson, T. W., Bowles, W. A., and Washburn, A. L., 1966, Hydrologic basin, Death Valley, California: U.S. Geol. Survey Prof. Paper 494–B, 138 p.

Irving, J. D., 1896, The stratigraphical relations of the Brown's Park beds of Utah: New York Acad. Sci. Trans., v. 15, p. 252–259.

Jefferson, M. S. W., 1897, The antecedent Colorado: Science, new ser., v. 6, p. 293–295.

Kinney, D. M., compiler, 1966, Geology—Natl. Atlas Sheet 74–75: Washington, D.C., U.S. Geol. Survey, scale 1:7,500,000.

Koons, E. D., 1945, Geology of the Uinkaret Plateau, northern Arizona: Geol. Soc. America Bull., v. 56, no. 2, p. 151–180.

—— 1948, Geology of the eastern Hualpai Reservation: Plateau, v. 20, no. 4, p. 53–60.

Lance, J. F., 1954, Age of the Bidahochi Formation, Arizona [abs]: Geol. Soc. America Bull. v. 65, no. 12, pt. 2, p. 1276.

LaRue, E. C., 1916, Colorado River and its utilization: U.S. Geol. Survey Water-Supply Paper 395, 231 p.

Lee, W. T., 1908, Geologic reconnaissance of a part of western Arizona: U.S. Geol. Survey Bull. 352, 96 p.

Lehner, R. E., 1958, Geology of the Clarkdale quadrangle, Arizona: U.S. Geol. Survey Bull. 1021–N, p. 511–592.

Lohman, S. W., 1965, Geology and artesian water supply of the Grand Junction area, Colorado: U.S. Geol. Survey Prof. Paper 451, 149 p.

Longwell, C. R., 1928, Geology of the Muddy Mountains, Nevada, with a section through the Virgin Range to the Grand Wash Cliffs, Arizona: U.S. Geol. Survey Bull. 798, 152 p.

—— 1936, Geology of the Boulder Reservoir floor, Arizona-Nevada: Geol. Soc. America Bull., v. 47, no. 9, p. 1393–1476.

—— 1946, How old is the Colorado River?: Am. Jour. Sci., v. 244, no. 12, p. 817–835.

—— 1960, Interpretation of levelling data in Smith, W. O., and others, Comprehensive survey of sedimentation in Lake Mead, 1948–49: U.S. Geol. Survey Prof. Paper 295, p. 33–38.

—— 1963, Reconnaissance geology between Lake Mead and Davis Dam, Arizona-Nevada: U.S. Geol. Survey Prof. Paper 374–E, 51 p.

McKee, E. D., 1951, Sedimentary basins of Arizona and adjoining areas: Geol. Soc. America Bull., v. 62, no. 5, p. 481–505.

McKee, E. D., Wilson, R. F., Breed, W. J, and Breed, C. S., eds., 1967, Evolution of the Colorado River in Arizona—A hypothesis developed at the Symposium on Cenozoic geology of the Colorado Plateau in Arizona, August 1964: Mus. Northern Arizona Bull. 44, 67 p.

MacNeil, F. S., 1965, Evolution and distribution of the genus *Mya*, and Tertiary migrations of Mollusca: U.S. Geol. Survey Prof. Paper 483–G, 51 p.

Maxson, J. H., 1950, Lava flows in the Grand Canyon of the Colorado River, Arizona: Geol. Soc. America Bull. v. 61, no. 1, p. 9–15.

Mears, Brainard, Jr., 1950, Cenozoic geomorphic history of the Oak Creek Canyon region, Arizona [abs.]: Geol. Soc. America Bull., v. 61, no. 12, pt. 2, p. 1557.

Merriam, Richard, and Bandy, O. L., 1965, Source of upper Cenozoic sediments in Colorado delta region: Jour. Sed. Petrology, v. 35, no. 4, p. 911–919.

Metzger, D. G., 1963, Progress report on geohydrologic investigation in the Parker-Blythe-Cibola area, in Investigation of the water resources of the Lower Colorado River area: U.S. Geol. Survey, open-file report, p. 15–19.

—— 1965, A Miocene(?) aquifer in the Parker-Blythe-Cibola area, Arizona and California: U.S. Geol. Survey Prof. Paper 525–C, p. C203–C205.

—— 1968, The Bouse Formation (Pliocene) of the Parker-Blythe-Cibola area, Arizona and California: U.S. Geol. Survey Prof. Paper 600–D, p. D126–D136.

Moore, R. C., 1926a, Origin of enclosed meanders on streams of the Colorado Plateau: Jour. Geology, v. 34, no. 1, p. 29–57.

—— 1926b, Significance of enclosed meanders in the physiographic history of the Colorado Plateau country: Jour. Geology, v. 34, no. 2, p. 97–130.

Morrison, R. B., 1965, Route from Denver, Colorado, to Salt Lake City, Utah, via the Denver and Rio Grande Western Railroad (Moffat Tunnel Route)—Field Conf. 1, Guidebook 1st day, Supp.—Internat. Assoc. Quaternary Research (INQUA), 7th Cong., U.S.A., 1965: [Lincoln, Nebr., Nebraska Acad. Sci.], 68 p.

Newberry, J. S., 1861, Geological report, in Ives, J. C., Report upon the Colorado River of the West: U.S. 36th Cong. 1st sess., Senate and House Exec. Doc. 90, pt. 3, 154 p.

Noble, L. F., 1914, The Shinumo quadrangle, Grand Canyon district, Arizona: U.S. Geol. Survey Bull. 549, 100 p.

Olson, J. C., Hedlund, D. C., and Hansen, W. R., 1968, Tertiary volcanic stratigraphy in the Powderhorn-Black Canyon region, Gunnison and Montrose Counties, Colorado: U.S. Geol. Survey Bull. 1251–C, 29 p.

Phoenix, D. A., 1963, Geology of the Lees Ferry area, Coconino County, Arizona: U.S. Geol. Survey Bull. 1137, 86 p.

Powell, J. W., 1875, Exploration of the Colorado River of the West and its tributaries: Washington, D.C., U.S. Govt. Printing Office, 291 p.

Repenning, C. A., and Irwin, J. H., 1954, Bidahochi Formation of Arizona and New Mexico: Am. Assoc. Petroleum Geologists Bull., v. 38, no. 8, p. 1821–1826.

Richmond, G. M., 1962, Quaternary stratigraphy of the La Sal Mountains, Utah: U.S. Geol. Survey Prof. Paper 324, 135 p.

Ritter, D. F., 1967, Rates of denudation: Jour. Geol. Education, v. 15, no. 4, p. 154–159.

Robinson, H. H., 1913, The San Franciscan volcanic field, Arizona: U.S. Geol. Survey Prof. Paper 76, 213 p.

Rocky Mountain Association of Geologists and others, 1951, Uinta Basin, Utah and Colorado, *in* Possible future petroleum provinces of North America—Rocky Mountain region: Am. Assoc. Petroleum Geologists Bull. v. 35, no. 2, p. 297–301.

Sears, J. D., 1924a, Geology and oil and gas prospects of part of Moffat County, Colorado, and southern Sweetwater County, Wyoming: U.S. Geol. Survey Bull. 751–G, p. 269–319.

—— 1924b, Relations of the Browns Park formation and the Bishop conglomerate and their role in the origin of Green and Yampa Rivers: Geol. Soc. America Bull., v. 35, no. 2, p. 279–304.

—— 1962, Yampa Canyon in the Uinta Mountains, Colorado: U.S. Geol. Survey Prof. Paper 374–I, 33 p.

Shawe, D. R., 1968, Stratigraphy of the Slick Rock district and vicinity, San Miguel and Dolores Counties, Colorado: U.S. Geol. Survey Prof. Paper 576–A, 104 p.

Smith, J. F., Jr., Huff, L. C., Hinrichs, E. N., and Luedke, R. G., 1963, Geology of the Capitol Reef area, Wayne and Garfield Counties, Utah: U.S. Geol. Survey Prof. Paper 363, 102 p.

Smith, P. B., 1960, Fossil Foraminifera from southeastern California deserts: U.S. Geol. Survey Prof. Paper 400–B, p. B278–B279.

Spieker, E. M., and Billings, M. P., 1940, Glaciation in the Wasatch Plateau, Utah: Geol. Soc. America Bull. v. 51, no. 8, p. 1173–1198.

Stern, T. W., Newell, M. F., Kistler, R. W., and Shawe, D. R., 1965, Zircon uranium-lead and thorium-lead ages and mineral potassium-argon ages of La Sal Mountains rocks, Utah: Jour. Geophys. Research, v. 70, no. 6, p. 1503–1507.

Strahler, A. N., 1948, Geomorphology and structure of the West Kaibab fault zone and Kaibab Plateau, Arizona: Geol. Soc. America Bull. v. 59, no. 6, p. 513–540.

Twenter, F. R., 1961, Miocene and Pliocene history of central Arizona: U.S. Geol. Survey Prof. Paper 424–C, p. C153–C156.

—— 1962, Geology and promising areas for ground-water development in the Hualapai Indian Reservation, Arizona: U.S. Geol. Survey Water-Supply Paper 1576–A, 38 p.

U.S. Geological Survey, 1932, Geologic map of the United States: Washington, D.C., scale 1:2,500,000; reprinted 1960.

Wahlstrom, E. E., 1947, Cenozoic physiographic history of the Front Range, Colorado: Geol. Soc. America Bull. v. 58, no. 7, p. 551–572.

Walcott, C. D., 1890, Study of a line of displacement in the Grand Canyon of the Colorado, in northern Arizona: Geol. Soc. America Bull. v. 1, p. 49–64.

Warner, M. M., 1966, Sedimentational analysis of the Duchesne River Formation, Uinta Basin, Utah: Geol. Soc. America Bull., v. 77, no. 9, p. 945–958.

White, C. A., 1889, On the geology and physiography of a portion of northwestern Colorado and adjacent parts of Utah and Wyoming: U.S. Geol. Survey 9th Ann. Rept., p. 677–712.

Williams, Howel, 1936, Pliocene volcanoes of the Navajo-Hopi country: Geol. Soc. America Bull., v. 47, no. 1, p. 111–172.

Wilmarth, M. G., 1938, Lexicon of geologic names of the United States (including Alaska): U.S. Geol. Survey Bull. 896, 2 v.: 2396 p.

Wilson, E. D., 1931, Marine Tertiary in Arizona: Science, new ser., v. 74, p. 567–568.

—— 1933, Geology and mineral deposits of southern Yuma County, Arizona: Arizona Bur. Mines, Bull. 134, Geol. Ser. 7, 236 p.

Wood, H. E., 2d, and others, 1941, Nomenclature and correlation of the North American continental Tertiary: Geol. Soc. America Bull., v. 52, no. 1, p. 1–48.

Woodring, W. P., 1931, Distribution and age of the marine Tertiary deposits of the Colorado Desert: Carnegie Inst. Washington Pub. 418, p. 1–25.

Wrucke, C. T., 1961, Paleozoic and Cenozoic rocks in the Alpine-Nutrioso area, Apache County, Arizona: U.S. Geol. Survey Bull. 1121–H, 26 p.

Young, R. A., 1966, Cenozoic geology along the edge of the Colorado Plateau in northwestern Arizona: Washington Univ., St. Louis, Mo., Ph. D. dissertation, 167 p., maps.

The Rapids and the Pools—Grand Canyon

By LUNA B. LEOPOLD

THE COLORADO RIVER REGION AND JOHN WESLEY POWELL

GEOLOGICAL SURVEY PROFESSIONAL PAPER 669–D

*The rapids and the profile of
the Colorado River*

Contents

Illustrations

THE RAPIDS AND THE POOLS— GRAND CANYON

By Luna B. Leopold

Abstract

Through the Grand Canyon the Colorado drops in elevation about 2,200 feet in 280 miles; most of this drop occurs in rapids that account for only 10 percent of the distance. Despite the importance of rapids, there are no waterfalls. Depth measurements made at $\frac{1}{10}$-mile intervals show that the bed profile is highly irregular, but the apparent randomness masks an organized alternation of deeps and shallows. Measurement of the age of a lava flow that once blocked the canyon near Toroweap shows that no appreciable deepening of the canyon has taken place during the last million years. It is reasoned that the river has had both the time and the ability to eliminate the rapids. The long-continued existence and the relative straightness of the longitudinal profile indicate that the river maintains a state of quasi-equilibrium which provides the hydraulic requirements for carrying the debris load brought in from upstream without continued erosion of the canyon bed. The maintenance of the alternating pools and rapids seems to be a necessary part of this poised or equilibrium condition.

GENERAL STATEMENT

In the dry glare of a sun-drenched afternoon, in the bitter chill of a thunderstorm wind, or in the purple evening, there is no respite from the incessant boom of the great river. One finds at times he has forgotten the ever-present roar of the rapids and, as if suddenly awakened, he hears it again. So persistent is the sound that I often wonder how the mind can put away the noise into some recess, even momentarily.

The river's boom is associated with a pervasive uneasiness which never leaves a man while he is clamped within the cliffs of the canyon. This uneasiness is not the reflection of a queasy stomach for, in fact, the dry air, the sun-dappled water, and the intense color tend to give a sense of exhilaration. Rather, the uneasiness is a subdued but undeniable cold fear which never departs.

To anyone who has been down the big river, the words in Powell's journals convey clearly the fact that even those courageous men had the same constant unrest.

They had more reason than we for a deep and troubled fear. On that first trip, no one knew whether high and vertical waterfalls might block completely any passage by boat. Clearly, there was no return upstream.

Powell (1875, p. 62), halfway through his trip, expressed his feelings this way: "* * * there are great descents yet to be made, but, if they are distributed in rapids and short falls, as they have been heretofore, we will be able to overcome them. But, may be, we shall come to a fall in these canyons which we cannot pass, where the walls rise from the water's edge, so that we cannot land, and where the water is so swift that we cannot return. Such places have been found, except that the falls were not so great but that we could run them with safety. How will it be in the future!"

In the hundreds of miles through which the river flows in a canyon section, the channel consists of an alternation of flat pools and steep rapids. Yet there are no waterfalls in the usual sense of the word. What John Wesley Powell feared the most does not exist. Why not? This seems a simple enough question, yet the answer is neither simple nor obvious.

This chapter is an attempt to explain, albeit incompletely, why rivers characteristically develop a uniform profile downstream, gradually decreasing in steepness. Despite this progressive flattening of slope, they tend to maintain an alternation of low-gradient deep pools and higher gradient riffles or rapid reaches. The general explanation will then be applied to the Colorado River in the Grand Canyon section to inquire in what ways, if any, a canyon alters a river's characteristic bed profile.

CONCEPT OF QUASI-EQUILIBRIUM

A river is both the route and the transporting agent by which rock and soil eroded off the continent are carried to the sea. The necessity for such movement lies merely in the energy possessed by any object as a result

131

of its elevation. Water falling on mountains as precipitation will flow downhill because of the pull of gravity, and in the course of its movement it will carry along bits of rock and soil. The water moving downhill is constantly replenished by more falling as precipitation, and therefore, through the action of the hydrologic cycle, the continents are gradually worn down. Though the water falls over a widespread area, it does not long remain so dispersed and gathers in the well-defined ribbons of a channel network.

No aspect of the work of rivers can be discussed without some reference to the concept of quasi-equilibrium and least work. The pool-and-rapid sequence, which is the major concern of this essay is integrally related to the concept.

Power is expended—that is, energy is mechanically converted into heat—throughout the natural world. Water converts its energy of elevation into heat as it flows downhill. A rolling rock does the same as it moves down a slope. Wind dissipates its energy as it blows from a high-pressure area to one of low pressure. The work done during such energy conversion tends to be uniformly distributed because any nonuniformity causes a concentration of work on the dissident or anomalous feature.

For example, a carpenter sawing a board strikes a nail. All the work of the saw is concentrated on the nail and little on the wood until the nail is eliminated. So also in planing a board. Any slight prominence or bump on the surface is reduced by the plane faster than the surrounding uniform surface.

These examples are analogous to the work done by flowing water in a river channel. The channel bed—considered over some miles of length—tends toward a uniform down-channel slope. If some unusual feature exists, such as a ledge of especially hard rock, a very large boulder, or a waterfall, the flowing water being locally blocked will flow over and around the obstacle with higher than usual velocity, undercutting the downstream edge and eroding the sides of the obstacle. Therefore, in accord with the general tendency referred to above, energy expenditure concentrates on the bumps of the streambed, tending to reduce them and to make the whole streambed uniform.

Such a tendency toward uniformity is, in the physical world, usually counterbalanced by other tendencies arising from other conditions that must be met. The tendency of the flowing water to erode and lower the streambed is counteracted first by the resistance of the rock or other riverbed materials. This is one of the simpler balances operating in the river system. There are others more complex. The river derives from tributaries and from its bed and banks a debris load of silt, sand, or gravel. This debris will accumulate anywhere along the river where the flow conditions make the capacity to transport less than the load brought in from upstream. The factors governing transport capacity, especially width, depth, velocity, and slope, adjust among themselves to keep in balance the transport capacity and the load to be carried. The ubiquitous form of the river profile—steep in the headwaters and gradually decreasing in gradient downstream—results from the internal adjustments among the hydraulic factors as tributaries introduce additional water and their debris load.

There is another constraint on the tendency for uniform river gradient which is of controlling importance in the present discussion of pools and rapids. Coarse debris, especially gravel, will not move downstream in a uniform sheet but will tend to bunch up in mounds separated by troughs. This concentration of coarse particles at some places on the riverbed, separated by zones of relative scarcity of similar rocks, results from the effect of one rock on another in close proximity. The closer rocks are spaced, the greater is the water flow required to move them. Gravel bars in rivers, then, are the result of the tendency for rocks to accumulate in groups. The phenomenon is strikingly similar to the tendency for automobiles on a highway to accumulate in groups separated by stretches of open road nearly devoid of cars, even though the highway is free of obstructions or causes for local slowdown.

The river channel, then, is a result of complicated interactions among many factors that tend to reinforce or oppose each other. The net result of their interaction is a more or less stable and self-adjusting system, having overall characteristics of uniformity, and, within restraints, of minimization of work. This stable but self-adjusting condition is often described as quasi-equilibrium.

RESPONSE OF A RIVER IN A ROCK CANYON

The question examined here is the extent to which confinement in a rock canyon alters the usual response of a river to the mechanical laws. Are the pools and rapids of a river in a great canyon analogous to the pools and riffles of a small trout stream, or are they of a different origin and nature? The question might best be approached by first describing the nature of the pools or flat reaches and the various kinds of rapids in the Grand Canyon.

Until the U.S. Geological Survey expedition down the Grand Canyon in 1965, there existed no measurements of water depth in any great canyon of the world except at isolated cross sections where a cable has been constructed for water-flow measurements or where a dam or bridge has been constructed. No continuous profile of any canyon riverbed had ever been taken. One reason for this is that a reliable depth measurement cannot be obtained in a swift current by sounding with a lead weight attached to a line. Where the water is deep the weight is swept downstream, and a vertical measurement is impossible. The modern sonic sounder is the only practical way of measuring depth. Such instruments, now widely used in boats, large and small, measure the length of time required for an energy pulse to reach the bed and return upward to the boat. This time lag is automatically converted into depth in feet. Even the sonic equipment fails at times to work satisfactorily in fast rapids, for reasons not known. I presume that air bubbles under the energy-transmitting transducer interrupt the signal.

A recording sounder like those used in oceangoing hydrographic vessels is of no use in a river because the boat proceeds downstream at a varying speed, so that the location at any particular moment must be separately determined. The simple scheme we have used requires merely that aerial photographs be taken beforehand. The photographs are printed on semi-matte paper in an unbroken roll, so that as the party progresses downstream, the pictures are unrolled successively. One man reads the depth dial and calls out the depth at about 5-second intervals. Another keeps collating the aerial photograph with identifiable features of the canyon, so that he knows where the boat is at any moment. He writes the depth directly on the photograph at the boat location. In the Grand Canyon and associated canyons of the Colorado River, these measurements were made through about 500 miles of river distance and totaled more than 6,000 separate readings of water depth.

In addition to the large number of depth readings made by echo sounding, a few cross sections were measured with a 100-pound lead weight in connection with current-meter measurements of water velocity (fig. 86).

The water-depth data discussed here were measured in June 1965, before the bypass tunnels at Glen Canyon Dam were closed. They represent, therefore, the conditions in the Grand Canyon essentially unaltered by major dams, though many dams were in operation in upper tributaries. The flow at the time of these measurements was 48,500 cfs (cubic feet per second) at Lees Ferry, though some losses occurred to bank storage, making the discharge decrease slightly downstream.

In order to get a broad picture of the Colorado River

channel at this flow, the median values of width and depth in lower Marble Canyon and middle Granite Gorge (mile 113 to mile 149) were 220 feet and 40 feet. The average velocity for these dimensions is computed to be 6.2 fps (feet per second) or 4.2 mph (miles per hour). The mean velocity through the rapids was generally 11 to 15 fps, or 7.5 to 10 mph.

The range of values of width and depth for selected river segments is shown in figure 87. The depth data represent values taken at 1/10-mile intervals in the first 139 miles below Lees Ferry, when the discharge was 48,500 cfs. The width data are measured from aerial photographs taken in the spring of 1965. The maximum depth measured in the Grand Canyon was 110 feet at mile 114.3.

The river flows alternately in long, relatively smooth pools and short, steep, and violent rapids (fig. 88). What constitutes a rapid is a matter of definition, but there are 93 steep reaches of various lengths between Lees Ferry and middle Granite Gorge, a distance of about 150 miles. In this reach, rapids average about 1.6 miles apart.

The water-surface gradient in the pools is less than 2 feet per thousand (0.002) and typically is about 5 feet in 10,000 (0.0005). In the rapids, on the other hand, the water surface falls from 5 to 17 feet per thousand (0.005–0.017). For example, in Badger Creek Rapids, the water surface falls 14 feet in 860 feet. The surface velocity above the rapids was measured at 7.0 fps and in the rapids, 11.0 fps, when the discharge was 48,500 cfs.

These figures may be made more meaningful by inspection of the profile of water surface and bed through part of Marble Canyon (fig. 89). The profile represents 6 miles of river and includes the rapids near the mouth of Unkar Creek. Upstream and down are pool reaches of relatively flat gradient (fig. 90).

The first impression transmitted by such a profile is the large variation in water depth. In the pool reach from mile 71 to Unkar Rapid, through which the water-surface slope remains essentially constant at 0.0008 foot per foot, the variation in water depth ranged from 6 to 74 feet, a change which occurred within a distance of 0.3 mile. The median value was 20 feet. Two-thirds of the individual readings were in the depth range from 13 to 30 feet.

The data suggest that long pools having low water-surface gradients tend to be deeper than other parts of the river. Nearly every rapid includes an unusually shallow section, but not all equally shallow places are a high-gradient rapid. Also, some deep holes occur in the rapids, but these generally are at or near the foot.

FIGURE 86.—Flow-measurement gear being readied for observations of velocity and depth. The 100-pound weight hangs below the current meter from a cable on the winch.

Types of Waves and Causes of Rapids

In attempting to ascertain the causes of rapids, it would be helpful if one knew the details of the sizes and types of boulders or the configuration of bedrock making up the riverbed through the rapids. As only depth soundings are available, one must infer what he can about the bed from other evidence. The character of the shoreline and the distribution of wave forms at the water surface provide some indication of what is hidden under water. To aid in drawing inferences about the causes of rapids, it is useful to categorize the forms seen on the surface, especially the relation of waves to the shoreline and to what is known about water depth.

Four types of waves can be distinguished in rapids. This fourfold classification is descriptive of the hydraulic form rather than the geomorphic cause of the rapids. It is a classification based on the origin of large waves or wave trains in rapids rather than an explanation of why rapids occur at a given place in a canyon. Each type of wave is shown diagrammatically in figure 91.

Waves below large rocks or outcrops.—A common cause of large waves is the chance occurrence of extremely large boulders or rock outcrops in the channel. These rock masses or blocks force water to pass over and around the obstruction. The water speeds up on the downstream side, causing a hole or deep trough in

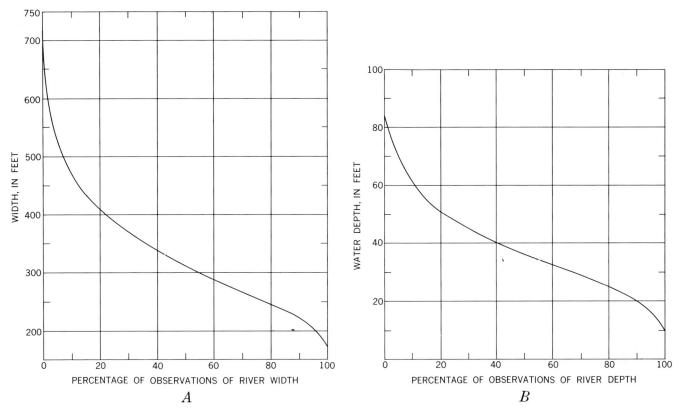

FIGURE 87.—Data on width and depth of Colorado River in Grand Canyon presented as smoothed frequency-distribution graphs. A, River widths. The graph shows, for example, that 20 percent of the width observations equaled or exceeded 410 feet, and that 50 percent of the observations equaled or exceeded 320 feet. Widths were measured at 1/10-mile intervals from aerial photographs of an 82-mile segment from mile 28 to mile 110 (miles measured as distances below Lees Ferry, Ariz.). B, River depth. The graph shows that 20 percent of the depth observations equaled or exceeded 51 feet, and that 50 percent of the observations equaled or exceeded 36 feet. Data represent values at 1/10-mile intervals in the 139 miles below Lees Ferry.

the water surface. Immediately below that, a standing wave occurs characterized by water leaping upward at the wave crest and continually breaking toward the upstream side.

Deep-water waves caused by convergences.—Convergence seems to be the most common cause of wave trains consisting of individual waves of large magnitude. As shown in figure 91, a narrowing of the channel forces water from along the side of the channel toward the center, often simultaneously from both banks, resulting in a pileup of water near the channel centerline and a train of waves (fig. 92) having wavelengths and amplitudes dependent upon the amount of flow and the amount of convergence.

Waves and riffles in shallow water.—The ordinary riffle seen in small streams generally results from shallow water. Often the shallow water is caused by a gravel bar (fig. 93) and sometimes by a low-angle fan being deposited in the channel from an entering tributary (fig. 90). The form of the bar or channel obstruction,

in large rivers as well as small, is a topographic hump on the streambed. There will usually be a deep pool immediately upstream, but over the obstructing bar the water will flow in a shallow and more or less uniform sheet at higher than usual velocities owing to the steep water slope on the downstream side of the obstructing bar.

Waves in deep but high-velocity water.—When large waves occur in a rapid, it is usually not possible to tell whether the water is shallow or deep. We have enough measurements to show that large waves can occur even in very deep water, but not associated with convergence, as described above.

Categorizing the surface features of rapids, as suggested above, leads to the conclusion that the typical alternation of pools and fast water is not the result of random occurrence of rock outcrops in the channel, tributary fans, or talus falls from adjoining cliffs. These causes of rapids are relatively obvious, but only a few

FIGURE 88.—Hance Rapids, caused principally by the debris cone from a tributary entering on the left bank.

of the rapids in the Grand Canyon can be explained by these, as will now be shown.

A channel obstruction causing a rapid can be formed by large blocks of rock falling into the river from adjacent high cliffs. In many places along the Colorado, one sees bedrock blocks whose dimensions are in hundreds rather than tens of feet. Sometimes these are seen as great blocks protruding from the river, but more often, their size can be appreciated when they are on the river margin or on the slopes beneath the enclosing cliffs. The depth soundings through some rapids show that the depth changes instantly from very deep to very shallow and just as quickly increases again. This strongly suggests that the boat has just passed a large block of cliff rock which fell into the river and is completely submerged. Even some of the big rapids seem to be caused primarily from rockfalls from the cliffs. Many rapids are so far from adjoining cliffs, however, that this explanation is improbable.

The second obvious reason for rapids in the great canyons is the occurrence of a fan of rock debris debouched from an entering tributary and partly blocking the river. Many tributaries, however, do not cause a rapid at all, although they are apparently equal in size to those that do.

Some rapids must be the result of outcrops of especially hard rock locally, but because such outcrops are submerged, the cause must be inferred. Lava Falls, one of the largest and most dangerous rapids in the Grand Canyon, seems to be of this sort. In middle Pleistocene time, basalt from a lava eruption partly filled the canyon. This lava flow later was eroded away. Its occurrence suggests such a cause for this steep and violent rapid.

Many rapids, however, do not seem to be explained by the three types of circumstances mentioned. Rather, they are associated with what seems at first glance to be a random occurrence of gravel accumulations, either as a central bar across the channel or as the channelward extension of a lateral gravel bar. In fact, these gravel accumulations are not random when viewed in terms of a long reach of channel. They have a roughly regular spacing as has long been observed in the occurrence of gravel riffles in small streams. Some support for this inference comes from the data on the number of rapids per unit distance mentioned earlier. In the first 150 miles below Lees Ferry, a reach dominated by the sedimentary rock in Marble Canyon, rapids average 1.6 miles apart. In the next 178 miles downstream, a reach dominated by the metamorphic rock of Granite Gorge,

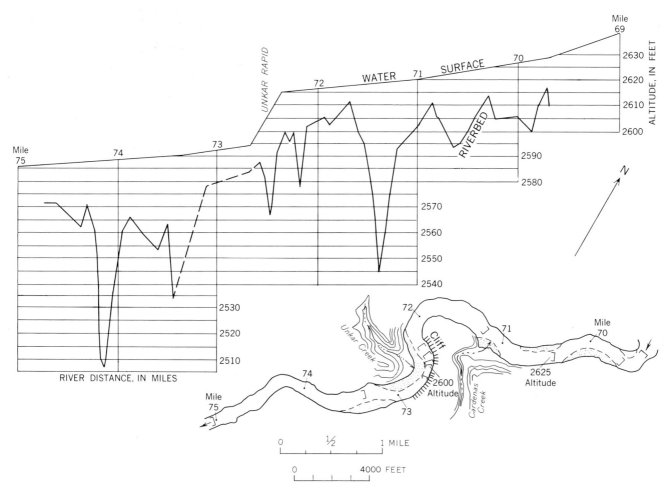

FIGURE 89.—Profile of water surface and riverbed in a 6-mile segment of the Grand Canyon near Unkar Rapid. Below is a sketch map of same reach showing position of 5-foot contours on the water surface and the location of mile points below Lees Ferry.

the spacing also averages 1.6 miles. The above data refer only to spacing of steep zones in the profile. Spacing of bars or shallow places not observable at the surface is a shorter distance.

Thus, the occurrence in canyon rivers of rapids separated by deeper pools, despite the seeming irregularity in any given locality, is apparently independent of the major bedrock type and the valley characteristics associated with different bedrock types. The alternation appears to be one aspect of channel adjustment toward maintaining stability or quasi-equilibrium and is typical in canyon rivers as well as in small streams on a wide and unconfined valley flat.

Another fact that suggests the existence of a quasi-equilibrium state is the long period of time that the Colorado River has maintained its present bed. It was mentioned above that in Pleistocene time, part of the canyon in the lower Granite Gorge was partly filled by

the outpouring of lava. By using a radioactive-decay method, McKee, Hamblin, and Damon (1968) determined the age of lava cropping out near the present river level in the vicinity of Toroweap as 1.16 m.y. (million years). They stated (p. 133), "This represents a minimum age of Grand Canyon, for at the time the lava formed, the Canyon was essentially as deep as it is today. Since that time the Colorado River has cut through the 550-foot lava dam at the mouth of Toroweap Valley * * *" plus certain additional strata. These authors go on to say (p. 135), "The negligible amount of canyon deepening during the last million years or more can scarcely be attributed to the hardness of the rock * * *. Probably the most important factor involved in the apparently retarded downcutting, however, is the stream gradient which is controlled by elevation above sea level."

FIGURE 90.—Looking downstream at Unkar Rapid, which was caused by tributary fan forcing river against cliff on the left bank.

To explain in different words the importance of this age determination: the river has had a long time to smooth out breaks in gradient resulting from outcrops of hard rock and from tributary fans or big rockfalls. The erosion of more than 500 feet of hard basalt would require more time and the expenditure of more stream power than would be necessary to dispose of even the largest tributary fan or rockfall observed anywhere in the canyon. Accordingly, one finds it difficult to avoid the conclusion that the river profile is essentially graded and that the alternation of smooth pools and steep rapids is a natural habit of the river, related to the achievement of an equilibrium condition probably equatable to a tendency toward minimum work.

The rapids in the Grand Canyon constitute the most important element in the river's approach to sea level. Considering the whole length of the Grand Canyon, the decrease in elevation of the water flowing through all the pools is small compared with the decrease resulting from even a few of the principal rapids. Figure 94 is a graph showing the proportion of the total elevation attributable to various distances. It can be seen that 50 percent of the total decrease in elevation takes place in only 9 percent of the total river distance. In half the total river length, 86 percent of the total elevation decrease is achieved. The asymmetry of this curve demonstrates the importance of the rapids in accounting for a large proportion of the total elevation drop. For example, in those rapids that have a slope of .01 or more (1 foot drop in 100 feet), 28 percent of the total elevation drop is accounted for.

The 10 largest rapids are listed below in order of decreasing water-surface gradient; these alone account for 19 percent of the total fall in the 150-mile river reach used as a sample.

List of steepest rapids, Lees Ferry to mile 150, Grand Canyon

	Slope in feet	Length in miles
House Rock Rapid	0. 0170	0. 3
Horn Creek Rapid	. 0168	. 4
75-Mile Rapid	. 0164	. 2
Badger Creek Rapid	. 0162	. 2
Zoroaster Creek Rapid	. 0150	. 2
76-Mile Rapid	. 0130	. 3
Unkar Rapid	. 0130	. 4
Tuna Creek Rapid	. 0130	. 2
Sockdologer Rapid	. 0126	. 4
Grapevine Rapid	. 0120	. 7
Total		[1] 3. 3

[1] Or 2.2 percent of 150 miles.

NOTE.—Total drop through 10 steepest rapids is 246 feet or 19.3 percent of total drop in 150 miles.

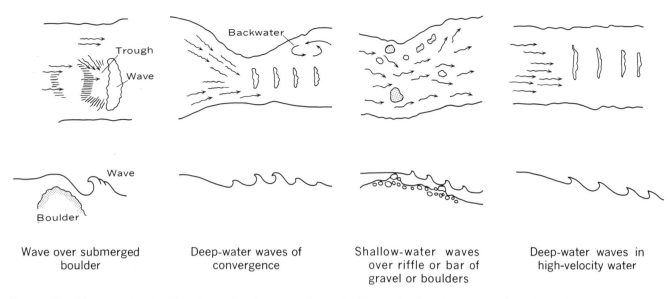

| Wave over submerged boulder | Deep-water waves of convergence | Shallow-water waves over riffle or bar of gravel or boulders | Deep-water waves in high-velocity water |

FIGURE 91.—Diagrams showing four types of water waves in rapids. Upper sketches show a plan view of the river; lower sketches indicate the inferred relation of waves to the bed configuration.

FIGURE 92.—A rapid due primarily to convergence where rockbound channel narrows in a part of Granite Gorge.

FIGURE 93.—Rapids unrelated to any tributary entrance and presumably caused by large gravel bar deposited on streambed.

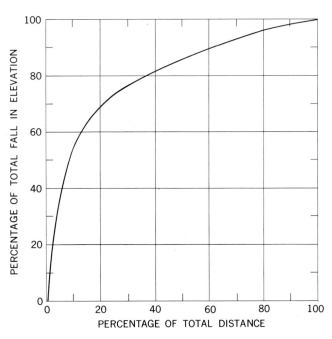

FIGURE 94.—Relation between the fall in elevation of the Colorado River and distance along the channel in the first 150 miles of the Grand Canyon below Lees Ferry.

The direction and speed of water through and below a rapid in the Grand Canyon illuminates some aspects of the bed form and profile. Commonly, immediately below a very steep rapid, a large part of the downstream flow will be thrown against one bank, particularly if that bank is a vertical cliff. When this occurs, the opposite side of the stream will invariably have a strong upstream current at the water surface, often forming half the total stream width. Between the downstream and upstream surface currents, then, a strong shear zone exists that will be characterized by boils or round domes of upwelling water. These boils are sporadic in size and intensity, as would be expected of turbulent eddies. The boils in the Grand Canyon may be as small as 3 feet in diameter or as large as 40 feet in diameter. The vertical component of upwelling water is distinctly shown by the dome-shaped topography of the water surface over the eddy. The amount of surface elevation or vertical superelevation of the water surface over the boil is a direct indication of the strength of the vertically directed upward current. We estimated that this vertical superelevation was as much as 1 foot, indicating a vertical velocity of 8 fps.

The presence of vertically directed water in the shear zone requires for continuity that there also be downward-directed motions. These seems to take the form of deep vortexes at the foot of the rapids, especially in the lee of large rocks that are partly submerged. Vortexes are also common in deep slow pools below rapids. The other source of downward vertical motion seems to be the diving of large amounts of water at the foot of a rapid; this water, because of the steep slope through the rapid, already has a downward component. The deep hole at the foot of many rapids, then, must represent scour by downwardly directed water, much of which must flow along the bed at high velocities downstream, later to appear broken into upwelling filaments that cause the described boils. Some indication of the intensity of the downward motion and the speed of water movement downstream at the bed is indicated by two types of observation.

On several occasions I put a fluorescein-dye marker in the river close to the shear zone at the foot of a large rapid. The bag enclosing the dye was buoyant, for it was the type designed for the use of pilots shot down at sea. In several of these trials, the dye bag immediately disappeared, and was dragged below the surface by the downward component. We circled in the pool for a considerable time, waiting to see where the dye marker would appear. In one instance it did not reach the surface again until it had been taken downstream nearly a quarter of a mile. The amount of time required for the marker to reappear provided an estimate of mean downstream velocity of the transporting filament, approximately 8 fps.

Current-meter velocity measurements in a reach just upstream of Unkar Rapid give another indication of the strength of the current near the bed. The cross sections and some velocity measurements are given in figure 95. Near the deepest part of cross section 3, where the depth was about 45 feet, the measured surface velocity was 11.4 fps, and an equal velocity was measured 1 foot above the bed.

It seems, then, that large amounts of water dive at the foot of a rapid to the bottom of the succeeding pool. Some of this water moves swiftly downstream near the bed, and filaments of it are projected to the surface in large boils having a high vertical velocity. This motion in the vertical plane is a part of another large-scale circulation in which most of the flow is confined to one-half of the river channel, whereas water in the other half of the channel is flowing upstream simultaneously at a velocity of as much as 10 or 12 fps. Such an eddy occurs downstream from the area shown in figure 95.

It is interesting that even the most experienced river boatmen greatly underestimate the depth of water in the Grand Canyon and the variability of depth. The extent of the downward and upward motions also was a surprise even to the most experienced.

One may well inquire whether the position and magnitude of the pools and the rapids change with time. Obviously, the period of observation of individual rapids is so short that an answer by direct observation is impossible. Certain inferences, however, may be drawn.

Those rapids caused by the accumulation of debris fans at the mouths of tributary canyons clearly cannot migrate away from the tributary mouth. Therefore, their position must be essentially fixed in geologic time.

A few rapids probably result from a sill or outcrop of especially hard rock upon which an overfall forms as the water cuts into less competent beds downstream. Lava Falls might well be attributed to such a cause, but no other major rapid. Therefore, the upstream migration of knickpoints caused initially by the occurrence of a local body of hard rock cannot account for the succession of rapids throughout the canyon length.

Rapids formed by local accumulation of large blocks falling directly into the river from adjacent cliffs would be expected to decrease in magnitude as these rocks gradually eroded away, but the position of such a rapid should not migrate upstream.

The great age of the lava that once dammed the river at Toroweap strengthens the conjecture that the river has had ample time to eliminate the sections having steep rapids. The rapids, therefore, must be relatively stable features.

Nature and Transport of Material on the Riverbed

The nature of the material on the riverbed can be inferred primarily from three kinds of observations. The bed was exposed to direct observation when the foundations were excavated for both Hoover and Glen Canyon Dams. In the foundation excavation for Hoover Dam, a sawed plank was found imbedded in sand and gravel 55 feet below the normal streambed elevation. This implies that the sand and gravel found in the canyon bottom moves to considerable depths during floods.

Most channel bars exposed at low flow consist of sand and cobbles. Large boulders occur primarily on fans directly attributable to debris from tributary canyons.

Though the streambed includes in places extremely large blocks of rock, for the most part the variation in water depth, typified by the bed profile shown in figure

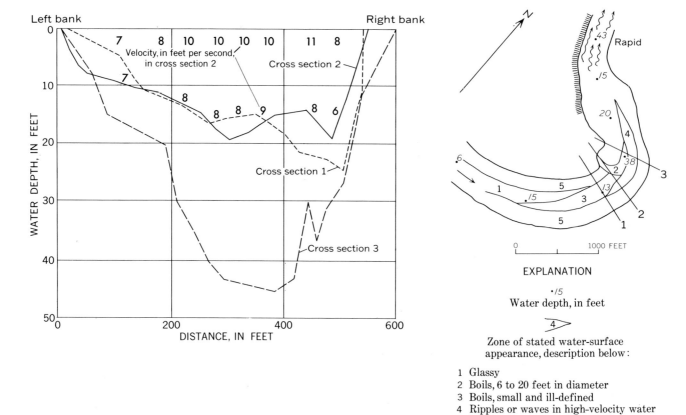

FIGURE 95.—Channel cross sections and sketch map, showing appearance of water surface near Unkar Rapid. Velocity measurements (fps) near the river surface and near the bed are shown for cross section 2.

89, seems to be caused by local scour in a bed composed primarily of sand and gravel. This is supported also by the particle sizes of sediment deposited at the head of Lake Mead; this sediment consisted of 45 percent sand and 55 percent silt and clay (Smith and others, 1960). The relatively fine texture of the bed material is perhaps most persuasively demonstrated by the fact that the riverbed is scoured deeply during floods in all observed sections of the river that were or are still unaffected by dams in the reaches immediately upstream. Data on the depth of riverbed scour during the spring run-off peak have been described previously at some length (Leopold and Maddock, 1953, p. 30–35). However, the previous discussions have, for the most part, omitted the changes throughout the nonflood season, which are important to the present discussion.

Figure 96 shows the changes in some of the principal hydraulic factors at Lees Ferry during a 10-month period from December 1947 to September 1948. These data represent conditions in the Grand Canyon prior to the construction of Glen Canyon Dam and several other dams farther upstream. The spring flood in 1948 was moderately high but far below the maximum of record.

The discharge was 92,100 second-feet on May 25. During this season, as the discharge increased progressively from about 10,000 second-feet, the water-surface elevation rose 11 feet, but simultaneously the mean elevation of the riverbed fell 16 feet. In other words, the accommodation of the river channel to the increased flow consisted of an increase in cross-sectional area achieved somewhat more by riverbed scour than increase in water-surface elevation. After the 1948 flood, the water-surface elevation returned to approximately its preflood value, but for several months after the flood recession, the average bed elevation remained 2 to 3 feet lower than in the preflood conditions. In the fall and winter months, the average elevation of the streambed rose gradually to its average springtime condition.

The hydraulic relations during such riverbed scour were discussed in detail by Leopold and Maddock (1953). The scour at Lees Ferry was shown to be associated with high suspended-load concentrations, and for a given discharge, during the recession side of the flood, the sediment load was smaller and the streambed elevation was lower than on the rising flood stage. The scour cannot be attributed merely to high velocity be-

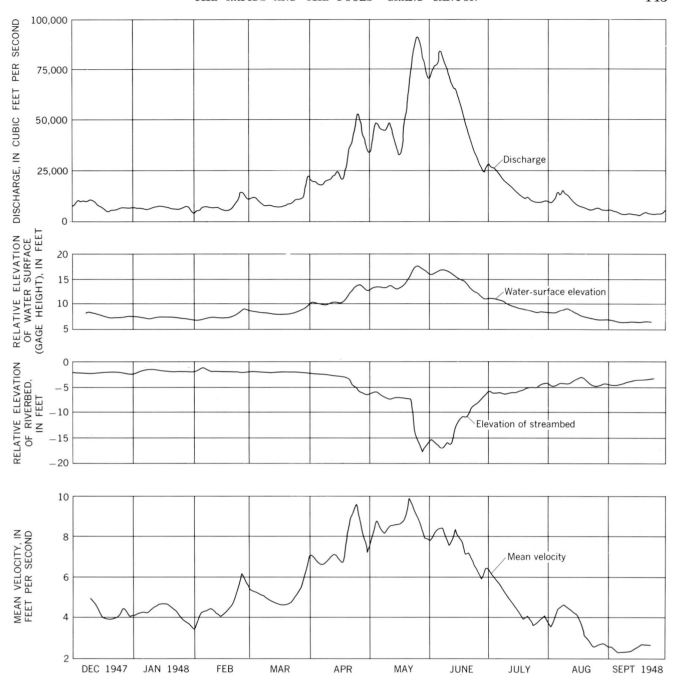

FIGURE 96.—Changes in discharge, water-surface elevation, bed elevation, and mean velocity during a 10-month period at the Lees Ferry measuring station, Colorado River. Note that the streambed had been scoured 16 feet between mid-April and late May as the discharge increased.

cause, as shown in figure 96, the most rapid rise of discharge was associated with deepening of the riverbed which was also coincident with a decrease in the mean water velocity. At the end of August 1948, when the discharge was the same as the preflood values of the preceding January, the mean velocity was lower than had typified the January conditions.

The stations at Grand Canyon and San Juan River at Bluff filled and then scoured on the rising flood stage; the bed changed but little on the falling stage. Thus, during a snowmelt flood, the Colorado River had a large variation in sediment load and changed the elevation of its streambed and the cross-sectional area of its flow as it simultaneously changed its mean water velocity.

These hydraulic adjustments were associated with a changed bed roughness in response to changes in sediment transport.

We see, then, a complicated adjustment of the riverbed roughness, cross-sectional area, and bed forms brought about by different conditions of water and sediment inflow.

Before the dams were built, the sediment transported through the Grand Canyon averaged about 143 million tons per year, as indicated by sediment accumulated in Lake Mead during the first 14 years of the reservoir's existence. The year-to-year variation in the amount of sediment transported through the canyon in the pre-dam condition was large. For example, in the year 1927, the measurements show that 480 million tons were transported past Grand Canyon station.

As the spring flood passed, not all the sand and gravel that was temporarily cut out of the streambed moved completely through the canyon into the lower reaches of the river. The interrupted motion of individual grains of sand or gravel cobbles was an alternation between transport and resting or waiting in a dune or bar for extended periods of time. The average downstream speed of a cobble was very much slower than the average speed of any water particle. For this reason, the total volume of riverbed scour during a flood is large compared with the volume of sediment accumulated in a downstream reservoir as a result of the same flood passage.

The low-gradient pools of a canyon river are visualized as local basins of semipermanent character cut into a bed consisting primarily of sand and gravel. These sections of the riverbed are scoured deeply during flood passage, and after the flood has passed they slowly regain their original topography.

I hypothesize that the areas of rapids, on the other hand, are nearly fixed features, consisting of heavy gravel, only the surface rocks of which move during flood periods. As in other smaller rivers in which we have made observations of marked rocks placed on river bars and riffles, the usual flood moves only rocks lying at or near the surface. These are immediately replaced, however, by similar rocks derived from upstream. Scour of the material of the rapids during a flood is, therefore, nearly inconsequential compared with the deep scour that occurs in the finer grained material of the pools or deeps nearby. Despite the ability of the river to transport the gravel and boulders that form the bulk of any given rapid, the flow mechanics require, for long-term stability, that the riverbed not be a smooth sloping plain, but consist of alternating deeps and shallows which, even through long periods of time, remain in a consistent geographic position.

The main difference between the bed topography in a deep narrow gorge like the Grand Canyon and the common gravel-bedded stream of less mountainous areas is a matter of scale. A river develops a profile connect-

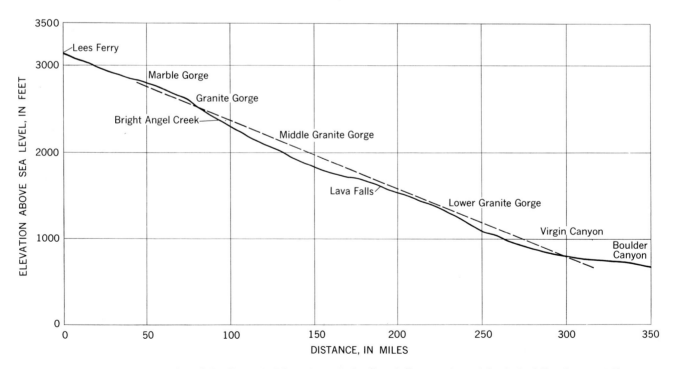

FIGURE 97.—Longitudinal profile of the Colorado River through the Grand Canyon. A straight dashed line drawn at the average gradient shows that the river profile, though somewhat irregular, is nearly straight.

ing the high-elevation headwaters with its mouth or base level by a channel which along its length represents a quickly attained quasi-equilibrium, constantly adjusted through geologic time as the elevation difference between headwaters and mouth is gradually reduced. The concavity of the profile in most rivers is primarily the result of increased discharge as tributaries enter along the river length. Along the Colorado River through the Grand Canyon, the addition of water from tributaries is negligible. The river profile through the Grand Canyon, when drawn at such a scale that the pool and rapids alternation is obscured, is nearly a straight line, as can be seen in figure 97.

SUMMARY

The Colorado River flows several hundreds of miles through a series of canyons, some of which are of very hard and resistant rock. The river seems encased in a vise so confining and limiting that any freedom of action or movement seems to be foreclosed. In fact, however, the river has nearly all the characteristics of an unconfined channel flowing in a broad flood plain, save one, the tendency to move laterally. The Colorado adjusts its depth and velocity by scour and fill of the bed in response to changes of debris load. It formed and maintains bed alternations of deep pool and shallow rapid by the construction of gravel bars, which maintain their size and position despite the trading of rocks on the bar surface. The river profile, except for the alternation of pool and rapid, is smooth and nearly straight.

Only in the lack of lateral migration as a result of the confining rock walls does the canyon river seem markedly different from a free or unconfined one. Yet the perfect form of some meanders entrenched in hard rock indicates that the river has no proclivity for lateral movement, for it has cut nearly vertically hundreds of feet, at least in some places, for periods of several millions of years. Why the canyon river does not erode laterally more than it does is simply not known.

The Grand Canyon section of the Colorado River, despite its impressive rapids, has the characteristics of a river in balance, maintaining its quasi-equilibrium poise by self-adjustment.

The great age and stability of the rapids do not result in all rapids being equal in size or declivity. Their magnitude ranges from small to great. Random variation alone might well have produced one or more rapids so steep or so nearly approaching a real waterfall that the Powell party would have been blocked. Powell took a long chance and was lucky as well as capable.

REFERENCES

Langbein, W. B., and Leopold, L. B., 1968, River channel bars and dunes—theory of kinematic waves: U.S. Geol. Survey Prof. Paper 422–L, 20 p.

Leopold, L. B., and Maddock, Thomas, Jr., 1953, The hydraulic geometry of stream channels and some physiographic implications: U.S. Geol. Survey Prof. Paper 252, 57 p.

McKee, E. D., Hamblin, W. K., and Damon, P. E., 1968, K–Ar age of lava dam in Grand Canyon: Geol. Soc. America Bull., v. 79, no. 1, p. 133–136.

Powell, J. W., 1875, Exploration of the Colorado River of the West and its tributaries: Washington, D.C., U.S. Govt. Printing Office, 291 p.

Smith, W. O., Vetter, C. P., Cummings, G. B., and others, 1960, Comprehensive survey of sedimentation in Lake Mead, 1948–49: U.S. Geol. Survey Prof. Paper 295, 254 p.